William McNally, Wilfrid Laurier University

CFO Workbook

Corporate Finance Online

First Edition

Stanley Eakins

East Carolina University

William McNally

Wilfrid Laurier University

Toronto

ISBN-10: 0134174836

ISBN-13: 9780134174839

Vice-President, CMPS: Gary Bennett

Editorial Director: Claudine O'Donnell

Acquisitions Editor: Megan Farrell

Marketing Manager: Jessica Saso

Project Manager: Richard Di Santo

Developmental Editor: Alanna Ferguson

Production Services: MPS North America LLC

1 2 3 4 5   19 18 17 16 15

Printed and bound in the United States of America[V0UD]

Table of Contents

Table of Contents

Preface

This document is a collection of workbooks. In each class, students will work alone or in small groups on the workbook. The instructor will circulate to answer questions and make short presentations as needed.

The course outline indicates the dates on which each workbook is used. Students are expected to bring the workbook to class along with a calculator or laptop.

Ratio Analysis (Ch.2, LO3)

1. Introduction

In this workbook you will:

- Learn the steps in ratio analysis
- Learn the types of ratios
- Learn about Activity Ratios
- Learn about Financing Ratios
- Learn about Profitability Ratios
- Learn about Du Pont Ratio Analysis

2. Steps in Ratio Analysis

- Usually you begin with a basic Du Pont ratio analysis.
  - o Then decide what additional ratios are appropriate given what you learn from the Du Pont ratio analysis.
- Cross-sectional Analysis: Compare ratios to industry norms.
  - o Evaluate reasons for discrepancies from industry norms.
- Time Series Analysis: Identify trends in ratios over time.
  - o Evaluate reasons for trends.
- If discrepancies arose because of underlying problems, evaluate alternative solutions to problems.

3. Types of Ratios

- Liquidity: working capital ratios, current, quick, etc.
- Activity ratios (AKA asset utilization ratios): total asset turnover, fixed asset turnover, inventory turnover, etc.
- Financing ratios: debt ratio, debt-equity, times-interest-earned, etc.
- Profitability ratios: ROE, ROA, gross profit margin, net profit margin, etc.
- Market ratios: EPS, P/E, M/B, etc.

4. Activity Ratios

Activity ratios measure asset utilization—dollars of sales per dollar of asset.

4.1 Total Asset Turnover

$$TAT = \frac{Sales}{Total\ Assets}$$

- TAT = Total Asset Turnover
- Represents dollar value of sales generated per dollar of assets invested in a business.
  - o An ideal business has no assets (e.g., network marketing business such as Amway, Mary Kay Cosmetics).

4.2 Fixed Asset Turnover

$$FAT = \frac{Sales}{Fixed\ Assets}$$

- FAT = Fixed Asset Turnover
  - o Provides a useful way of evaluating businesses with large amounts of fixed-assets (e.g., steel, auto, manufacturing, etc.).

Compare Ford to Daimler Benz. Which company is more efficient in its use of total assets and fixed assets? Complete the table that follows the financial statements below.

	Ford	Daimler Benz
Sales	146,917	117,982
Cost of sales	125,234	92,457
SG&A	9,002	10,472
Other	208	4,849
Depreciation	4,174	4,368
EBIT	8,299	5,836
Interest	3,689	884
Other Income (Loss)	2,391	5,187
Earnings Before Taxes	7,001	10,139
Income Taxes	– 147	1,419
Net Income	7,148	8,720
Cash & Cash Equivalents	36,568	19,171
Accounts Receivable	87,309	30,804
Inventories	7,708	17,349
Other Current Assets	19,984	3,117
Total Current Assets	151,569	70,441
Other Assets	22,841	66,910
Fixed Assets, Net	27,616	21,779
Goodwill & Intangible Assets		9,388
Total Assets	202,026	168,518
Accounts Payable	19,531	9,086
Short-term Debt and Current Portion Long-term	16,251	39,567
Other Current Liabilities	40,462	10,455
Total Current Liabilities	76,244	59,108
Long-term Debt	98,437	46,447
Other Liabilities	598	19,600
Total Liabilities	175,279	125,155
Common Shares	3,089	15,735
Retained Earnings	23,658	27,628
Owner's Equity	26,747	43,363
Total Liabilities and Owner's Equity	202,026	168,518

	Ford	Daimler Benz
Total Asset Turnover		0.70
Fixed Asset Turnover	5.32	

4.3 Inventory Turnover

$$\text{Inventory Turnover} = \frac{\text{COGS}}{\text{Inventory}}$$

- COGS = Cost of Goods Sold
- You can also use sales in the numerator.
- If the rate is too high, then there is too little inventory. This may cause loss of sales due to stocks and high costs from excessive re-ordering.
- If the rate is too low, then inventory is too high. This may cause losses due to obsolescence. High costs are due to warehousing, financing and insurance.

Compare Metro to Safeway. Which company is more efficient in its use of total assets and which company manages its inventory better? Complete the table that follows the financial statements below.

	Metro	Safeway
Sales	11,402,800	36,139,100
Cost of Sales	9,237,000	26,645,100
SG&A	1,344,600	7,914,700
Other	40,000	-
Depreciation	179,600	943,900
EBIT	601,600	635,400
Interest	41,100	273,000
Other Income (Loss)	358,600	– 26,400
Earnings Before Taxes	919,100	336,000
Income Taxes	203,700	89,700
Net Income	715,400	246,300
Cash & Cash Equivalents	80,800	4,647,300
Accounts Receivable	300,200	1,211,400
Inventories	781,300	2,089,600
Other Current Assets	27,100	515,400
Total Current Assets	1,189,400	8,463,700
Other Assets	323,000	753,800
Fixed Assets, Net	1,328,400	7,537,500
Intangible Assets	365,100	-
Goodwill	1,855,600	464,500
Total Assets	5,061,500	17,219,500
Accounts Payable	1,004,900	3,376,400
Short-term Debt and Current Portion Long-term	14,400	252,900
Other Current Liabilities	187,000	2,227,100
Total Current Liabilities	1,206,300	5,856,400
Long-term Debt	650,000	3,890,800
Other Liabilities	397,800	1,597,200
Total Liabilities	2,254,100	11,344,400
Common Shares	641,500	1,288,200
Retained Earnings	2,165,900	4,586,900
Owner's Equity	2,807,400	5,875,100
Total Liabilities and Owner's Equity	5,061,500	17,219,500

	Metro	Safeway
Total Asset Turnover		2.10
Inventory Turnover	11.82	

5. Financing Ratios

- Financing ratios are used to evaluate a borrower.
- The decision to lend depends on:
  - How much debt does the borrower already have?
  - Solvency. Can the borrower handle their current interest payments and can they repay the principal?
  - Collateral. Is there any available, or do other lenders have a claim on most of it?

5.1 Measuring the Amount of Debt

$$\text{Debt Ratio} = \frac{\text{Total Liabilities}}{\text{Total Assets}}$$

- Can also use total debt in numerator.
  - Total debt = short-term debt + long-term debt

$$\text{Debt-to-Equity Ratio} = \frac{\text{Total Liabilities}}{\text{Owner's Equity}}$$

- Can also use total debt in numerator.

5.2   Measuring Solvency 1: Time Interest Earned

$$\text{Times Interest Earned} = \frac{\text{EBIT}}{\text{Interest}}$$

- EBIT = Earnings Before Interest and Taxes
- Measures the ability of the company to meet the interest expense with operating income.
- Represents the number of times EBIT is larger than the interest expense.

5.3   Measuring Solvency 2: Cash Flow to Debt

$$\text{Cash Flow to Debt Ratio} = \frac{\text{Net Income} + \text{Depreciation}}{\text{Total Liabilities}}$$

- Measures the ability of the company to repay the principal.
- Represents the proportion of total liabilities that could be paid off this year if all available cash was devoted to that task.
- Depreciation is added back to Net Income because depreciation is a non-cash charge.
- Can also use total debt in denominator.
    - o Total debt = short-term debt + long-term debt

5.4   Collateral

$$\text{Asset Coverage Ratio} = \frac{\text{Collateral}}{\text{Debt}}$$

- Collateral = long-term tangible assets
  - ○ Long-term tangible assets = Total assets – intangibles – A/P
  - ○ Subtract intangibles because they are bad collateral.
  - ○ Accounts Payable (A/P) have a claim against inventory, and that inventory is bad collateral.
- Debt
  - ○ Total debt = short-term + long-term debt

5.5   Exercise

Compare Carriage Services to StonMor Partners. Both companies are in the death care (AKA funeral) business. They each have lots of assets, including land (cemeteries) and prepaid funerals and burials. Which company is managing its debts better? Which would you lend to? Complete the table that follows the financial statements below.

	Carriage Services	StonMor Partners
Total Revenues	221,432	246,641
COGS and SG&A	168,009	230,710
Depreciation	11,577	9,548
Earnings Before Interest and Taxes	41,846	6,383
Other Income	0	– 6,649
Interest Expense	10,017	21,070
Income Before Income Taxes	31,829	– 21,336
Provision for Income Taxes	13,362	– 2,304
Net Income from Continuing Operations	18,467	– 19,032
Cash	4,432	12,175
Accounts Receivable	19,162	55,115
Inventories	16,056	-
Other Current assets	-	26,289
Total Current Assets	39,650	93,579
Merchandise Trusts	167,810	431,556
Long-term Accounts Receivable	47,255	78,356
PP&E, Net	152,933	85,007
Cemetery Property	86,617	316,469
Goodwill	222,118	48,034
Deferred Changes and Other Non-current Assets	11,471	108,557
Cemetery Perpetual Care Trust Investments	47,986	311,771
TOTAL ASSETS	775,839	1,473,329
Current Portion of LT Debt	11,218	2,916
Accounts Payable and Other Liabilities	12,661	37,269
Accrued Liabilities	19,355	1,512
Total Current Liabilities	43,235	41,697
Other Long-term Liabilities	4,013	1,527
Long-Term Debt	253,311	289,016
Deferred Cemetery Revenues	273,989	581,585
Care Trusts' Corpus	47,820	311,771
Deferred Liabilities	-	140,213
Total Liabilities	622,367	1,365,809
Redeemable Preferred Stock	200	
Common Stock	202,683	
Accumulated Deficit	– 34,144	
Treasury Stock, At Cost	– 15,267	
Total Stockholders' Equity	153,272	107,520
TOTAL LIABILITIES AND SHAREHOLDERS EQUITY	775,839	1,473,329

	Carriage	StonMor
Debt Ratio	80%	
Times Interest Earned		0.30
Cash Flow to Debt	5%	
Asset Coverage Ratio		4.75

1   Which company has more debt?
A)   Carriage Services
B)   StonMor

2   Which company has a greater capacity to pay its interest?
A)   Carriage Services
B)   StonMor

3   Which company can repay its principal owing more quickly?
A)   Carriage Services
B)   StonMor

4   Which company has more available collateral per dollar of liabilities?
A)   Carriage Services
B)   StonMor

6.   Profitability Ratios

6.1   Gross Profit Margin

$$\text{Gross Profit Margin} = \frac{\text{Sales} - \text{Cost of Goods Sold}}{\text{Sales}}$$

- Reflects the product price mark-up over the marginal cost of production.
- Companies with pricing power (the power to set price) have large gross margins.
- Price power is due to:
  o   Market structure (i.e., oligopoly or monopoly)

14

o Barriers to entry (i.e., tariffs, quotas, patents, innovation, learning curve, etc.)

6.2 Operating Profit Margin

$$\text{Operating Profit Margin} = \frac{\text{Sales} - \text{Cost of Goods Sold} - \text{SG\&A} - \textit{Depreciation}}{\text{Sales}} = \frac{\text{EBIT}}{\text{Sales}}$$

- Reflects the product price mark-up over average cost of production (which includes fixed costs).

6.3 Net Profit Margin

$$\text{Net Profit Margin} = \frac{\text{Net Income}}{\text{Sales}}$$

- Represents profit to owners as a percentage of sales.

6.4 Return on Assets

$$\text{Return on Assets} = \text{ROA} = \frac{\text{Net Income}}{\text{Total Assets}}$$

- Supposed to measure overall corporate profitability per dollar of assets.
  - o However, the numerator doesn't measure corporate profitability. It measures profit to owners because interest is deducted.
  - o Regardless, ROA is widely used.

6.5 Return on Owner's Equity

$$\text{Return on Owner's Equity} = ROE = \frac{\text{Net Income}}{\text{Owner's Equity}}$$

- Measures owners' return.
- The numerator represents profit to owners.
- The denominator is an estimate of their investment in the company.

6.6 Apple's Profit in 2012

Use the data below to calculate the Apple's profitability ratios for 2012. Complete the table that follows.

Selected Financial Information
Apple Inc.
Year End Sept 29, 2012
($000s)

Sales	156,508,000
Cost of Sales	87,846,000
EBIT	55,241,000
Net Income	41,733,000
Total Assets	176,064,000
Owner's Equity	118,210,000

Selected Profitability Ratios
Apple Inc.
Year End Sept 29, 2012

Gross Profit Margin	
Operating Profit Margin	
Net Profit Margin	
ROE	
ROA	

6.7 Apple's Profit and Its Products

The table below shows Apple's profitability ratios from 1983 to 2013. The table also shows the introduction dates of Apple's major products. Steve Jobs was CEO of Apple from the date of incorporation until he was fired in Spring 1985. He was invited back to lead Apple in July 1997. Jobs passed away on October 5, 2011. Complete the 2012 values and answer the questions that follow.

Fiscal Year*	Gross Profit Margin	Operating Profit Margin	Net Profit Margin	ROE	ROA	Product	Introduction Date
2013	37.6%	28.7%	21.7%	30.0%	17.9%		
2012							
2011	40.5%	31.2%	23.9%	33.8%	22.3%		
2010	39.4%	28.2%	21.5%	29.3%	18.6%	iPad	27-Jan-2010
2009	36.0%	21.0%	15.6%	20.5%	10.6%		
2008	34.3%	19.3%	14.9%	23.0%	12.2%	MacBook Air, iPhone 3G	15-Jan-2008 09-May-2008
2007	34.0%	18.4%	14.6%	24.1%	13.8%	iPhone	29-Jun-2007
2006	29.0%	12.7%	10.3%	19.9%	11.6%	iPod Nano, MacBook Pro	07-Sep-2005 10-Jan- 2006
2005	29.0%	11.8%	9.6%	17.9%	11.6%		
2004	27.3%	3.9%	3.3%	5.4%	3.4%	iPod Mini	06-Jan-2004
2003	27.5%	0.0%	1.1%	1.6%	1.0%		
2002	27.9%	0.3%	1.1%	1.6%	1.0%	iPod	23-Oct-2001
2001	23.0%	−6.4%	−0.5%	−0.6%	−0.4%		
2000	27.1%	6.5%	9.8%	19.1%	11.6%		
1999	27.6%	5.9%	9.8%	19.4%	11.6%		
1998	24.9%	4.4%	5.2%	18.8%	7.2%		
1997	19.3%	−15.1%	−14.8%	−87.1%	− 24.7%		
1996	9.8%	−14.1%	−8.3%	−39.7%	− 15.2%		
1995	25.8%	6.2%	3.8%	14.6%	6.8%		
1994	25.5%	5.7%	3.4%	13.0%	5.8%		
1993	34.2%	1.4%	1.1%	4.3%	1.7%		
1992	43.7%	11.4%	7.5%	24.2%	12.6%	PowerBook 100	21-Oct-1991
1991	47.5%	7.1%	4.9%	17.5%	8.9%		
1990	53.1%	12.8%	8.5%	32.8%	16.0%		
1989	49.0%	12.0%	8.6%	30.6%	16.5%		
1988	51.1%	15.2%	9.8%	39.9%	19.2%		
1987	51.3%	14.0%	8.2%	26.0%	14.7%	Macintosh II	02-Mar-1987
1986	53.1%	14.4%	8.1%	22.2%	13.3%	Macintosh Plus	16-Jan-1986
1985	41.7%	7.7%	3.2%	11.1%	6.5%	Apple LaserWriter	01-Jan-1985
1984	42.0%	6.0%	4.2%	13.8%	8.1%	Macintosh	01-Jan-1984
1983	48.5%	3.0%	7.8%	20.3%	13.8%	Apple IIe	01-Jan-1983

*Fiscal year-end is the last Saturday in September.

5   Which era featured the highest profitability for Apple?
     A)   MacIntosh
     B)   iPod
     C)   iPhone
     D)   iPad

6   Which was the lowest profit year for Apple and its owners?
     A)   The year Steve Jobs was fired.
     B)   The year Steve Jobs was hired back.
     C)   The year Steve Jobs died.

7   Which product had the highest mark-up over marginal cost?
     A)   MacIntosh
     B)   iPhone
     C)   iPad

8   In 2013, iPhones accounted for 54% of sales. What is the trend in
     smartphone price mark-ups (over marginal cost) in the last three years
     shown in the table?
     A)   Increasing
     B)   Decreasing
     C)   Flat

9   What is the best reason for your answer to the last question?
     A)   Increasing competition from Samsung, HTC, Sony, Blackberry,
           etc.
     B)   Higher marketing expenses
     C)   Higher taxes
     D)   Steve Jobs' death

10   In the modern era, which product appeared to be most profitability for
     Apple?
     A)   iPod
     B)   iPhone
     C)   iPad

11   What is your forecast for Apple's profitability in 2014 and beyond?
     A)   Increasing
     B)   Decreasing
     C)   Flat

7. Du Pont Ratio Analysis

The Du Pont Ratio Analysis is a method of analyzing financial statements to explain changes (or differences) in profitability.

Profit is measured by Return on Owner's Equity, ROE.

7.1 Derivation of Du Pont Equation

$$\text{ROE} = \frac{\text{Net Income}}{\text{Owner's Equity}} = \frac{NI}{E}$$

Trick #1

Multiply ROE by one (1), but define 1 as Total Assets over Total Assets (TA/TA):

$$\text{ROE} = \frac{NI}{E} \times \frac{TA}{TA}$$

$$\text{ROE} = \frac{NI}{TA} \times \frac{TA}{E}$$

12   What is NI/TA?
- A) Net Profit Margin
- B) Total Asset Turnover
- C) Gross Margin
- D) Return on Assets

7.2   TA/E

Balance Sheet

Assets	Liabilities & Owner's Equity
Current Assets	**Current Liabilities**
	Long-term Liabilities
Fixed Assets	**Owner's Equity (E)**

13   Consider the balance sheet above. What is the sum of the left-hand side?
   A)   Net Fixed Assets
   B)   Working Capital
   C)   Total Assets

14   Define the sum of current liabilities and long-term liabilities as Debt and denote it as D. Notice that Owner's Equity is denoted E. What is the sum of Debt and Equity? (D + E =?)
   A)   Total Liabilities
   B)   Total Assets
   C)   Total Accruals

15   Use your answer to the last question to simplify the ratio of TA/E. (Hint: substitute your answer from the last question into the numerator and simplify.)
   A)   TA/E = D/E − 1
   B)   TA/E = E/D − 1
   C)   TA/E = 1 + D/E
   D)   TA/E = 1 + E/D

7.3 Back to the Du Pont Equation

We now know that we can express ROE as:

$$ROE = ROA \times \left[1 + \frac{D}{E}\right]$$

Where

D = current plus long-term liabilities

- 1 + D/E = the equity multiplier
- The equity multiplier reflects the amount of borrowing (AKA leverage).
- Because D includes current liabilities, it is never equal to zero even for companies with no bank borrowing or outstanding bonds. But, firms with no borrowing will have an equity multiplier only a little larger than one. Firms with a lot of borrowing have an equity multiplier that is much bigger than one.

16   According to the Du Pont equation, if leverage increases, then ROE will
_____.

A)   Increase
B)   Decrease
C)   Stay the same

7.4 Simplify ROA

$$ROA = \frac{\text{Net Income}}{\text{Total Assets}} = \frac{NI}{TA}$$

Trick #2

Multiply ROA by one (1), but define 1 as Sales over Sales (S/S):

$$ROA = \frac{NI}{TA} \times \frac{S}{S}$$

Rearrange:

$$ROA = \frac{NI}{S} \times \frac{S}{TA}$$

17 What is the ratio of NI/S?
   A) Net Profit Margin
   B) Total Asset Turnover
   C) Gross Margin
   D) Return on Assets

18 What is the ratio of S/TA?
   A) Net Profit Margin
   B) Total Asset Turnover
   C) Gross Margin
   D) Return on Assets

7.5   Back to the Du Pont Equation

We now know that we can express ROE as:

$$\text{ROE} = \text{ROA} \times \left[1 + \frac{D}{E}\right]$$

OR

$$\text{ROE} = \text{Net Profit Margin} \times \text{Total Asset Turnover} \times \left[1 + \frac{D}{E}\right]$$

19 According to the Du Pont equation, if total asset turnover increases, then ROE will _____.
   A) Increase
   B) Decrease
   C) Stay the same

20 According to the Du Pont equation, if net profit margin decreases, then ROE will _____.
   A) Increase
   B) Decrease
   C) Stay the same

21 According to the Du Pont equation, overall firm-level profitability as measured by ROA is the product of the following two factors:
  A) Leverage and profit
  B) Liquidity and leverage
  C) Productivity and efficiency
  D) Profitability and efficient asset utilization

8. Using Du Pont Ratio Analysis

In this section you are going to use the Du Pont method to compare the profit (ROE) of two companies and to evaluate changes in profit over time for the two companies. Selected financial values for the two companies are given in the table below.

Both companies are technology companies focused primarily on smartphones. Successful is larger than Unsuccessful, so its accounting numbers have been scaled down to make it comparable and to hide its identity. (Try to guess the identity of each company.)

	Successful Inc.			Unsuccessful Inc.		
	2013	2012	2011	2013	2012	2011
Income Statement						
Sales	17,091	15,651	10,825	11,073	18,423	19,907
Cost of Goods Sold	10,661	8,785	6,443	7,639	11,856	11,082
R&D	448	338	243	1,509	1,556	1,351
SG&A	1,083	1,004	760	2,111	2,600	2,400
Net Income	3,704	4,173	2,592	(646)	1,164	3,411
Assets						
Inventory	176	79	78	603	1,027	618
Accounts Receivable	2,409	2,128	1,373	2,353	3,062	3,955
Net Fixed Assets	1,660	1,545	778	2,395	2,733	2,504
Total Assets	20,700	17,606	11,637	13,165	13,731	12,875
Accounts Payable	3,622	3,259	2,388	1,064	744	832
Owner's Equity	12,355	11,821	7,662	9,460	10,100	8,938

	Successful Inc.			Unsuccessful Inc.		
	2013	2012	2011	2013	2012	2011
Du Pont Ratios						
ROE		35.3%	33.8%	−6.8%	11.5%	38.2%
1+D/E	1.68		1.52	1.39	1.36	1.44
ROA	17.9%	23.7%	22.3%	−4.9%		26.5%
Total Asset Turnover	82.6%	88.9%		84.1%	134.2%	154.6%
Net Profit Margin	21.7%	26.7%	23.9%		6.3%	17.1%
Working Capital Ratios						
Days Inventory	6	3	4	29	32	20
Days Receivables	51	50	46	78	61	73
Operating Cycle						
Days Payables	124	135	135	51	23	27
Cash Cycle						
Profitability Ratios						
Gross Margin		43.9%	40.5%		35.6%	44.3%
R&D/Sales		2.2%	2.2%	13.6%	8.4%	6.8%
SG&A/Sales	6.3%	6.4%	7.0%		14.1%	12.1%

22   What is the trend in sales for each company?
  A)   Increasing for Successful; decreasing for Unsuccessful.
  B)   Increasing for Successful; increasing for Unsuccessful.
  C)   Decreasing for Successful; decreasing for Unsuccessful.
  D)   Decreasing for Successful; increasing for Unsuccessful.

23   If sales decline, then any ratio with sales in the denominator will tend to
        _____. (Assuming the numerator doesn't fall as much as sales.)
  A)   Increase
  B)   Decrease
  C)   Stay the same

24 What is happening to ROE across time for Successful?
  A) Increasing
  B) Decreasing
  C) Staying the same

25 Which Du Pont factor(s) is (are) the primary determinant(s) of the change in ROE at Successful?
  A) Leverage
  B) Net profit margin
  C) Total asset turnover
  D) Net profit margin and total asset turnover

26 What is happening to ROE across time for Unsuccessful?
  A) Increasing
  B) Decreasing
  C) Staying the same

27 Which Du Pont factor(s) is (are) the primary determinant(s) of the change in ROE at Unsuccessful?
  A) Leverage
  B) Net profit margin
  C) Total asset turnover
  D) Net profit margin and total asset turnover

28 What is the biggest difference between Successful and Unsuccessful?
  A) Leverage
  B) Net profit margin
  C) Total asset turnover

29 Between 2011 and 2013, Successful Inc.'s operating cycle has _____ and its cash cycle has _____.
  A) Lengthened, shortened
  B) Shortened, lengthened
  C) Lengthened, lengthened
  D) Shortened, shortened

30 Why?

31   Between 2011 and 2013, Unsuccessful Inc.'s operating cycle has
     _____ and its cash cycle has _____.
     A)   Lengthened, shortened
     B)   Shortened, lengthened
     C)   Lengthened, lengthened
     D)   Shortened, shortened

32   Why?

33   Regarding working capital management, what makes Successful better
     than Unsuccessful?
     A)   It holds less inventory.
     B)   It collects from customers more quickly.
     C)   It is slower to pay its suppliers.
     D)   All of the above

34   What is the trend over time for the Gross Margin Ratio for Successful?
     A)   Increasing
     B)   Decreasing
     C)   Staying the same

35   What is the trend over time for the Gross Margin Ratio for
     Unsuccessful?
     A)   Increasing
     B)   Decreasing
     C)   Staying the same

36   Analyze the Profitability Ratios.
     A)   Looking at Gross Margins, what is the difference between
          Successful and Unsuccessful?
     B)   What are the trends in SG&A/Sales and R&D/Sales for the two
          companies?
     C)   How do the trends in the profitability margins relate to the trends
          in net profit margin for each company?

Solutions

Trend in Sales (#22, #23)

    a. Sales are increasing for Successful and decreasing for Unsuccessful. The declining sales is likely due to increased ratios with sales in the denominator (i.e., net profit margin) unless Unsuccessful can reduce the values in the numerator at the same rate as sales.

ROE across time for Successful? (#24, #25)

    a. Successful experienced high but declining ROE between 2011 and 2013. While the net profit margin has declined slightly, the biggest driver for the decline is a reduction in total asset turnover.

ROE across time for Unsuccessful? (#26, #27)

    a. Unsuccessful had a high ROE in 2011, but profitability fell dramatically over the following two years and the company posted a loss in 2013. The decline in ROE was due to a decline in net profit margin and a large decline in total asset turnover.

Differences between Successful and Unsuccessful (#28)

    a. The big difference is that Successful has a larger net profit margin than Unsuccessful.

Analyze the Working Capital Ratios (#29, #30, #31, #32, #33)

    a. Successful's operating and cash cycles have lengthened over time due to slower collection from customers and faster payment of suppliers. Unsuccessful's operating cycle has lengthened due to larger inventory and slower collections. The Cash cycle has moved in the opposite direction (shortened) due to slower payments to customers.

    b. Successful manages every part of its working capital better than Unsuccessful. It holds less inventory, it collects from customers more quickly and it is slower to pay its suppliers.

Analyze the Profitability Ratios (#34, #35, #36)

    a. Gross margins decline for both companies across time. This is likely due to increased competition in the market for smartphones.

b. Successful has managed to maintain its gross margin at a higher level than Unsuccessful.
c. SG&A/Sales and R&D/Sales is level for Successful but declining for Unsuccessful. These trends reinforce the trend of gross margin and result in a large decline in net profit margin for Unsuccessful but only a slightly decline in net profit margin for Successful.

Introduction to TVM (Ch.3, LO1– LO3)

1. Introduction

In this workbook you will:

- Learn about why we need time value of money mathematics
- Learn about time lines
- Learn how to find the future value in one period
- Learn to find the present value of an amount due in one period
- Learn about asset valuation
- Learn how to find the future value with multiple compounding periods
- Learn how to solve for the compound average interest rate
- Learn how to solve for the length of time it takes money to grow
- Learn about future and present values with non-annual compounding
- Learn about effective interest rates

2. Introduction to the Time Value of Money (TVM)

- TVM is the tool for valuing capital goods and claims against those goods (i.e. securities).
- **Definition:**
  A capital good is a good that yields services in the future as well as in the present (e.g., cars, homes, factories—all durables).
- Search for the YouTube video called "What is the time value of money Moneyweek investment tutorials." Stop at 2:15.
- Humans prefer money now to money later. Thus, $1 today is not equal to $1 in one year. The $1 next year is worth less. TVM provides a set of exchange rates that allow us to convert dollars that arrive at different times into a common currency. Once they are so converted, we can evaluate them and make decisions.

1   You can have $100 right now or $100 in one year. When do you want it?
   A)   Now
   B)   In one year

3. The Time Line

This time line represents two periods.

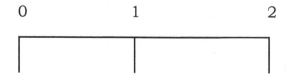

- Time t = 0 is the beginning of the first period.
- Time t = 1 is the end of the first period.
- You can also think of t = 1 as the start of the second period. Think of it as midnight on New Year's Eve.
- Time t = 2 is the end of the second period.

If there is an amount under an end point, it means the amount is paid (or received) at that point in time. For example, $100 received in one year is shown as:

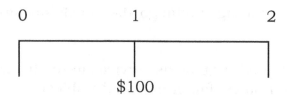

Typically, a receipt is shown as a positive value and a payment is shown as a negative value.

4. Future Value in One Period

Example: A bank offers 10% interest. You invest $100 today. How much interest will you earn over the year?

$Interest = i \times PV_0 = 0.1 \times \$100 = \$10$

Where
PV_0 = the present value (at t = 0) = $100
i = the interest (or growth) rate (for one period) = 0.10

How much will money will you have at the end of Year 1?

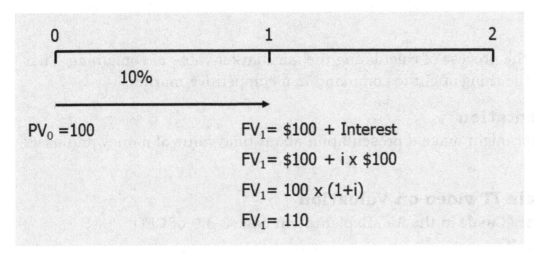

The future value of something that grows at a constant rate in one period is given by:

$$FV_1 = PV_0 \times (1 + i) \qquad \text{Eq. 1}$$

Where
FV_1 = the future value (at t = 1)
PV_0 = the present value (at t = 0)
i = the growth rate (for one period)

ANSWER:

5. Present Value in One Period

An investment pays $100 in one year's time. How much will you pay for it today? If you put money in the bank today, then you can earn an interest rate of 10%. (Hint: Solve for PV_0 using Eq.1.)

ANSWER:

PV_0 =

6. Valuing an Asset

Definition:

Valuation is the process of calculating the fair market value of something. That is, the price the thing ought to command in a competitive market.

6.1 Presentation

The instructor might make a presentation about time value of money and asset valuation.

6.2 Explain IT video on Valuation

Check out the "Castle in the Air" Explain It on page 3.3.9 of CFO.

7. Future Value with Compounding

Definition:

The process of leaving your money and any accumulated interest in an investment for more than one period (reinvesting the interest) is known as compounding.

You invest $100 for 2 years at 10% per annum. What is it worth after 2 years? Assume that you do not remove interest after one year.

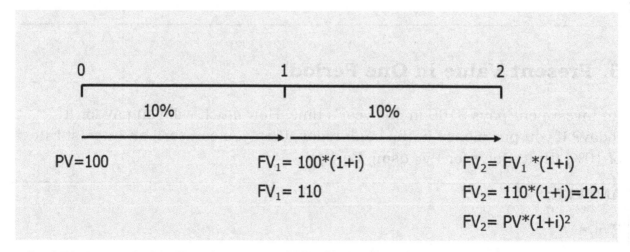

The future value of something that grows at a constant rate for n periods is given by:

32

$$FV_n = PV_0 \times (1 + i)^n \qquad \text{Eq. 2}$$

Where
FV_n = the future value
PV_0 = the present value (at $t = 0$)
i = the interest rate (for one period)
n = the number of periods

7.1 Future Value Explore It

Check out the future value Explore It on page 3.2.5 of CFO.

7.2 Future Value Examples

What is the future value of $1,000 in 35 years at 5%?

ANSWER:
FV_{35} =

What is the future value of $1,000 in 35 years at 12%?

ANSWER:
FV_{35} =

7.3 Future Value Self-Test

Check out the future value self-test on page 3.2.5 of CFO.

It's Time to Do a Self-Test

1. Practise computing the future values. Answer

8. Solve for i

8.1　The Arithmetic Mean

You buy a share (unit) in a mutual fund for $10. After one year the unit's price rises to $20. The following year it falls back to $10. See the diagram below.

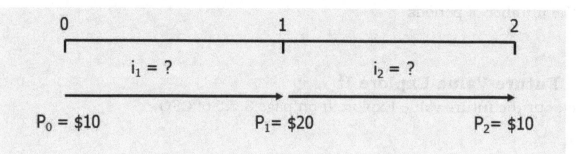

What is the interest rate in the first year?

ANSWER:

$i_1 =$

What is the interest rate in the second year?

ANSWER:

$i_2 =$

What is the average interest rate for the two years?

ANSWER:

$(i_1 + i_2)/2 =$

2　Does your answer to the last question seem like a correct representation of the return that you earned on the two year mutual fund investment?
   A)　No
   B)　Yes

8.2   Compound Average Rate

Use Eq. 2 to solve for i given PV, FV and n.

If FV = 10, PV = 10 and n = 2, then what is i?

ANSWER:

i =

---

3   Does your answer to the last question seem like a correct
       representation of the return that you earned on the two year mutual
       fund investment?
       A)   No
       B)   Yes

N.B. Mutual funds are required (by law) to report their compound average
return and not their arithmetic average return.

9. Solve for n
Use Eq. 2 to solve for n given PV, FV and i.

Assume inflation is 2% every year. A chocolate bar costs $1 today. When will it
cost $2 (in how many years)?

ANSWER:

n =

9.1   Solve for n Explore It
Check out the "Solve for n" Explore It on page 3.2.11 of CFO.

10. Non-Annual Compounding

10.1 Definitions

- m = number of compounding periods in the year.
  - o With semi-annual compounding, m = 2
  - o With monthly compounding, m = 12
- i/m = periodic rate
  - o Represents the interest rate over a compounding interval.

10.2 Example

Sophisto Bank pays a 10% interest rate with semi-annual compounding. What is m and what is the periodic interest rate (for a half-year)?

ANSWER:

m =

i/m =

Sophisto Bank pays 10% with semi-annual compounding. You deposit $100 in the bank. How much is in the account at the end of the first half year?

ANSWER:

FV =

Sophisto Bank pays 10% with semi-annual compounding. You deposit $100 in the bank. How much is in the account at the end of the first year?

ANSWER:

FV =

10.3 Non-Annual Compounding Explore It

Check out the "Future Value with Non-annual Compounding" Explore It on page 3.2.14 of CFO.

10.4 Two Steps for Non-annual Compounding

- STEP 1: Match the interest rate to the length of the compounding period.
  - o periodic rate = i/m
  - o If $i = 12\%$, $m = 2$, then $i/m = 6\%$
  - o If $i = 12\%$, $m = 4$, then $i/m = 3\%$
- STEP 2: Adjust the number of periods.
  - o If there are five years ($n = 5$) with semi-annual compounding ($m = 2$), then there are 10 periods ($n \times m$).

10.5 FV with Non-annual Compounding

$$FV_n = PV_0 \times (1 + i/m)^{n \times m} \qquad \text{Eq. 3}$$

Where

FV_n = the future value

PV_0 = the present value (at $t = 0$)

i/m = the periodic interest rate (for one compounding period)

$n \times m$ = the number of compounding periods

What is the future value of a $1,500 deposit after 20 years with an annual interest rate of 8% compounded quarterly?

ANSWER:

FV =

10.6 Non-annual Compounding Self-Test

Check out the non-annual compounding self-test on page 3.2.14 of CFO.

It's Time to Do a Self-Test

6. Practise computing future values with multiple compounding periods per year. [Answer]

11. Effective Interest Rate

AKA: Effective Annual Rate (EAR)

Simplisto Bank pays a 10% interest rate with no compounding. You deposit $100 in the bank. How much is in the account at the end of the first year?

ANSWER:

FV =

---

4   Which bank do you like better?
- A)   Sophisto (with semi-annual compounding)
- B)   Simplisto

5   What interest rate does Simplisto Bank need to offer (with no compounding) to compete with Sophisto?
- A)   10%
- B)   10.1%
- C)   10.15%
- D)   10.25%

10.25% is the effective interest rate equivalent to 10% compounded semi-annually.

$$EIR(i,m) = (1 + i/m)^m - 1 \qquad \text{Eq. 4}$$

Where
m = the number of compounding periods in the year
i = the quoted (nominal) rate
i/m = the periodic interest rate (for one compounding period)

Octo Bank pays a 8% interest rate compounded quarterly. What is the effective interest rate?

ANSWER:

EIR =

Your credit card charges you interest of 19.99% compounded daily. What is the effective interest rate?

ANSWER:

EIR =

11.1 EIR Self-Test

Check out the effective interest rate self-test on page 3.2.17 of CFO.

It's Time to Do a Self-Test

7. Practise computing effective interest rates. Answer

Solutions

PV in One Period (5)

$PV_0 = 90.91$

Future Value with Compounding (7.2)

$FV_{35} = 5,516.02$
$FV_{35} = 52,799.62$

Solve for i (8.1, 8.2)

$i_1 = 1$ (100%)
$i_2 = -0.5$ (-50%)
$(i_1 + i_2)/2 = 0.25$ or 25%
$i = [FV_n/PV_0]^{1/n} - 1$
$i = 0$

Solve for n (9)

The trick is to remember the following rule of logarithms:
$\ln(y^x) = x * \ln(y)$
$n = \ln[FV_n/PV_0]/\ln(1+ i)$

$n = 35$

Non-annual Compounding (10.2, 10.5)

$m = 2$ and $i/m = 0.10/2 = 0.05$
$FV = \$105$
$FV_1 = \$110.25$
$FV = \$1,500 \times (1 + 0.08/4)^{20 \times 4} = \$7,313.16$

Effective Interest Rate (11)

$FV = \$100 \times (1.10) = \$110$
$EIR = 0.0824$
$EIR = 0.2212$

Annuities (Ch.4, LO1–LO3)

1. Introduction
In this workbook you will:

- Learn how to calculate the future value of an ordinary annuity
- Learn how to calculate the present value of an ordinary annuity
- Learn about equations of value and focal dates
- Learn how to solve retirement planning problems
- Learn how to handle imbedded annuities
- Learn about perpetuities

2. Future Value of Ordinary Annuities

- **Definition:**
  An annuity is a stream of equal cash flows that are paid out (or received) at regular time intervals.

Example:

- You expect to receive $1,000 at the end of each of the next five years. You will invest each payment in a bank account paying 12% interest. How much will you have in the bank when the fifth payment arrives?

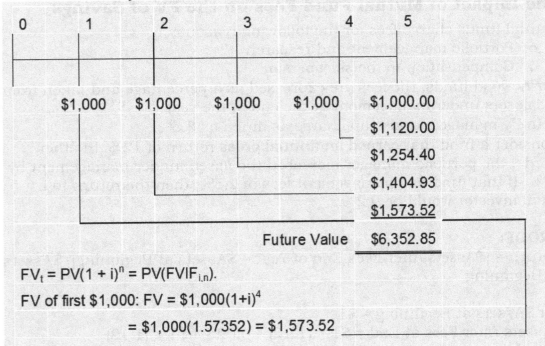

$$FV_t = PV(1 + i)^n = PV(FVIF_{i,n}).$$

FV of first $1,000: $FV = \$1,000(1+i)^4$

$$= \$1,000(1.57352) = \$1,573.52$$

- The future value of the annuity is just the sum of the future values of the payments:

$$FV_{annuity} = PMT_1 \times (1+i)^{n-1} + PMT_2 \times (1+i)^{n-2} + \ldots + PMT_{n-1} \times (1+i)^1 + PMT_n \times (1+I)^0$$

- With the annuity formula, the future value is:

$$FV_{annuity} = PMT \times \frac{(1+i)^n - 1}{i} \qquad \text{Eq. 1}$$

- Think of the annuity formula as a collection of future value problems completed in one step.
- Instead of the formula, sometimes we use this acronym:

$$FVIFA_{i,n} = \frac{(1+i)^n - 1}{i}$$

You expect to receive $1,000 at the end of each of the next five years. You will invest each payment in a bank account paying 12% interest. How much will you have in the bank when the fifth payment arrives? (Hint: Use Eq.1.)

ANSWER:

$FV_{annuity} =$

2.1 The Impact of Mutual Fund Fees on the FV of Savings

- Mutual funds charge fees for the following reasons:
    o Portfolio management and research
    o Compensation to the salesperson
- For no-load funds, the fees are expressed as a percentage and taken from the assets under management at the end of the year.
- Actively managed funds can charge as much as 3.5%.
- Consider a fund that earned an annual gross return of 12%. In other words, the portfolio manager increased the assets under management by 12%. If that fund had management fees of 2.5%, then the return to a retail investor would be 9.2%.

PROOF:
Return = [$Assets After Fees End of Year – $Assets at Beginning]/$Assets at Beginning

Let $Assets at Beginning = $1
$Assets After Fees at End = $1 × (1.12) – 0.025 × $1 × (1.12)
$\qquad\qquad\qquad\qquad$ = $1 × (1.12) × (1 – 0.025)

42

$$= \$1.092$$

Return = [1.092 − 1]/1 = 0.092 or 9.2%

At the end of each month you save $600 which you invest in a mutual fund. The fund earns 12% per annum (assume this is equal to 1% per month) and charges no fees. If you save for 30 more years, how much will you have at retirement?

ANSWER:

$FV_{annuity}$ =

Let's change the last question and introduce mutual fund fees. Instead of earning 12% per annum, you will earn 9.2% (or 0.7667% per month which is 9.2%/12). What is the future value of your monthly savings of $600 per month (for 30 years) at this lower interest rate?

ANSWER:

$FV_{annuity}$ =

1   When you shop for mutual funds, how big a fee do you want to pay?
    A)   0%
    B)   1%
    C)   2.5%
    D)   Who cares about a couple of percent per annum?

2.2   FV Annuity Explore It
Check out the future value annuity Explore It on page 4.1.6 of CFO.

2.3   FV Annuity Self-Test
Check out the FV annuity self-test on page 4.1.8 of CFO.

It's Time to Do a Self-Test

1. Practise computing the future value of annuities. Answer

3. Present Value of Ordinary Annuities

Example:

You match three numbers in the lottery and win $5,000. They will pay you $1,000 at the end of each of the next five years. What is the present value of your prize if the interest (discount) rate is 12%?

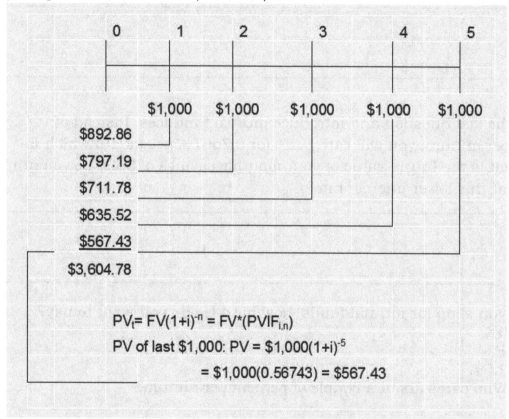

- The present value of the annuity is just the sum of the present values of the payments:

$$PV_{annuity} = PMT \times \left[\frac{1}{(1+i)^1} + \frac{1}{(1+i)^2} + \cdots + \frac{1}{(1+i)^n} \right]$$

- With the annuity formula, the present value is:

$$PV_{annuity} = PMT \times \frac{1 - \frac{1}{(1+i)^n}}{i} \qquad \qquad \text{Eq. 2}$$

- Think of the annuity formula as a collection of present value problems completed in one step.

- Instead of the formula, sometimes we use this acronym:

$$PVIFA_{i,n} = \frac{1 - \frac{1}{(1+i)^n}}{i}$$

You are going to receive $1,000 at the end of each of the next five years. What is the present value of your money if the interest rate is 12%?

ANSWER:
$PV_{annuity} =$

You want a retirement income of $90,000 a year (at the end of each year). You expect to live for 25 years after retirement. You expect to earn 4% on your savings. How much do you have to invest at retirement to achieve your goal?

ANSWER:
$PV_{annuity} =$

You invest $173.55 in a bank that pays interest of 10%. After one year you withdraw $100 and after two years you withdraw another $100. How much is left in the account after the second withdrawal?

ANSWER:
Balance after 2 years =

3.1 PV Annuity Explore It
Check out the present value annuity Explore It on page 4.2.5 of CFO.

3.2 PV Annuity Self-Test
Check out the PV annuity self-test on page 4.2.5 of CFO.

It's Time to Do a Self-Test

5. Practise computing the present value of an annuity. Answer

4. Equation of Value, Focal Date and Retirement Planning

4.1 Definitions
- An equation of value (EOV) is the equation we use to solve time value of money problems.
  - In this course, all of the problems have one unknown so you just need one EOV.
- Equation of value is an equality between cash inflows and outflows after they have all been accumulated or discounted to a common point in time.
- Focal date is the common point in time.
- Sometimes the EOV is simple like the FV and PV annuity formulas given above (Eq.1 and Eq.2). Sometimes, like in the retirement planning problem below, it is more complicated.

4.2 Basic Retirement Planning Problem
Consider the time line below.

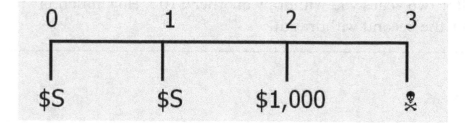

- You will save an amount S for two years at Date 0 and Date 1. You will retire and then withdraw $1,000 at Date 2. At Date 3 your retirement is over. Permanently!
- The amount you save, S, is the same each year and is the unknown value in this problem.
- The interest rate is i = 10%.
- To solve for S, you need an equation of value.

46

4.3 Intuition for Retirement Planning EOV

- This is the creative part of the problem.

2   What principle should you use to build an equation of value for a retirement planning problem?
       A)   inflows = outflows
       B)   savings = withdrawals
       C)   All of the above

4.4 EOV Proposal #1

Savings = Withdrawals

$S + S = \$1,000$

$S = 1,000/2 = \$500$

Let's double-check our solution of S = $500 and see if it accumulates to $1,000 at Date 2. You invest $500 in a bank that pays interest of 10%. One year later you invest another $500. After another year how much do you have in the bank?

> **ANSWER:**
>
> FV =

3   Given your answer to the last question, is $500 the correct amount to save?
   A)   Yes
   B)   No

4   What was wrong with the Proposal #1 equation of value?
   A)   It didn't have a focal date.
   B)   You can't operate on money that occurs at different points in time until you have accumulated (or discounted) the money to a common point in time.
   C)   It ignores the time value of money.
   D)   All of the above

4.5   EOV Proposal #2

- Let Date = 0 be the focal date.
- Move all of the money to Date = 0.
- Then equate savings and withdrawals.

STEP 1: Move savings to Date 0

PV of savings at Date 0 = S + S/(1.10)

STEP 2: Move withdrawal to Date 0

PV of withdrawal at Date 0 = $1,000/(1.10)^2

STEP 3: Equate savings and withdrawals

S + S/(1.10) = $1,000/(1.10)^2
(1.10)S + S = $1,000/(1.10)
2.10*S = 909.09
S = $432.90

Let's double-check our solution of S = $432.90 and see if it accumulates to $1,000 at Date 2. You invest $432.90 in a bank that pays interest of 10%. One year later you invest another $432.90. After another year how much do you have in the bank?

ANSWER:
FV =

4.6 EOV Proposal #3

Let the focal date be Date 2. Follow the three steps shown above. Step 1: Move the savings to Date 2. Step 2: Move the withdrawal to Date 2. (It's already there!) Step 3: Equate and solve for S. What is the equation of value and what is the amount you should save?

ANSWER:
EOV =
S =

4.7 EOV Proposal #4

Let the focal date be Date 1. Follow the three steps shown above. What is the equation of value and what is the amount you should save?

ANSWER:
EOV =
S =

4.8 Conclusions

5   When you solve a time value of money problem do you need a focal date?
   A)   Yes
   B)   No

6   Does it matter what date you pick?
   A)   Yes
   B)   No

49

7   Why did we pick Date 1 in the retirement planning problem?

8   When you do a time value problem, should you draw a time line?
    A)   Yes. In addition to helping you organize the data it may also help
          you to pick a focal date and it may even help you see the equation
          of value.
    B)   No. I don't have enough time.

4.9   A More Realistic Retirement Planning Problem

How much should you save each year for retirement given the following
assumptions?

- You are 30 years old today.
- You will start saving on your 31st birthday.
- You will save every year up to (and including) your 60th birthday.
- You will retire on your 60th birthday.
- You will start withdrawing your retirement income on your 61st birthday.
    o   Q: How will you live for the year after your 60th birthday? A: Don't
         worry about it! These assumptions let us use ordinary annuities.
- Your retirement withdrawal is $90,000 per year.
- You will make your last withdrawal on your 85th birthday.
- The interest rate is 5%.
- The time line is shown below.

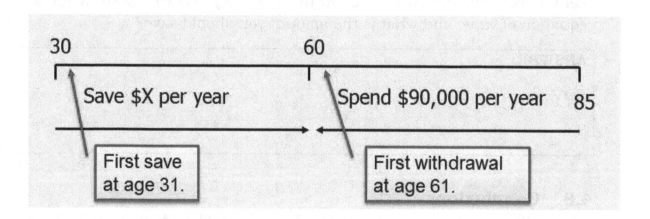

ANSWER:

X =

50

4.10 An Even More Realistic Retirement Planning Problem

How much should you save each month for retirement given the same assumptions as above with the following changes?

- You save and withdraw monthly and not annually.
  - o m = 12
  - o Your first save is one month after your 30th birthday.
  - o Your first withdrawal is one month after your 60th birthday.
- The interest rate is different when you work compared to when you are retired.
  - o When you work you earn 6% per annum (or 0.06/12 = 0.005 per month).
  - o When you retire you earn 4% per annum (or 0.04/12 = 0.0033333 per month).
  - o Why? Because you take less risk in retirement, which means you have fewer stocks in your portfolio and more bonds. Bonds earn lower returns than stocks.

ANSWER:

X (per month) =

4.11 An Even More Realistic Retirement Planning Problem

How much should you save each month for retirement given the same assumptions as above with the following changes?

- You want to leave $500,000 to your children when you die.
  - o You die the day after your 85th birthday.

ANSWER:

X (per month) =

---

5.   Imbedded Annuities

Nicole is diligent and, starting on her 19th birthday, she saves $1,000 at the end of each year (earning 10%) until she is 25, at which time she stops saving and invests her accumulated savings in a savings account that pays interest of 10%. Paris doesn't start saving until she is 26, at which time she starts saving $1,000 a year at 10%. Who has more at age 65?

Paris' problem is the future value of an ordinary annuity. Time 0 is her 25th birthday. Time 1 is her 26th birthday (when the savings really begin) and the final deposit is on her 65th birthday. (Hint: Draw a time line.)

ANSWER:

FV =

Nicole's problem is an imbedded annuity. We will use an ordinary annuity. Time 0 is her 18th birthday (nothing happens). Time 1 is her 19th birthday (when the savings really begin) and the final deposit is on her 25th birthday. What is the future value of her deposits on her 25th birthday? (Hint: Draw a time line.)

ANSWER:

FV =

Part 2 of Nicole's problem. After her 25th birthday she takes her accumulated savings (your answer to the last problem) and leaves them in the bank until her 65th birthday. She earns 10%. How much is in the bank on her 65th birthday?

ANSWER:

FV =

---

9   Who has more money at age 65?

  A)   Nicole

  B)   Paris

  C)   That's not the point. The point is that the two numbers are very
          close. If we had used an interest rate of 10.2491%, then the two
          numbers would have been equal. There are two other points: 1)
          imbedded annuities are a little tricky so always draw a time line;
          and 2) a small amount of money deposited sooner can equal a
          large amount of money deposited later, so start saving for
          retirement as soon as you can.

5.1   Imbedded Annuity Self-Test

Check out the imbedded annuity self-test on page 4.3.5 of CFO.

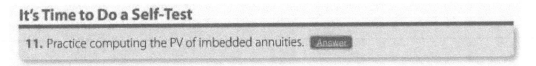

It's Time to Do a Self-Test

11. Practice computing the PV of imbedded annuities. Answer

6.   Perpetuities

6.1   Definition

If the annuity payments continue to infinity, then the stream of payments is called a perpetuity.

6.2   Future Value of a Perpetuity

You will deposit $100 in a bank at the end of every year starting one year from today. You earn 3% per annum in the account. How much will be in the account at the end of time? (Assume annual compounding.)

ANSWER:

FV =

6.3   Present value of a Perpetuity

You will receive $100 at the end of every year starting one year from today. The interest rate is 10% per annum. The payments will continue forever. What is the present value of the payments?

$$PV = \frac{PMT}{i}$$

ANSWER:

PV =

You will receive $100 at the end of every year starting one year from today. The interest rate is 10% per annum. The payments will continue for 30 years. What is the present value of the payments?

ANSWER:

PV =

10   You need to find the present value of a long series of payments but you aren't sure how long the series will last. Is there any material harm in assuming that the series is a perpetuity?

A)   If the series is long and/or the interest rate is fairly high, then the two techniques yield about the same answer.

B)   Who cares? The perpetuity formula is so much simpler than the annuity formula.

C)   Both A and B are correct.

D)   I am busy, so you had me at B.

Solutions

<u>FV of Annuity</u> (2, 2.1)

$FV_{annuity}$ = $6,352.85
$FV_{annuity}$ = $2,096,978.48
$FV_{annuity}$ = $1,145,301.06

<u>PV of Annuity</u> (3)

$PV_{annuity}$ = $3,604.78
$PV_{annuity}$ = $1,405,987.19

There will be nothing left in the account after two years. Alternatively, the balance after one year is $173.55 × (1.10) = 190.9090. Then withdraw $100 which reduces the account to $90.90. With 10% interest, this will grow to $100 to exactly match your withdrawal at the end of the second year.

<u>EOV, Focal Date and Retirement</u> (4.4, 4.5, 4.6, 4.7, 4.9, 4.11)

FV = $1,155
FV = $1,000

Focal Date = 2:
$S*(1.10)^2 + S*(1.10) = \$1,000$
S = $432.90

Focal Date = 1:
$S*(1.10) + S = \$1,000/1.10$
S = $432.90

X = $19,092.07 per year
X = $1,414.51 per month
X = $1,597.92 per month

<u>Imbedded Annuities</u> (5)

$FV_{annuity}$ = $442,592.56
$FV_{annuity}$ = $9,487.17
FV = $429,382.30

<u>Perpetuities</u> (6.2, 6.3)

FV = ∞
PV = 1,000
PV$_{annuity}$ = \$942.69

Loans (Ch.4, LO4)

1. Introduction

In this workbook you will:

- Calculate balloon loan payments
- Calculate amortized loan payments
- Understand the re-investment rate assumption implicit in streams of payments like amortized loans
- Calculate car loan payments
- Solve for the total amount of interest in an amortized loan
- Solve for the interest rate in a loan given the payments
- Calculate car lease payments
- Create a loan amortization schedule
- Calculate the principal outstanding on a loan
- Calculate mortgage payments

2. Loan with a Balloon Payment

Definition:

A balloon payment is a lump-sum payment made at the maturity of the loan to repay some (or all) of the principal and interest. The simplest balloon payment includes all interest and principal.

The equation of value for a balloon loan is:

$$\text{Principal} = \text{Balloon}/(1 + i)^n$$

A friend wants to borrow \$1,000 and repay the interest and principal (a balloon repayment) in full at the end of three years. Your investment alternatives yield 10%. How much money do you want from him in three years? (Hint: How much would you have after three years if you put the money in the bank?)

ANSWER:

Balloon =

---

3. Amortized Loan

Definition:

An amortized loan features identical, regular, end-of-period payments that are a blend of interest and principal.

- Suppose your friend (from the question above) wants to make three equal payments to repay the interest and principal. How large should those payments be to assure that you earn 10%? (The principal of the loan is $1,000.)
- Hint: Shouldn't the three equal payments have the same present value as the principal to make you indifferent between them? Then you exchange two equal things.

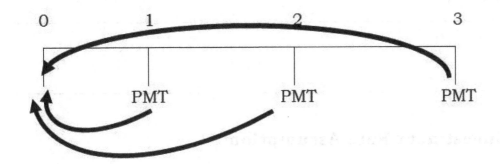

- The PV of the payments (as shown on the time line) is:

$$PV = PMT \times (1.10)^{-1} + PMT \times (1.10)^{-2} + PMT \times (1.10)^{-3}$$

If the PV of the payments must equal the principal, $1,000, then what is PMT?

ANSWER:

PMT =

3.1 Equation of Value for Amortized Loan

- Amortized loan payments are an ordinary annuity: they are all the same size, they occur at regular time intervals and they occur at the end of each period.
- The equation of value for an amortized loan is:

Principal = PMT × PVIFA$_{i\%,n}$

$$PVIFA_{i,n} = \frac{1 - \dfrac{1}{(1+i)^n}}{i}$$

- The right-hand side of the equation of value is what we did above when we found the present value of the three payments.

3.2 Solve for Amortized Loan Payments

An amortized loan has a principal of $10,000, an interest rate of 15% and a term of five years. What are the loan payments? (Hint: Use the equation of value to solve for PMT.)

ANSWER:

PMT =

3.3 The Re-investment Rate Assumption

You expect to receive $402.11 at the end of the year for the next three years. (The first payment is one year from today.) You will invest those payments in the bank as you receive them and you expect to earn 5%. How much will you have in the bank after the third payment arrives?

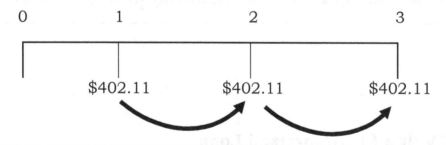

ANSWER:

FV =

60

1   As a lender, which do you prefer: the balloon ($1,331) or the amortized loan payments re-invested at 5%?
    A)   Balloon
    B)   Amortized loan payments
    C)   Indifferent

You expect to receive $402.11 at the end of the year for the next three years. (The first payment is one year from today.) You will invest those payments in the bank as you receive them and you expect to earn 10%. How much will you have in the bank after the third payment arrives?

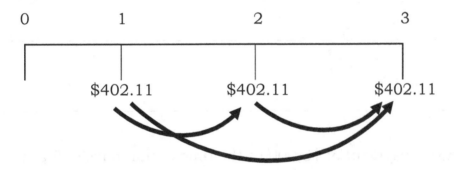

ANSWER:

FV =

---

2   As a lender, which do you prefer: the balloon ($1,331) or the amortized loan payments re-invested at 10%?
    A)   Balloon
    B)   Amortized loan payments
    C)   Indifferent

3   True or False. The lender only earns 10% if he/she can re-invest the loan payments at 10%.
    A)   True
    B)   False

4   Which of the following are correct about amortized loans?
    I.   Lenders earn interest in the payments.
    II.   Lenders earn interest by re-investing the payments.
    A)   I
    B)   II
    C)   I and II

3.4 Car Loan

Car loans are amortized loans. You want to buy the BMW550. The price is $82,900 (plus dealer charges of $1,015). BMW financial services offers a loan (called purchase financing) with a 72 month term and an annual rate of 8% (APR). How much are the monthly payments? (Remember you must also borrow enough to pay the 13% HST on the purchase, so the principal of the loan is (82,900 + 1,015) × 1.13. The monthly interest rate is i/m where I = 8% and m = 12.)

ANSWER:

PMT =

What if you make a down-payment of $5,000 at the time of purchase? What is the equation of value with a down-payment and what are the new monthly payments?

ANSWER:

EOV:

PMT =

3.5 Car Loan Explore It
Check out the car loan Explore It on page 4.4.7 of CFO.

3.6 Solve for the Total Amount of Interest

What is the sum of all payments on the BMW car loan from Section 3.4? (Use the payments with no down payment.)

ANSWER:
Sum of PMTs =

What is the principal of the BMW car loan from Section 3.4?

ANSWER:
Principal =

5   What is included in amortized loan payments?
- I.   Interest
- II.   Principal
  - A)   I
  - B)   II
  - C)   I and II

How much interest do you pay (in total) on the BMW car loan from Section 3.4 with no down payment?

ANSWER:
Interest =

3.7   Solve for the Interest Rate

You loaned $1,000 to a friend. He will make annual payments of $416.35 at the end of the year for the next three years. (The first payment is one year from today.) What annual rate, i, are you earning on this deal?

Hint: Use the equation of value to solve for i:

Principal = PMT × (1/i) × [1 − (1 + i)$^{-n}$]

Substitute what you know:

1,000 = 416.35 × (1/i) × [1 − (1 + i)$^{-3}$]

- Hard algebra
- Impossible for n > 5
- Use trial-and-error (Hint: try 11%, 12% or 13%)

ANSWER:

i =

You loaned $1,000 to a friend. He will make annual payments of $341.69 at the end of the year for the next three years. (The first payment is one year from today.) He will also make a single payment of $200 at maturity (three years from today). Draw the time line of payments for this loan.

ANSWER:

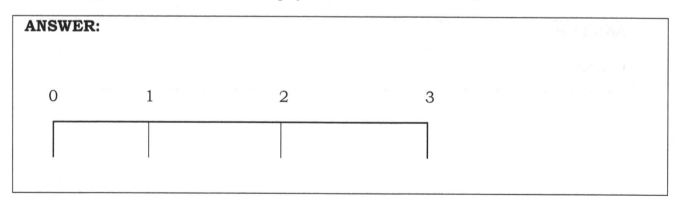

What is the equation of value for this new loan? (Hint: Equate the principal to the PV of payments.)

ANSWER:

Equation of Value =

What annual rate, i, are you earning on this deal? (Hint: Try 9%, 10% and 11%.)

ANSWER:

i =

4. Car Lease

You loaned $1,000 to a friend. He will make annual payments of $314.75 at the beginning of the year for the next three years. (The first payment is made today.) He will also make a single payment of $200 at maturity (three years from today). Draw the time line of payments for this loan.

ANSWER:

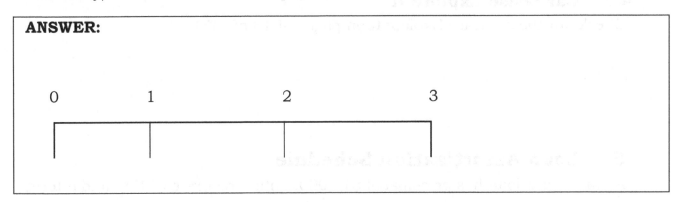

What is the equation of value for this new loan? (Hint: Equate the principal to the PV of payments.)

ANSWER:

Equation of Value =

What annual rate, i, are you earning on this deal? (Hint: Try 9%, 10% and 11%.)

ANSWER:

i =

You want to lease the BMW550. The price is $82,900 (plus dealer charges of $1,015). BMW financial services offers a lease with a 48 month term and an annual rate of 8% (APR). The lease requires that you make a lump-sum payment at the end-of-term of $34,818 (called the buyout). The lease payments are made at the beginning of each month. How much are the monthly payments? (Tax is paid on all payments including the monthly payments and the buyout.)

ANSWER:

Before tax PMT =

After-tax payment = 1.13 × PMT

4.1   Car Lease Explore It

Check out the car lease Explore It on page 4.4.13 of CFO.

5.   Loan Amortization Schedule

An amortized loan has principal of $10,000, an interest rate of 15% and a term of five years. What are the loan payments?

ANSWER:

PMT =

● You borrowed $10,000 at 15% as above. How much interest do you owe at the end of the first year?

ANSWER:

$Interest$_1$ =

You borrowed $10,000 as above. At the end of the first year you make your first payment (calculated two questions ago). Some of that payment covers the interest that you owe (calculated in the last question) and the remainder is a repayment of principal. How much principal remains owing after the first payment?

ANSWER:

$Balance Owing$_1$ =

● You start the second year owing the amount calculated in the last question. How much interest do you owe at the end of the second year? (The interest rate is 15%.)

ANSWER:

$Interest$_2$ =

Complete the following table.

Year	Payment	Interest	Repayment of Principal	Balance Owing
1	$2,983.16			
2	$2,983.16			
3	$2,983.16			
4	$2,983.16			
5	$2,983.16			

●

6   The amount of interest in each amortized loan payment is the same in every payment over the life of the loan.
A)   True
B)   False

7   Over time, each amortized loan payment makes a larger repayment of the principal.
A)   True
B)   False

You are standing at the end of the second year having just made your second payment (see time line below). Using your amortization table, how much do you owe?

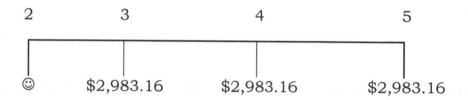

ANSWER:

$Balance Owing$_2$ =

You are standing at the end of the second year having just made your second payment (see time line above). What is the present value of the remaining payments when discounted at the loan rate?

ANSWER:

PV of remaining payments$_2$ =

8   What is the easiest way to find the principal outstanding on an amortized loan?
A)   Use an amortization table
B)   Find the present value of the remaining payments

68

5.1   Amortized Loan Explore It

Check out the amortized loan Explore It on page 4.4.9 of CFO.

6.   Mortgages

6.1   Mortgages are Amortized Loans

You borrow $300,000 to buy a home. The amortization period (n) is 25 years. You elect to make monthly payments (m = 12). The bank quotes you a rate of 4%. What are your monthly payments on the mortgage?

> **ANSWER:**
>
> PMT =

6.2   Effective Interest Rates on Mortgages

What is the effective interest rate of 4% compounded monthly?

> **ANSWER:**
>
> EIR =

What is the effective interest rate of 4% compounded semi-annually?

> **ANSWER:**
>
> EIR =

6.3 Mortgage Regulation in Canada

- In Canada, the effective rate that mortgage lenders can charge is capped at the effective interest rate obtained with semi-annual compounding.
  - o In the example above, that is the answer to the second EIR question.
- In the mortgage example above, if the borrower pays $1,583.51 per month, then the lender earns an EIR of 4.074%, which violates the law.
- Warning: the payment calculation we did above is incorrect because the periodic rate that we used ($i/m = 0.04/12 = 0.00333$) is too high.
- We need to find a periodic rate that has an EIR equal to the maximum of 4.04%. That unknown periodic rate, j, is defined over the payment interval m.
- The borrower chooses m when they select the payment frequency of the mortgage. The choices are: quarterly (for farmers only), monthly, semi-monthly ($m = 24$), bi-weekly ($m = 26$), weekly ($m = 52$).
- The EIR of j is:

    $$EIR(j,m) = (1 + j)^m - 1$$

- The EIR of j must equal the EIR of the bank's quoted rate when compounded semi-annually:

    $$EIR(i,2) = (1 + i/2)^2 - 1$$

    Where i = the annual rate quoted by the bank

- Now, equate the two EIRs and solve for j:

    $$EIR(j,m) = EIR(i,2)$$
    $$(1 + j)^m - 1 = (1 + i/2)^2 - 1$$
    $$j = (1 + i/2)^{2/m} - 1$$

What is "j" for a mortgage with a quoted rate of 4% and monthly payments?

ANSWER:
j =

N.B. Carry a lot of significant digits with "j", as the solution is very sensitive to rounding.

6.4 Canadian Mortgage Payments Done Correctly

You borrow $300,000 to buy a home. The amortization period (n) is 25 years. You elect to make monthly payments (m = 12). The bank quotes you a rate of 4%. What are your monthly payments on the mortgage? (Hint: Use "j" for the PVIFA.)

ANSWER:

PMT =

Solutions

Loan with a Balloon Payment (2)

Balloon = $1,331

Amortized Loan (3, 3.2, 3.3)

PMT = $402.11
PMT = $2,983.16

FV = 1,267.65
FV = 1,331

Car Loan (3.4, 3.6)

PMT = $1,662.57
EOV: Principal = Down payment + PMT $\times$ (1/i) $\times$ [1 – (1 + i)$^{-n}$]
PMT = $1,574.90

Sum of PMTs = $119,705.12
Principal = $94,823.95
Interest = $24,881.17

Solve for the Interest Rate (3.7)

i = 12%
EOV: Principal = PMT $\times$ (1/i) $\times$ [1 – (1 + i)$^{-n}$] + Lump-sum $\times$ (1 + i)$^{-n}$
i = 0.10 or 10%

Car Lease (4)

EOV: Principal = PMT $\times$ (PVIFA-due) + Lump-sum $\times$ (1 + i)$^{-n}$
i = 0.11 or 11%

PMT = $1,421.25
After-tax PMT = $1,606.01

<u>Loan Amortization Schedule</u> (5)

PMT = $2,983.16
$Interest_1$ = 1,500
Principal owing after first payment = $8,516.84
$Interest_2$ = 1,277.53

	Payment	Interest	Repayment	Balance
1	$2,983.16	$1,500.00	$1,483.16	$8,516.84
2	$2,983.16	$1,277.53	$1,705.63	$6,811.22
3	$2,983.16	$1,021.68	$1,961.47	$4,849.74
4	$2,983.16	$727.46	$2,255.69	$2,594.05
5	$2,983.16	$389.11	$2,594.05	$0.00

$Balance Owing_2$ = $6,811.22
PV of payments = 6,811.22

<u>Mortgages</u> (6.1, 6.2, 6.3, 6.4)

PMT = $1,583.51
EIR = 0.04074 or 4.074%
EIR = 0.0404 or 4.04%
j = 0.0033059
PMT = $1,578.06

Risk and Return (Ch.5)

1. Introduction

In this workbook you will:

- Learn to calculate holding period returns
- Learn to calculate the expected return on a single asset
- Learn about risk
- Learn how to calculate and interpret the standard deviation of returns for a single asset
- Learn how to calculate the return on a portfolio
- Learn about diversification
- Learn how to calculate covariance and correlation

2. History of Risk and Return

Your instructor will make a brief presentation on the history of risk and return as well as explain random variables and probability distributions.

3. Holding Period Return

You bought one share last year for $17. Today, one year later, you sold it for $20. Today you also received the company's annual dividend of $0.50. What is the dividend yield on your investment?

> **ANSWER:**
> $D_1/P_0 =$

What is the capital gain rate on your investment?

> **ANSWER:**
> $(P_1 - P_0)/P_0 =$

What is the sum of the dividend yield and capital gain rate?

> **ANSWER:**
> $D_1/P_0 + (P_1 - P_0)/P_0 =$

What is the total return (AKA holding period return) on your investment?

> **ANSWER:**
> $(P_1 - P_0 + D_0)/P_0 =$

4. Expected Return

Definition:

- The expected value measures central tendency for probability data. It is a weighted average. Multiply each outcome by its probability and sum them.
- It is the value we would expect to get on average after repeated trials.
- For symmetric, uni-modal distributions, expected value is also the most "likely."

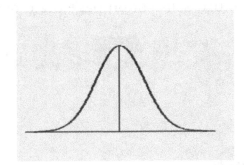

The formula for expected value is:

$$E(k) = Pr_1 k_1 + \ldots + Pr_n k_n \qquad \text{Eq. 1}$$

Where
E = the expectations operator
i indexes the states of nature; there are n states
Pr_i = the probability of state i
k_i = the outcome of the random variable k in state I; for stocks, k is the return on the stock in state i

You are playing a game of chance. The croupier rolls a fair die. You get one dollar times the face value of the die (i.e., $1 for 1, $2 for 2, etc.). What is your expected payoff for the game?

> **ANSWER:**
> Expected payoff =

You are interested in buying shares of ACME Inc. The states of nature, returns and probabilities for the stock are shown in the table below. What is your expected return for the stock?

States of Nature	Return	Probability
1. Good economic conditions	+10%	0.4
2. Bad economic conditions	−5%	0.6

ANSWER:
E(k) =

4.1 Expected Return Self-Test

Check out the expected return self-test on page 5.2.6 of CFO.

5. Practise computing the expected return. Answer

5. Risk

5.1 Definition of Risk

Definition:
Risk is the possibility that something bad will happen.

In finance, bad = earning a smaller return than you expected or, worse, losing money.

Definition:
Risk (for finance) is the possibility of earning small (or negative) returns.

1   Is it risky to jump from a flying airplane with no parachute?
   A)   Yes
   B)   No, it's suicidal.

2   Is it risky to invest all of your retirement savings in lottery tickets?
   A)   Yes
   B)   No

5.2 Measurement of Risk

- Risk is measured by variance and standard deviation of returns.
  - o It is only used for securities with symmetric returns distributions such as stocks and investments in capital assets, NOT options (or lotteries!)

Definitions:

- Variance and standard deviation are measures of spread or dispersion of the outcomes around the expected value.
- Variance is the probability weighted sum of the squared deviations from the expected value.
- Standard deviation is the square-root of variance.

$$Standard\ Deviation = \sqrt{\sum_{i=1}^{n} (k_i - E(k))^2 \times Pr_i}$$

Where

E(k) = the expected return

i indexes the states of nature; there are n states

Pr_i = the probability of state i

k_i = the return in state i

What is the standard deviation of returns for ACME?

States of Nature	Probability	Return	$[k - E(k)]^2$	$Pr*[k - E(k)]^2$
1. Good economic conditions	0.4	+10%		
2. Bad economic conditions	0.6	–5%		

ANSWER:
Standard Deviation =

77

5.3   Interpretation of Standard Deviation

3   If a friend asks you to forecast ACME's return for next year, what do you tell them?
    A) k_{Good} = 10%
    B) k_{Bad} = −5%
    C)   E(k) = 1%

Given your forecast, if the Good state occurs, then how wrong will you be?

> **ANSWER:**
> Forecast error =

4   What is the best interpretation for $(k - E(k))^2$?
    A)   Squared deviation from expected value
    B)   Forecast error squared
    C)   All of the above

5   What is a synonym for a forecast error?
    A)   Surprise
    B)   Shock
    C)   Bolt from the blue

6   Do risky investments have bad surprises?
    A)   Yes
    B)   You bet they do

7   Isn't variance just the probability weighted average of the squared surprises?
    A)   Yes
    B)   Now that you mention it, yes it is.

8   To have a high variance, what do you need?
    A)   Big surprises
    B)   High probability events
    C)   High probability of big surprises

5.4 Standard Deviation Explore It

Check out the standard deviation Explore It on page 5.3.2 of CFO.

5.5 Types of Surprises

- In the capital asset pricing model (which we are building in this and the next few workbooks) we sort surprises into two categories: 1) market-wide surprises; and 2) firm- or industry-specific surprises.
  - o Market-wide surprises affect all (or almost all) companies in the stock market.
  - o Firm- or industry-specific surprises affect one or a few companies.
- See if you can categorize the following surprises:

Surprise	Type
Big Box Electronics Inc. has grappled with two years of declining same store sales. The CEO said, "Consumer electronics is a very, very soft market. Smartphones, tablets and TVs are becoming commoditized."	
Banks posted higher profits due to increased retail lending.	
Toll Brothers Home Construction Inc. posted higher profits this quarter due to an increase in new housing starts. Housing starts hit their highest level in the last two years.	
Copper stocks could be set to rally this year as analysts sound the alarm on the metal's inventory levels.	
GM Inc. stock fell again today as it announced another recall affecting 300,000 vehicles due to a faulty ignition switch.	

5.6 Interpretation of Standard Deviation

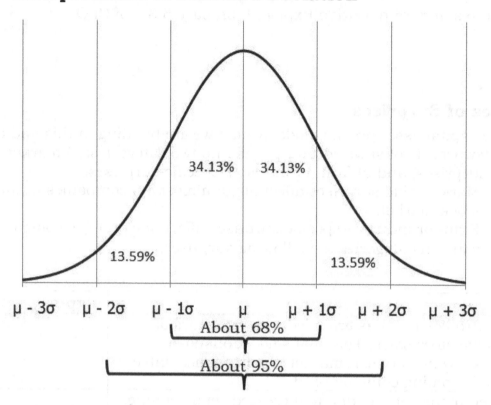

ACME Inc. shares have an expected return of 1% (E(k) = μ = 1%) and a standard deviation of 7.35%. (Assume that the returns on ACME are normally distributed.) What is the probability of getting a return greater than 15.70%? (Hint: How many standard deviations is 15.7% away from the mean?)

ANSWER:
Prob(k > 15.70%) =

---

6. Portfolio Returns

- A portfolio is a collection of assets.
- Portfolios can include real estate, stocks, gold, bonds, etc.

6.1 Trading Account Balance Approach

	0	1
Transactions		
Stock 1:	Buy 6 shares @ $10 per	Sell 6 shares @ $12 per
Stock 2:	Buy 2 shares @ $20 per	Sell 2 shares @ $22 per

How much is your total investment at time 0?

ANSWER:
$Inv_0 =$

How much do you have at Time 1?

ANSWER:
$Sale\ Proceeds_1 =$

What is the return on your portfolio over the year?

ANSWER:
$k_p =$

6.2 Formula Approach

The formula for the return on a portfolio is:

$$k_p = w_1 k_1 + ... + w_n k_n \qquad\qquad \text{Eq. 2}$$

Where
k_p = the return on the portfolio
k_1 = the return on the first security
w_1 = the proportion invested in the first security

$$w_1 = \frac{\$\ \text{value of purchase of stock 1}}{\text{Total amount of investor's equity}}$$

What are the portfolio weights for stocks 1 and 2?

ANSWER:
$w_1 =$
$w_2 =$

What are the returns for stocks 1 and 2?

ANSWER:
$k_1 =$
$k_2 =$

81

What is the portfolio return?

ANSWER:
$k_p =$

6.1 Portfolio Return Self-Test
Check out the portfolio return self-test on page 5.4.5 of CFO.

9. Practise computing the portfolio return.

7. Portfolio Risk

7.1 First Impressions About Portfolio Risk

9   To build a low risk portfolio you simply collect low risk (low standard deviation) stocks and avoid high standard deviation stocks.
   A)   True
   B)   False
   C)   Maybe

7.2 Portfolio Risk Example

- The following table shows the returns for two stocks across three states of nature.

Company	Weather Conditions	Returns on Venus
Venus Bathing Suits	Sunny Year	33%
	Normal Year	12
	Rainy Year	–9

	Weather Conditions	Returns on Gill
Gill Waterproof Jackets	Sunny Year	–9%
	Normal Year	12
	Rainy Year	33

If the states of nature are all equally likely, then what is the expected return for Venus?

ANSWER:
$E(k) =$

10   What is the standard deviation of returns for Venus?
    A)   0%
    B)   The same as Gill and pretty big

11   If you had \$10,000 to invest, which would you prefer—Venus or Gill?
    A)   Venus
    B)   Gill
    C)   Not sure. They have the same expected return and standard deviation.

If you had \$10,000 to invest and bought \$5,000 worth of Venus stock and the same amount of Gill stock, what are the portfolio weights for your two-stock portfolio?

ANSWER:
$w_V =$
$w_G =$

What is the return on your two-stock portfolio in a sunny year?

ANSWER:
$k_p =$

What is the return on your two-stock portfolio in a rainy year?

ANSWER:
$k_p =$

12   What is the standard deviation of returns for the portfolio across the three states of nature?
    A)   0%
    B)   25%
    C)   100%

13   What elements of the Venus/Gill example drive the extreme result
      regarding the standard deviation of returns?
      A)   The returns of the two stocks are perfectly negatively correlated.
      B)   The 50/50 portfolio weights
      C)   The negative correlation and the 50/50 weights

Definition:

Diversification is the act of giving something variety. In the context of investing,
diversification manages the risk of a portfolio by including a variety of assets.

14   Diversification _____:
      A)   Reduces risk.
      B)   Increases expected return.
      C)   Reduces risk and expected return.
      D)   Reduces risk and increases expected return.

15   Diversification works best when the stocks in the portfolio have
      _____ correlations.
      A)   Negative
      B)   Positive
      C)   Zero

16   To maximize diversification, stocks should be negatively correlated
      across _____ .
      A)   Time
      B)   Economic states of nature
      C)   Weather
      D)   Industries

17   A portfolio of stocks can potentially have less risk than the least risky
      stock in the portfolio.
      A)   True
      B)   False

8. Covariance and Correlation

8.1 Covariance

The formula for covariance is:

$$COV(k_1, k_2) = \sum_{i=1}^{n} Pr_i [k_{1i} - E(k_1)][k_{2i} - E(k_2)]$$

(1)	(2)	(3)	(4)	(5)	(6)	(7)
States of Nature	Prob	Stock N, k_n	TSX 60, k_m	$[k_n - E(k_n)]$	$[k_m - E(k_m)]$	(2)*(5)*(6)
1.	0.3	0%	5%			
2.	0.2	10%	12%			
3.	0.2	10%	8%			
4.	0.3	20%	15%			
SUM						

What is the covariance between Stock N and the TSX 60 if both have an expected return of 10%?

ANSWER:
COV =

8.2 Correlation

The formula for correlation is:

$$Corr(k_1, k_2) = \rho_{1,2} = \frac{COV(k_1, k_2)}{\sigma_1 \sigma_2}$$

What is the correlation between Stock N and the TSX 60 if their standard deviations are 7.746% and 4.074%, respectively?

ANSWER:
Corr =

The correlation between Stock 1 and Stock 2 is 0.5. Stock 1 has a standard deviation of 55% and Stock 2 has a standard deviation of 45%. What is the covariance between Stock 1 and Stock 2?

ANSWER:
COV =

8.1 Correlation Explore It

Check out the correlation Explore It on page 5.5.5 of CFO.

Solutions

Holding Period Return (3)

$D_1/P_0 = 0.02941$
$(P_1 - P_0)/P_0 = 0.17647$
$D_1/P_0 + (P_1 - P_0)/P_0 = 0.20588$

Expected Return (4)

Expected payoff = 3.5
$E(k) = 0.01$

Risk (5.2, 5.3, 5.6)

Standard Deviation = 0.0735 or 7.35%
Forecast error = +9%
$Prob(k > 15.70\%) = 2.5\%$

Portfolio Returns (6.1, 6.2)

$Inv_0 = \$100$
Sale Proceeds$_1$ = $116
$k_p = 0.16$
$w_1 = 0.6; w_2 = 0.4$
$k_1 = 0.2; k_2 = 0.1$
$k_p = 0.16$

Portfolio Risk (7.2)

$E(k) = 0.12$
$w_V = 0.5$ and $w_G = 0.5$
$k_p = 0.12$
$k_p = 0.12$

Covariance and Correlation (8.1, 8.2)

1	0.3	0%	5%	−10%	−5%	0.0015
2	0.2	10%	12%	0%	2%	0
3	0.2	10%	8%	0%	−2%	0
4	0.3	20%	15%	10%	5%	0.0015
		0.1	0.1			0.003

COV = 0.003
Corr = 0.95
COV = 0.12375

Portfolio Theory I (Ch. 6, LO1)

1. Introduction
In this workbook you will:

- Learn about diversifiable and non-diversifiable risk
- Learn how to calculate the variance of a two-asset portfolio
- Learn how diversification depends critically on correlation
- Learn how the variance of a large portfolio is entirely determined by correlation (covariance)
- Learn about Markowitz's efficient set
- Learn about risk-free assets
- Learn about the new efficient set and the importance of the market portfolio
- Learn about value weighted portfolios, stock market indices and exchange traded funds

2. Naïve Diversification
Watch the "Types of Risk" Explain It Video on page 6.1.6 about naïve diversification.

3. Types of Risk
- Unsystematic Risk
    - Represents risks particular to individual companies or industries.
    - Unsystematic risk = diversifiable risk
    - Refers to the risk that *can* be eliminated through diversification.
    - AKA: "firm-specific risk"
- Systematic Risk
    - Represents risks that affect most (or all) firms.
    - Systematic risk = non-diversifiable risk
    - Refers to the risk that *cannot* be eliminated through diversification.
    - AKA: "market risk"

1 Diversification eliminates _____ risk.
- A) Systematic
- B) Unsystematic
- C) Total
- D) Portfolio

4. The Mathematics of Diversification

4.1 The Variance of a two-Asset Portfolio

The formula for the return on a two-asset portfolio is:

$k_p = wk_1 + (1 - w)k_2$

Where
k_p = the return on the portfolio
k_1, k_2 = the returns on the two assets
w = the portfolio weight on the first asset
$(1 - w)$ = the portfolio weight on the second asset (since there are only two)

- Note: since the returns on the two assets are random variables, the return on the portfolio is a function of two random variables and so is also a random variable.
- From mathematical statistics, the standard deviation of a linear function of two random variables is:

$$\sigma_p = \sqrt{w^2 \sigma_1^2 + (1-w)^2 \sigma_2^2 + 2w(1-w)\rho_{1,2}\sigma_1\sigma_2} \qquad \text{Eq.1}$$

Where

σ_p	= standard deviation of returns on the portfolio
w	= portfolio weight of Asset 1
$\sigma_1(\sigma_2)$	= standard deviation of returns on Asset 1 (Asset 2)
$\rho_{1,2}$	= correlation between the returns on Assets 1 and 2

Recall (from definition of correlation) that:

$COV(k_1, k_2) = \rho_{1,2}\sigma_1\sigma_2$

You have a two-asset portfolio with stocks A and B. Data are provided in the table below. You have 25% of your wealth in Stock A and the correlation between the stocks is –1. What is the expected return on the portfolio and what is the standard deviation of returns?

	Asset	
	A	**B**
Expected Return	0.06	0.10
Standard Deviation	0.04	0.10
Variance	$(0.04)^2$	$(0.10)^2$

ANSWER:
$E(k_p) =$
$\sigma_p =$

You have a two-asset portfolio with Stocks A and B. Data are provided in the table above. The correlation between the stocks is –1. Complete the table below.

Portfolio Weights		Correlation = –1	
A (w)	B (1 – w)	E(k_p)	σ_p
1	0	0.06	0.04
0.75	0.25		0.005
0.50	0.50		0.03
0.25	0.75		
0	1	0.10	0.10

Plot the five pairs of points from your table above on the following graph. Connect the points with a line. These are the feasible combinations of return and risk available with the two assets, A and B, when their correlation is –1.

Return and Risk with Correlation = –1

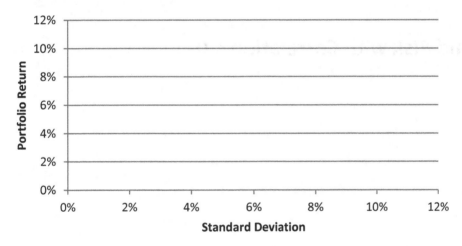

91

You have a two-asset portfolio with Stocks A and B. Data are provided in the earlier question. The correlation between the stocks is 0. Complete the following table.

| Portfolio Weights | | Correlation = 0 | |
A (w)	B (1 − w)	E(k$_p$)	σ$_p$
1	0	0.06	0.04
0.75	0.25		0.039
0.50	0.50		0.054
0.25	0.75		
0	1	0.10	0.10

Plot the five pairs of points from your table above on the following graph. Connect the points with a line. These are the feasible combinations of return and risk available with the two assets, A and B, when their correlation is 0.

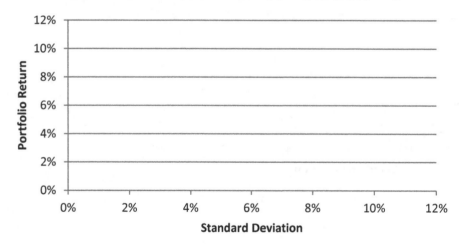

Return and Risk with Correlation = 0

You have a two-asset portfolio with Stocks A and B. The correlation between the stocks is +1. The expected return and standard deviations of various portfolios are provided in the table below. Plot the five pairs of points from the table on the graph below. Connect the points with a line. These are the feasible combinations of return and risk available with the two assets, A and B, when their correlation is +1.

Portfolio Weights		Correlation = +1	
A (w)	B (1 – w)		
1	0	0.06	0.04
0.75	0.25	0.07	0.055
0.50	0.50	0.08	0.07
0.25	0.75	0.09	0.085
0	1	0.10	0.10

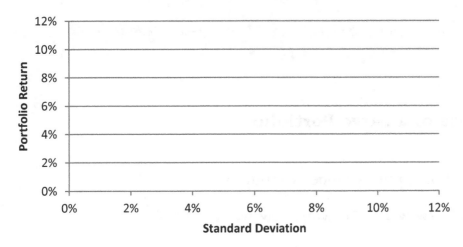

Return and Risk with Correlation = +1

2   Consider a two-asset portfolio with non-zero portfolio weights. As you increase the correlation of the two assets, the variance of the portfolio

_____.

A)   Increases
B)   Decreases
C)   Remains unchanged
D)   Increases and then decreases

3   Consider portfolios of two assets. When the correlation between the assets is _____, the standard deviation of portfolio returns is a simple weighted average of the standard deviations of the two assets.
   A)   +1
   B)   −1
   C)   0

4   Consider portfolios of two assets. When the correlation between the assets is _____, you cannot form a portfolio that has less standard deviation than the asset with the lowest standard deviation.
   A)   +1
   B)   −1
   C)   0

4.2 Two-Asset Portfolio Risk Self-Test

Check out the portfolio risk self-test on page 6.1.5 of CFO.

> **2.** Practise calculating the standard deviation of a two-asset portfolio. [Answer]

4.3 The Variance of a Large Portfolio

For a three-asset portfolio, the variance is equal to:

$$\sigma_p^2 = w_1^2\,\sigma_1^2 + w_2^2\sigma_2^2 + w_3^2\sigma_3^2 + 2w_1\,w_2\sigma_{1,2} + 2w_1\,w_3\sigma_{1,3} + 2w_2\,w_3\sigma_{2,3} \qquad \text{Eq.2}$$

Where
$\sigma_{1,2}$ = the covariance between the returns on asset 1 and 2

- Note that there are three variance terms and six covariance terms.
   - The formula only shows three covariance terms but each is multiplied by 2 because the covariance of 1 with 2 is the same as 2 with 1.
- In general, for n-assets there are n variance terms and $(n^2 - n)$ covariance terms.
- Now, consider an equally weighted portfolio. That is, all of the portfolio weights are given by w = (1/n), where n is the number of assets in the portfolio.

- Let n get big, like 1,000 assets. Then there is a lot of variance and covariance terms. The formula for the portfolio variance is:

$$\sigma_p^2 = \left(\frac{1}{n}\right)^2 [\sigma_1^2 + ... + \sigma_n^2] + \left(\frac{1}{n}\right)^2 [\sigma_{1,2} + ... + \sigma_{n,n-1}] \qquad \text{Eq. 3}$$

- The first term is all of the variance terms. They are all multiplied by the portfolio weight-squared, which is $(1/n)^2$. There are n variance terms in the square brackets.
- The second term is all of the covariance terms. Each covariance is multiplied by the product of the two portfolio weights, which is $(1/n) \times (1/n)$ or $(1/n)^2$. There are $(n^2 - n)$ covariance terms in the square brackets.

TRICK:

By definition, a sample average is the sum of the items in the sample divided by the number of items in the sample:

$$\overline{X} = \frac{1}{n}\sum_{i=1}^{n} x_i$$

We can re-arrange this definition to solve for the sum of items in the sample:

$$\sum_{i=1}^{n} x_i = n\overline{X}$$

In words, the sum of a bunch of things can be replaced by the average times n.

Let's apply the trick to Eq.3. In the first square brackets there is a sum of n variance terms. Let's replace that with the product of the average variance times n:

$$\sigma_p^2 = \left(\frac{1}{n}\right)^2 [n\overline{\sigma}^2] + \left(\frac{1}{n}\right)^2 [\sigma_{1,2} + ... + \sigma_{n,n-1}]$$

In the second square brackets there is a sum of $(n^2 - n)$ covariance terms. Let's replace that with the product of the average covariance times $(n^2 - n)$:

$$\sigma_p^2 = \left(\frac{1}{n}\right)^2 [n\overline{\sigma}^2] + \left(\frac{1}{n}\right)^2 [(n^2 - n)\overline{\sigma}_{i,j}]$$

Now simplify the n's:

$$\sigma_p^2 = \left(\frac{1}{n}\right)\overline{\sigma^2} + \left(1 - \frac{1}{n}\right)\overline{\sigma}_{ij}$$

5   What happens to the portfolio variance as n gets very large? As n approaches infinity, the portfolio variance approaches:
        A)   Infinity
        B)   Zero
        C)   The average variance
        D)   The average covariance

6   How do you construct a large portfolio with low risk (variance)?
        A)   Buy stocks with a low variance of returns.
        B)   Buy stocks with a low average covariance.

7   On May 14, a Russian rocket carrying a \$275 million telecommunications satellite failed and burned up shortly after launch. The lost Express AM4R satellite was built by Astrium, a European aerospace company. Astrium's share price fell after the accident due to the loss. You are considering including shares of Astrium in your (large) portfolio. How will the inclusion affect the variance of your portfolio?
        A)   Increase variance, because the stock has a high variance of returns.
        B)   Decrease variance, because the stock has low covariance with the returns on most other stocks.

5.   Markowitz Diversification

Consider the following thought experiment:
- There are nearly 2,000 stocks on the Toronto Stock Exchange. Assume that we have a database with the expected returns, variance of returns and covariance of returns for every stock and pair of stocks.
- Now, consider every possible portfolio combination of those 2,000 stocks. Start with single stock portfolios, then pairs of two, sets of three, etc.
- Don't forget that you can vary the portfolio weights for all combinations.
    - o For example, even with two stocks, you can have weights of 1%/99%, 2%/98%, etc.
- Now work out the expected return and standard deviation of returns for every portfolio. You are going to have a lot of return and standard deviation pairs.
- Finally, plot all of those combinations on a figure, like we did earlier for the two-asset portfolios. You would get something like the following:

The Feasible Set and the Efficient Set

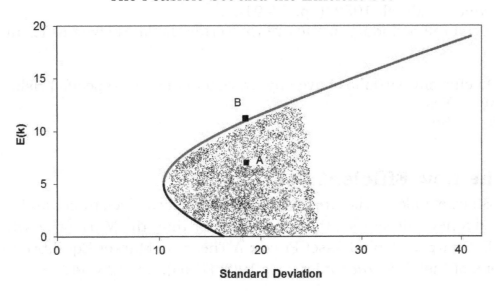

- The shaded area in the figure represents the set of all feasible return/risk combinations that we calculated (in our imagination) above.
- The boundary of the set is very bell behaved: it is a rectangular hyperbola.

8   Consider portfolios A and B shown in the feasible set figure. Which do you prefer?
- A)   A
- B)   B, because it has the same risk as A, but a higher expected return.

Definition:

An efficient portfolio is the portfolio with the highest return for any given level of risk.

9   What is the efficient set of portfolios in the figure, above?
- A)   The combination of portfolios A and B
- B)   The boundary line below the vertex
- C)   The shaded interior of the set
- D)   The boundary line above the vertex

- Harry Markowitz discovered the efficient set and is the father of portfolio theory. His Ph.D. dissertation at the University of Chicago led to his

97

famous 1952 article titled "Portfolio Selection" published in the *Journal of Finance* in March 1952, (pp. 77–91).

- We call the boundary line above the vertex the Markowitz Efficient Set.

10   Do efficient portfolios have any unsystematic (firm-specific) risk?
   A)   Yes
   B)   No

6.   The New Efficient Set

William Sharpe added a risk-free asset to Markowitz's efficient set and discovered a new efficient set that is even better than the Markowitz set. See William F. Sharpe. "Capital Asset Prices: A Theory of Market Equilibrium under Conditions of Risk." *Journal of Finance* 19(3) (1964), pp. 425–442.

6.1 The Risk-Free Asset

11 What is the default probability of a Government of Canada bond?

    A) 0%, since Government of Canada promises are backed by its ability to tax.

    B) More, since total provincial and federal debt exceeds $125,000 per family and there isn't much likelihood of repayment.

Assumption: Assume that the Government of Canada's default probability is zero.

12 Is a Government of Canada coupon bond risk-free? That is, when you buy it, do you know your return with certainty?

    A) Yes, the return is equal to the yield to maturity.

    B) No, the yield is only approximately equal to the return. The final return depends on coupon re-investment rates.

13 A truly risk-free asset is issued by the Government of Canada (no default risk) and has no coupon re-investment problem. Which of the following is such an asset?

    A) Government of Canada 30 year 4% coupon bond

    B) Government of Canada 10 year 2% coupon bond

    C) Government of Canada 1 year T-bill

Consider a one year T-Bill with a face value of $100 that sold for $98.0392 today. If the economy is normal in one year, then the government will pay you the face value of $100 and you will have earned a return of 2%. This information is shown in the middle row of the table below.

State of Nature	Probability	Face Value	T-Bill Return
Weak Economy	20%		
Normal Economy	60%	$100	2%
Strong Economy	20%		

What if the economy is weak or strong? How will that affect the expected payment from the federal government in one year and what is the corresponding return in each state? (Complete the final two columns of the table.)

What is the expected return and variance of returns for the T-Bill?

$$Standard\ Deviation = \sqrt{\sum_{i=1}^{n}(k_i - E(k))^2 \times Pr_i}$$

Where
E(k) = the expected return
i indexes the states of nature; there are n states
Pr_i = the probability of state i
k_i = the return in state i

States of Nature	Probability	Return	$[k - E(k)]^2$	$Pr*[k - E(k)]^2$
1. Weak Economy	0.2			
2. Normal Economy	0.6	2%		
2. Strong Economy	0.2			

ANSWER:
Variance =

What is the covariance of returns on the T-Bill with the returns on anything else?

ANSWER:
Covariance =

6.2 Portfolios of One Risky and One Risk-free Asset

Consider forming a two-asset portfolio. One asset is the risk-free asset, a T-Bill. The other asset is a large equity mutual fund. Data on the two assets is provided in the table below. Answer the questions that follow.

Asset	Expected Return	Standard Deviation
Mutual Fund	12%	17.15%
T-Bill	5%	0%

If your portfolio weights are 0.5/0.5, what is the expected return on the portfolio?

ANSWER:
E(k_p) =

If your portfolio weights are 0.5/0.5, what is the standard deviation of the portfolio? (Hint: Use Eq.1 but keep in mind that the variance of returns on the risk-free asset is zero and so is the covariance.)

ANSWER:
σ_p =

You now have the return and risk for three portfolios of the two assets. One portfolio is the risk-free asset alone, one is the mutual fund alone and the third is the 50/50 mix. Plot the risk and return combinations on the following graph and connect the points with a line. (Hint: if you try other weights you will see that they all lie on the line.)

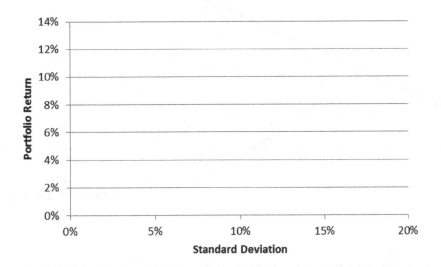

14   When you make two-asset portfolios with the risk-free asset and any other risky asset, the resulting set of risk-return combinations lies on a _____.

A)   Curved line
B)   Rectangular hyperbola
C)   Straight line

William Sharpe discovered this well-behaved geometry and added it to Markowitz's efficient set. Specifically, he created two-asset portfolios by combining the risk-free asset with each of the portfolios along Markowitz's efficient set. The most interesting two-asset portfolio is the one with efficient portfolio M, which produces the risk-return combinations along the tangent line at point M, shown in the Figure below.

The New Efficient Set

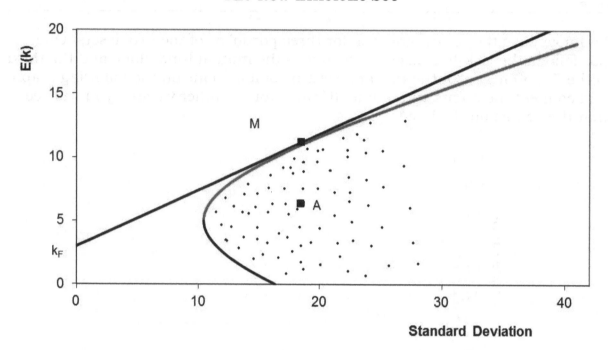

15   Look at the tangent line through M on the figure above and compare it to the Markowitz efficient set. Which is better?
A)   The Markowitz efficient set
B)   The straight line through M

102

16   Is it possible to form a two-asset portfolio with the risk-free asset and any other efficient portfolio that beats the two-asset portfolio with M?
   A)   Yes
   B)   No

- Sharpe called the line through M the "new efficient set."
- He reasoned as follows:
  1. Everyone will pick a portfolio on the new efficient set because it offers the highest returns for each level of risk.
  2. Peoples' position on the line will depend on their risk tolerance. Those fearing risk will be closer to k_F. Those with more risk tolerance will be closer to point M or higher.
  3. Regardless of position, all investors will have a simple two-asset portfolio with: 1) the risk-free asset; and 2) portfolio M.
  4. If everyone holds their risky assets in the form of portfolio M, then M must include every risky asset.
- M is called the market portfolio because it includes every asset in the market for capital assets.
- M is a value-weighted portfolio. (See the next section for an explanation.)
- If we define the universe of capital assets to be stocks, then M is a portfolio including all of the stocks where the portfolio weight of each stock is its proportionate value.

7.   Value-Weighted Portfolios

Definition:

A value-weighted portfolio is a portfolio where the portfolio weight of each asset is equal to its proportionate value.

Consider a small stock market with two stocks, 1 and 2. Data for the two stocks over two days are shown in the table. Answer the questions that follow.

	Stock 1		Stock 2		Total
DAY	Price	#Shares	Price	#Shares	
1	$10	6	$20	2	
2	$12	6	$22	2	

What is the total value of both shares on Day 1 and Day 2?

ANSWER:
$V_1 =$
$V_2 =$

What is the proportionate change in the value of shares over the two days?

ANSWER:
$(V_2/V_1)-1 =$

What is the proportion of Stock 1's value to the total value of all shares on Day 1?

ANSWER:
$w_1 =$

Note: Owning everything in the market is a value weighted portfolio. If you owned everything in this market on Day 1, then you would have a two-asset portfolio. A total of 60% of your wealth is in Stock 1 and that is also its relative value as a proportion of the value of all stocks in this market.

What are the returns on the two stocks from Day 1 to Day 2?

ANSWER:
$k_1 =$
$k_2 =$

Consider a portfolio with three shares of Stock 1 and one share of Stock 2 built on Day 1. What is the portfolio weight on Stock 1?

ANSWER:
$w_1 =$

Consider a portfolio with three shares of Stock 1 and one share of Stock 2 built on Day 1. What is the portfolio weight on Stock 1?

ANSWER:
$w_2 =$

Consider a portfolio with three shares of Stock 1 and one share of Stock 2 built on Day 1. What is the return on the portfolio from Day 1 to Day 2?

ANSWER:
$k_p =$

17   The rate of return on a value-weighted portfolio is equal to the weighted average of the returns on the component assets where the weights are equal to the proportionate values of the assets.
A)   True
B)   False

18   To build a value weighted portfolio, calculate the relative values in the base period.
A)   True
B)   False

19   Any portfolio that has the same weights as a value portfolio will have the same return as the value weighted portfolio.
A)   True
B)   False

8.   Stock Market Indexes and ETFs

- To follow Sharpe's theory, we need to invest in the market portfolio. If we focus on exchange traded equities on the TSX only, there are about 2,000 stocks in the market portfolio. Few investors have enough wealth to buy 2,000 stocks.
- Some stock market indexes can be good proxies for the market portfolio.
  - o They are value-weighted.
  - o Their returns are highly correlated with the market's return.
  - o They include fewer stocks.
- Mimicking an index still requires buying dozens or hundreds of stocks, which is beyond the wealth of most investors. The solution is an exchange traded fund (ETF).
- This section explains indexes and ETFs.
- We use ETFs to implement Sharpe's theory.

8.1 Stock Market Indices

- There are lots of different indices: different stocks in the index and different weighting schemes.
  - o TSX/S&P 60; S&P 500; Dow Jones Industrial; Hang-Sen; FTSE
- Weighting schemes are
  - o Price weighted
  - o Value weighted
- We will focus on value weighted.
- The Dow is price weighted. Ignore it from now on!

8.2 Example of a Value-Weighted Index

- Consider the two-stock market in the value-weighted portfolio example above.
- To construct a two-stock value-weighted index for that market on Day 2, take the total value of the shares on the market (on Day 2) over their value in a base year. Day 1 is the base year.

$$\text{Index}_t = \text{Multiplier} \times \frac{\text{Aggregate Market Value}_t}{\text{Aggregate Market Value}_0}$$

What is the ratio of V_2 to V_1? Multiply that by 100 and we have our index. What is the index value on Day 2?

ANSWER:
$100 \times V_2/V_1 =$

---

20   The percentage change in a value weighted index is equal to the percentage change in the value of the index's bundle of stocks.
   A)   True
   B)   False

21   The percentage change in a value weighted index is equal to a weighted average of the percentage changes in the component stocks weighted by their relative values.
   A)   True
   B)   False

22   If you actually purchased the stocks in an index, your return would be greater than the index's return because of _____.
   A)   Dividends
   B)   Gravity

To control for this, all index companies report a "total return" index which incorporates dividends. Use the total returns version for all portfolio purposes.

For more information, Google "S&P 500 total returns index."

8.3 Exchange Traded Funds

- Even if the S&P/TSX 60 is a good proxy for the Canadian "market" portfolio, it is still very expensive to buy 60 different stocks.
- Solution = iShares S&P/TSX 60 Index ETF

- o Managed by BlackRock
- o Ticker symbol = "XIU"
- o Google "ishares TSX"
- o Check out the MER (Management expense ratio).
- o The ETF is a single exchange-traded security that mimics the index, which, in turn, is a good proxy for the market portfolio.
- Watch the YouTube video "Thrasher University: What is an ETF?"

Solutions

The Variance of a Two-Asset Portfolio (4.1)

$E(k_p) = 0.09$

$\sigma_p = 0.065$

Portfolio Weights		Correlation = −1	
		$E(k_p)$	σ_p
w = 1	(1 − w) = 0	0.06	0.04
w = 0.75	(1 − w) = 0.25	0.07	0.005
w = 0.50	(1 − w) = 0.50	0.08	0.03
w = 0.25	(1 − w) = 0.75	0.09	0.065
w = 0	(1 − w) = 1	0.10	0.10

Portfolio Weights		Correlation = 0	
		$E(k_p)$	σ_p
w = 1	(1 − w) = 0	0.06	0.04
w = 0.75	(1 − w) = 0.25	0.07	0.039
w = 0.50	(1 − w) = 0.50	0.08	0.054
w = 0.25	(1 − w) = 0.75	0.09	0.0757
w = 0	(1 − w) = 1	0.10	0.10

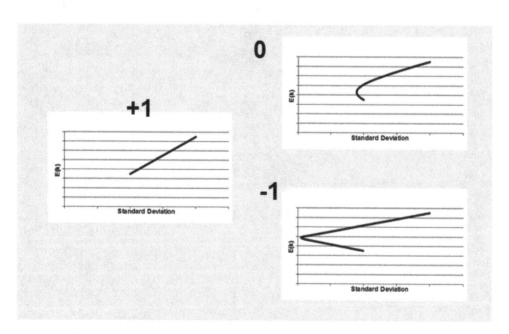

The Variance of a Large Portfolio (4.3)

$\sigma_p^2 = $ the average covariance

The Risk-Free Asset (6.1)

Variance = $0.2 \times (0.02 - 0.02)^2 + 0.6 \times (0.02 - 0.02)^2 + 0.2 \times (0.02 - 0.02)^2 = 0$

Covariance = 0, since the T-Bill deviation from expected value is always zero.

Portfolio of One Risky and One Risk-Free Asset (6.2)

$E(k_p) = 0.085$
$\sigma_p = 0.0858$

Value-Weighted Portfolio (7, 8.2)

$V_1 = \$100$
$V_2 = \$116$
$(V_2/V_1) - 1 = 0.16$
$w_1 = 0.6$
$k_1 = 0.2$
$k_2 = 0.1$
$w_1 = 0.6$
$k_p = 0.16$

$V_2/V_1 = 1.16$
Index = 116

Portfolio Theory II (Ch.6, LO2–LO3)

1. Introduction

In this workbook you will:

- Learn about non-diversifiable risk and its measure, beta
- Learn how to estimate beta
- Learn the properties of beta
- Learn about return and risk for two-asset portfolios with the risk-free asset
- Learn how to draw portfolio possibility lines
- Learn about buying on margin (borrowing)
- Learn about the Treynor Index
- Learn to conduct performance evaluation with the Treynor Index
- Learn about market equilibrium and the security market line

2. Non-diversifiable Risk

2.1 Relevant Risk for a Market Portfolio Holder

- Assume that you own the market portfolio, as Sharpe's theory suggests you should.
- Recall that standard deviation measures total risk.
- Total risk has two parts:

    Total risk = Non-diversifiable + Diversifiable

1 Is there any diversifiable risk in the market portfolio?
   A) Yes
   B) No

2 Do you care about diversifiable risk?
   A) Yes
   B) No

3 Since standard deviation measures total risk, is standard deviation a relevant measure of risk for you?

A) Yes
B) No

2.2 Marginal Risk

- You need a measure of marginal risk:
  - Marginal risk is the change in risk of the market portfolio caused by changing your holdings of one stock.

Sharpe shows that the variance of the market portfolio can be expressed as:

$$\sigma_M^2 = \left[w_{1M} COV(k_1, k_M) + \ldots + w_{NM} COV(k_N, k_M) \right] \qquad \text{Eq. 1}$$

Where
w_{iM} = the portfolio weight of stock i in the market portfolio
$COV(k_i, k_M)$ = the covariance between stock i and the market portfolio

Look at Eq. 1. If you increase your portfolio weight on Stock 1 by one unit, how much does the variance on the market portfolio change? (Hint: Take the first derivative. Calculus warning!)

ANSWER:
$$\frac{\partial \sigma_M^2}{\partial w_1} =$$

2.3 Definition of Beta

- Standardize the measure of marginal risk by dividing it by the variance of returns on the market portfolio:

$$\beta_i = \frac{COV(k_i, k_M)}{\sigma_M^2}$$

- Beta is our measure of non-diversifiable risk.
- Beta, β, is our measure of the contribution of stock "i" to the risk of a market portfolio.
- Since the market portfolio is only exposed to non-diversifiable (AKA systematic) risk, Beta measures the quantity of non-diversifiable risk.
- High beta assets have a lot of non-diversifiable risk.

2.4 The Non-Diversifiable Risk Principle

- **Principle:** Since you can eliminate diversifiable risk for free by diversifying, only non-diversifiable risk is relevant in the pricing of risky securities.

Assume that you have all of your retirement savings invested in one stock, SureThing Inc. You are exposed to a lot of diversifiable risk. To compensate for the risk you demand a return of 20%. SureThing pays annual dividends that will grow in perpetuity at 5%. The next dividend, in one year, will be $1. How much will you pay for the shares?

ANSWER:
$P_0 =$

All other investors hold the market portfolio. They see less risk in SureThing because they are well diversified and only see the marginal (non-diversifiable) risk. On average, everyone else requires a return of 10% for SureThing. What is the market price for SureThing?

ANSWER:
$P_0 =$

4   Given the market price, will you buy any shares of SureThing?
   A)   No, they are too expensive.
   B)   Yes

5   Since you don't trade, does your perception of risk impact the pricing of SureThing?
   A)   No
   B)   Yes

6   Since diversification is free, stock prices will reflect only the risk that cannot be eliminated for free: non-diversifiable risk.
   A)   True
   B)   False

2.5 The Intuition for Beta

- The graph below shows returns on the market portfolio from 1960 to 2010. Dips indicate bear markets and rallies reflect bull markets. The two other lines show returns over time for two other portfolios: one is a portfolio of defensive stocks and the other is a portfolio of cyclical stocks.

- Cyclical stocks move up and down by more than the market.
- Defensive stocks move up and down by less than the market.

The Market, Cyclicals and Defensives

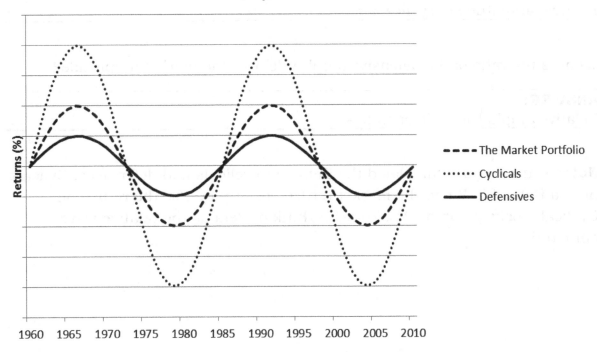

Definition:

Wave amplitude is the height of a peak or depth of a trough relative to the equilibrium point (middle).

Wave Amplitude

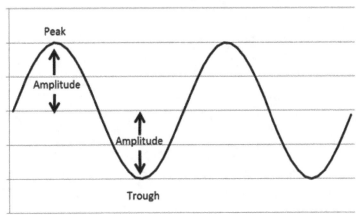

Look at the wave amplitude for the market portfolio and for cyclicals. (Hint: Use the horizontal lines.) What is the ratio of the cyclical amplitude over the market amplitude?

ANSWER:
Relative amplitude of cyclicals =

What is the ratio of the defensive amplitude over the market amplitude?

ANSWER:
Relative amplitude of defensives =

Note: You have just calculated the Betas for cyclicals and defensives. Cylicals have a Beta of 2. When the market return goes up by 1%, the return on Cyclical stocks go up by 2%. You can think of Beta as the relative wave amplitude.

2.6   Estimating Beta

The table below presents monthly returns for the market portfolio and for a stock. Plot the data points on the graph below the table. Plot the market returns on the x-axis.

	Returns	
	Market	Stock
January	5.0%	10.0%
February	3.5%	8.0%
March	0.0%	0.0%
April	2.5%	4.0%
May	−7.5%	−15.0%

Scatter Plot of Stock Returns and Market Returns

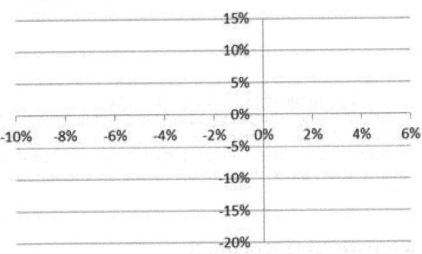

Add a line of best fit to the points on your graph. What is the slope of that line? (Hint: Slope = Rise over run.)

ANSWER:
Slope =

- Beta = The slope of the line of best fit
- If you estimate the slope using an ordinary least squares regression, then the formula for OLS estimate of the slope parameter is given by:

$$\beta_i = \frac{COV(k_i, k_M)}{\sigma_M^2}$$

- The equation that you are estimating is:
$$k_i = a_i + B_i \times k_M + e$$

- The line is called the "characteristic line."

7   Which of the following is the correct interpretation of the slope parameter, B?
   A)   The return on the stock when the market return is zero.
   B)   The change in the return on the stock when the market return changes by 1.
   C)   The return on the stock when the market return is 1%.

Last month the return on the market was 2% and the return on the stock was 3%. Next month, analysts expect the market to generate a return of 3%. What return do you expect from the stock if its beta is 2?

ANSWER:
$k_i =$

8   What is the R^2 statistic for your line of best fit?
   A)   Nearly 0% since the data points don't lie far from the line.
   B)   Nearly 100% since the data points don't lie far from the line.
   C)   Nearly 0% since the data points are spread far away from the line.
   D)   Nearly 100% since the data points are spread far away from the line.

2.7   Characteristic Line Explore It

Check out the characteristic line Explore It on page 6.2.6 of CFO.

2.8 Properties of Beta

- The beta of a portfolio is equal to the weighted average of the betas of the component assets:

$$\beta_p = w_1\beta_1 + \ldots + w_n\beta_n$$

Where

w_i = portfolio weights

9   What is the Beta for the market portfolio? Hint #1: The covariance of something with itself is equal to its variance (i.e., $COV(X,X) = Var(X)$). Hint #2: Look back at the formula for beta.
   A)   −1
   B)   0
   C)   +1

10   The covariance of the returns on the risk-free asset with the returns on any other asset is zero because the risk-free asset's returns do not deviate from their expected value (i.e., $COV(k_F,k_i) = 0$). What is the Beta for the risk-free asset?
   A)   −1
   B)   0
   C)   +1

3.   Portfolios with a Risk-Free Asset

3.1   The Return and Beta of a Two-Asset Portfolio

Consider forming a two-asset portfolio. One asset is the risk-free asset, a T-Bill. The other asset is the stock of a beverage company called Electric Coolade Inc. The table below provides data on the two assets. Answer the questions that follow.

Asset	Expected Return	Beta
Electric Coolade	12%	1.25
T-Bill	5%	0

If your portfolio weights are 0.5/0.5, what is the expected return on the portfolio?

> **ANSWER:**
> $E(k_p) =$

If your portfolio weights are 0.5/0.5, what is the beta of the portfolio?

> **ANSWER:**
> $\beta_p =$

You now have the return and risk for three portfolios of the two assets. One portfolio is the risk-free asset alone, one is Electric Coolade alone and the third is the 50/50 mix. Plot the risk and return combinations on the graph below and connect the points with a line. This is called a Portfolio Possibility Line.

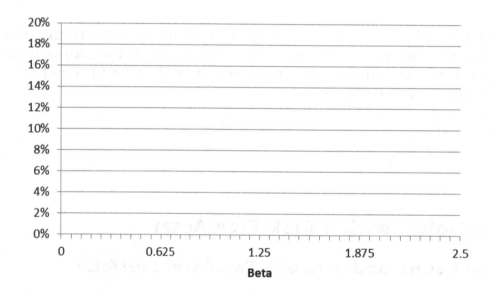

11   When you make other two-asset portfolios with Electric Coolade and the risk-free asset using other portfolio weights, the resulting set of risk-return combinations lie on _____.
   A)   The portfolio possibility line above
   B)   Other portfolio possibility lines
   C)   Cannot be represented in the space above

3.2   Buying on Margin (Borrowing)
Definition:

- Buying on margins means borrowing some money and buying more than you can afford with your own equity.
  - Equity = your money (AKA: your "margin")
- With borrowing, Total purchase = equity + borrowed money

- Where do you borrow money?
  - Your stock broker
    - Control over margin account creates security for the broker.
    - Therefore, the broker lends at a low rate (e.g., prime).
  - Personal line of credit
  - Short selling T-Bills!
    - Margin buying as a two-asset portfolio of: long one risky and short one risk-free asset.

3.3 Borrowing by Short-Selling a T-Bill

- If you aren't clear on short selling, then now is a good time to learn.
  - o Google "short-selling."
  - o Check out the YouTube video "Thrasher University: What is Short Selling?"

12   When you buy a government T-Bill, what is your position in T-Bills?
A)   Long
B)   Short
C)   Margined
D)   Optioned

13   When you buy a government T-Bill, are you borrowing or lending?
A)   Borrowing
B)   Lending

14   When the government issues (sells) a T-Bill, is it borrowing or lending?
A)   Borrowing
B)   Lending

15   When the government issues (sells) a T-Bill, what is its position in T-Bills?
A)   Long
B)   Short

- We are assuming that you can issue your own T-Bills and sell them along-side the government. In essence, we are assuming that you can borrow at the same rate as the government.

The yield on a one-year government T-Bill is k_F. You issue your own one-year T-Bill with a face value of $(1 + k_F)$. What price will you receive when you auction it?

> **ANSWER:**
> $P_0 =$

3.4 A Portfolio with Borrowing (Margin)

You have \$1 to invest, but want to buy \$2 of the Electric Coolade Inc. To borrow the extra money you sell a T-Bill with auction proceeds of \$1 (and face value of $\$1*(1 + k_f)$.

What is your equity investment?

> **ANSWER:**
> Equity =

What is the portfolio weight on Electric Coolade? (Hint: portfolio weight is the value of the purchase divided by your equity investment.)

> **ANSWER:**
> $w_{EC} =$

What is the portfolio weight on the risk-free asset? (Hint: You didn't purchase the risk-free asset, you sold it.)

> **ANSWER:**
> $w_F =$

Given the portfolio weights that you just calculated, what is the expected return and beta on the portfolio?

> **ANSWER:**
> $E(k_p) =$
> $\beta_p =$

120

Plot this new risk and return combination on the graph from Section 3.1.

16   Which of the following is true about the new portfolio possibility line?
    A)   It is an extension of the original line.
    B)   It has doubled the length of the original line.
    C)   All of the points to the right of the risk and return for Electric
          Coolade represent margin portfolios.
    D)   All of the above are true.

3.5   Portfolio Possibility Line Explore It

Check out the portfolio possibility line Explore It on page 6.3.9 of CFO.

4. The Treynor Index

The formula for the Treynor Index is:

$$\text{Treynor Index}_i = \frac{E(k_i) - k_F}{\beta_i}$$

- The numerator is the excess of the asset's return over the risk-free return.
    - ⭕ The excess return is also called the risk premium.
- The Treynor Index measures the excess return per unit of beta risk.
    - o It is a reward-to-risk ratio.

What is the Treynor Index for Electric Coolade? (Use the data from the earlier example.)

> **ANSWER:**
> T =

What is the slope of the portfolio possibility line that you drew above? (Hint: Use rise over run.)

> **ANSWER:**
> Slope =

17   The Treynor index is equal to the slope of the portfolio possibility line.
   A)   True
   B)   False

5.   Performance Evaluation with the Treynor Index

You are presented with the choice between Asset A or Asset B. Use the data in the following table to answer the questions that follow.

	Asset A	Asset B	Risk-Free
Expected Return	12%	15%	5%
Beta	1.25	2.25	0
Treynor Index			

What are the Treynor Indexes for the two assets?

> **ANSWER:**
> $T_A =$
> $T_B =$

18   Which asset provides a greater excess return per unit beta risk?
   A)   A
   B)   B

Draw the portfolio possibility lines for Assets A and B on the graph below.

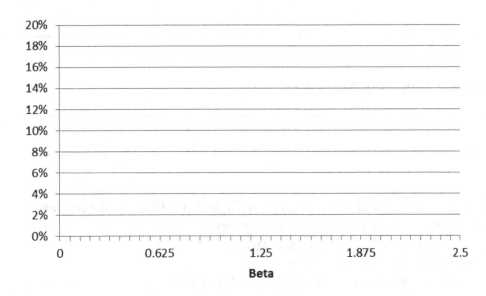

19   Which line is steeper?
   A)   Asset A
   B)   Asset B

6. Capital Market Equilibrium

6.1 Trading Due to Disequilibrium

20 Since Asset A is better than Asset B, you will want to buy it. The supply of the shares is fixed. What will happen to Asset A's price as a result of your demand?
   A) The price will rise due to excess demand.
   B) The price will fall due to excess demand.
   C) Prices are not affected by demand and supply.

Assume that Asset A was expected to pay a liquidating dividend of $10 in one year's time. (And then wind up operations.) It was originally trading at $8.93 (to yield an expected return of 12%). Your buying pushed the price to $8.99. What is the new expected return on A?

ANSWER:
$E(k_A)$ =

What is the new Treynor Index for Asset A?

ANSWER:
T_A =

21 Since Asset B is worse than Asset A, you will sell it. What will happen to Asset B's price as a result of the excess supply?
   A) The price will rise due to excess supply.
   B) The price will fall due to excess supply.
   C) Prices are not affected by demand and supply.

Assume that Asset B was expected to pay a liquidating dividend of $20 in one year's time. (And then wind up operations.) It was originally trading at $17.39 (to yield an expected return of 15%). Your selling pushed the price down to $17.20. What is the new expected return on Asset B?

ANSWER:
$E(k_B)$ =

What is the new Treynor Index for Asset B?

ANSWER:

$T_B =$

Draw the portfolio possibility lines for Assets A and B based on the new prices and expected returns.

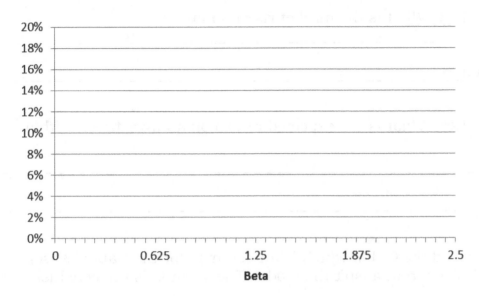

22   Which line is steeper?
    A)   Asset A
    B)   Asset B
    C)   They are both the same.

In equilibrium, all securities have the same Treynor index and plot on the same line: The Security Market Line.

23   What is the formula for the market's Treynor Index?
    A) $[E(k_M) - k_F]/B_M$
    B) $[E(k_M) - k_F]/1$
    C) $[E(k_M) - k_F]$
    D)   All of the above

All Treynor indexes are the same, so we can equate the Treynor Index for security i (a random security) and the Treynor Index for the market:

$$\frac{E(k_i) - k_f}{\beta_i} = E(k_M) - k_f$$

Which simplifies to:

$$E(k_i) = k_f + \beta_i \cdot \left[E(k_M) - k_f\right] \qquad \text{Eq.2}$$

- $[E(k_m) - k_f]$ is called the market risk premium.
- This formula says that the expected return on asset i is equal to the risk-free rate plus beta times the market risk premium.

$k_f = 4\%$ and $E(k_m) = 12\%$. What is the market risk premium?

ANSWER:
Market Risk Premium =

$k_f = 4\%$ and $E(k_m) = 12\%$. What is the expected return on an investment with a Beta of 1.5?

ANSWER:
$E(k)$ =

- Eq.2 is often called the CAPM which is an acronym for the Capital Asset Pricing Model. The formula isn't the model. The formula is the conclusion of the model.
- This formula calculates the equilibrium or "fair" rate of return for an asset. That is its long-term average.

24 Is the following a valid criticism of the model? "There may be some truth in the CAPM, but over the last year many stocks gave a substantially higher return than the CAPM predicted and many gave a substantially lower return."
   A)   Yes
   B)   No

- Eq.2 is the equation for the security market line.
- Here is a picture of the security market line (assuming that $k_M = 12\%$ and $k_F = 5\%$).

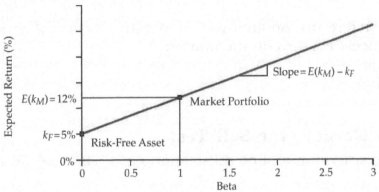

Figure 6.6 Security Market Line

6.2 Security Market Line Explore It

Check out the security market line Explore It on page 6.3.18 of CFO.

6.3 Security Market Line Questions

25   What is the y-axis intercept of the SML?
  A) k_F
  B) $E(k_M) - k_F$
  C)   B (Beta)
  D) $E(k_M)$

26   What is the slope of the SML?
  A) k_F
  B) $E(k_M) - k_F$
  C)   B (Beta)
  D) $E(k_M)$

27   A mutual fund manager expects her portfolio to earn a rate of return of 9% this year. $\beta = 0.8$, $k_f = 4\%$ and $E(k_m) = 11\%$. Should you invest in her mutual fund?
  A)   Yes
  B)   No
  C)   Not enough information

28   The SML implies that if you could find an investment with a negative beta, its expected return would be less that of the risk-free rate.
  A)   True

B) False

29   The expected return on an investment with a beta of 2 is twice as high
      as the expected return on the market.
      A)   True
      B)   False

6.4   Security Market Line Self-Test

Check out the security market line self-test on page 6.3.20 of CFO.

It's Time to Do a Self-Test

21. Practise computing expected returns using the SML. `Answer`

7.   Mutual Fund Performance Analysis with the SML

Consider the following historical data on two mutual funds, the market
portfolio and the risk-free rate.

	Prudent	Zenith	Market	Risk-Free
Return	8.3%	12.5%	12.0%	5.0%
Std Dev	8.5%	23.5%	18.0%	0.0%
Beta	0.47	1.50	1	0

Plot the Security Market Line and then show Prudent and Zenith on the graph.
Which is better?

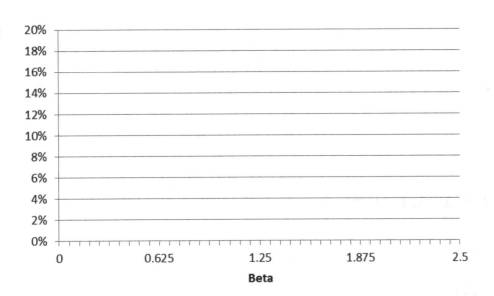

What are the Treynor Indexes for the two funds?

ANSWER:
$T_P =$
$T_Z =$

Could you have beaten Zenith by buying the market on margin? What portfolio weights would have accomplished this? (Hint: Build a two-asset portfolio with the risk-free asset and the market portfolio. Set the beta of that portfolio equal to Zenith's beta (1.5). Solve for the portfolio weight on Zenith.)

ANSWER:
w =

What return would you have earned on your replicating portfolio? By how much would you have beaten Zenith?

ANSWER:
$k_p - k_Z =$

Solutions

<u>Marginal Risk</u> (2.2)

$$\frac{\partial \sigma_M^2}{\partial w_1} = COV(k_1, k_M)$$

<u>Non-Diversifiable Risk Principle</u> (2.4)

P_0 = $6.67
P_0 = $20

<u>Intuition for Beta</u> (2.5)

Relative amplitude of cyclicals = 2
Relative amplitude of defensives = 0.5

<u>Estimating Beta</u> (2.6)

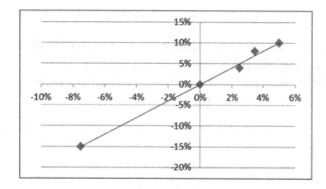

Slope = 2
The return on the stock should be 3% + 2% = 5%.

<u>Portfolios with a Risk-Free Asset</u> (3.1, 3.3)

$E(k_p)$ = 8.5%
β_p = 0.625

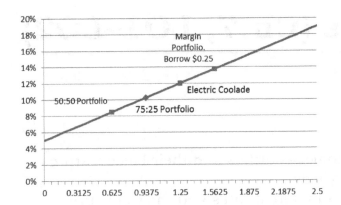

$P_0 = \$1$

A Portfolio with Borrowing (3.4)

Equity = $1
$w_{EC} = 2$
$w_F = -1$
$E(k_p) = 19\%$
$\beta_p = 2.5$

Treynor Index (4, 5)

$T = 0.056$ or 5.6%
Slope = 0.056

$T_A = 0.056$
$T_B = 0.044$

Capital Market Equilibrium (6.1, 7)

$E(k_A) = 0.1123$
$T_A = 0.0499$

$E(k_B) = 0.1628$
$T_B = 0.05$

Market Risk Premium = 0.08 or 8%
$E(k) = 0.16$

$T_A = 0.07$
$T_B = 0.05$

$w = 1.5$
$k_p - k_Z = 0.03$ or 3%

Rates and Bonds (Ch.7, LO1–LO2)

1. Introduction

In this workbook you will:

- Learn the definition of fixed income securities and their basic features
- Learn about zero coupon bond yields
- Learn about the term structure of interest rates and the yield curve
- Learn about the determinants of the shape of the yield curve
- Learn how inflation affects interest rates and bond yields
- Learn about the expectations theory
- Learn about forward rates
- Learn about the maturity preference theory
- Learn about default
- Learn about liquidity

2. Fixed Income Definitions and Features

- Fixed income securities:
    - A class of securities that pay a fixed income to the holder.
    - The class includes bonds.
- Bonds:
    - A debt security, like an IOU.
    - Bond issuers borrow money from bond investors.
    - The issuers agree to repay the principal amount (Face Value) of the loan on the maturity date.
    - A bond represents a loan from the holder to the issuer.

2.1 Zero Coupon Bond

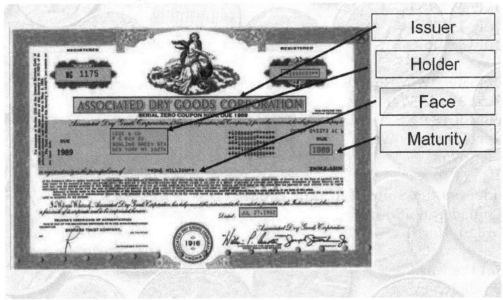

2.2 Coupon Bond

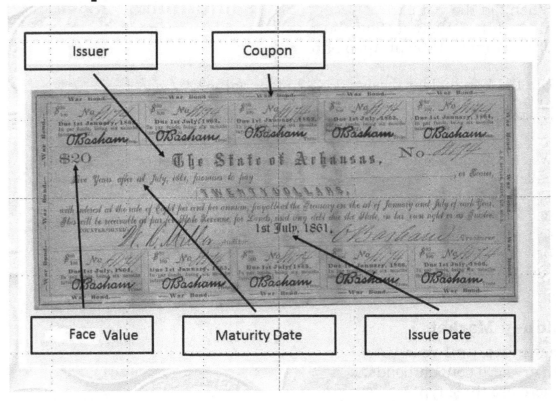

Notes:
- The coupons are dated every six months starting six months from the issue date of July 1, 1861.
- Each coupon is for $0.80.

1   What is the maturity date of the bond?
     A)   July 1, 1864
     B)   July 1, 1865
     C)   July 1, 1866

2   The bond says "War Bond" all around it. What was the war?
     A)   First World War
     B)   War of 1812
     C)   Revolutionary War
     D)   Civil War

3   What side was the State of Arkansas on?
     A)   Confederate (South)
     B)   Union (North)

4   Who won the war?
     A)   Confederacy
     B)   Union

5   When did the war end?
     A)   July 3,1863 at Gettysburg
     B)   April 9, 1865 at Appomattox

6   Did the bondholder receive the $20 face value?
     A)   Yes
     B)   No

7   When a bond issuer (borrower) does not pay interest or principal it is
     called _____.
     A)   Default
     B)   Delinquency
     C)   Noncompliance
     D)   Non-service

2.3   Money Market

- Maturities < = 1 year
- All are zero coupon bonds.
- There are three types:
  - Canadian Treasury Bills
    - Issued by Government of Canada with minimum face value of $1,000.
    - Common maturity is 91 days (182 and 364 days).
  - Commercial Paper

- Issued by highly rated private companies.
- Have no collateral. Issued for working capital needs.
  o Bankers' Acceptance
    - Like commercial paper.
    - Bank guarantees company's ability to pay. Bank pays holder in event of default by issuer.
    - Issuers are less credit-worthy than issuers of commercial paper.

Value of Bonds Outstanding End of Year Canadian Money Market ($000,000,000)				
	Commercial Paper	Bankers Acceptance	T-Bills	Total
1996	47.2	34.0	16.0	97.1
2000	131.1	51.5	18.0	200.6
2010	53.6	45.8	34.8	134.3
2011	54.4	47.9	34.8	137.1
2013	54.7	58.3	50.5	163.5
Source: Table F2, "Banking and Finance Statistics", Bank of Canada				

8   In 2013, which type of security had the largest share of the money market?
   A)   Commercial Paper
   B)   Bankers' Acceptance
   C)   T-Bills

9   Between 1996 and 2013, which type of money market security increased its share of the market by the largest amount?
   A)   Commercial Paper
   B)   Bankers' Acceptance
   C)   T-Bills

10   What caused the increase in borrowing by the federal government?
   A)   Out-of-control spending by the Martin and Harper governments
   B)   The financial crises of 2008
   C)   A lax attitude amongst today's taxpayers about intergenerational theft
   D)   All of the above

3. Zero Coupon Bonds

3.1   Zero Coupon Bond Cash Flows

Time Line of Cash Flows for Zero Coupon Bond

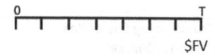

A zero coupon bond generates one cash flow: the face value paid at maturity to the holder.

3.2   Zero Coupon Bond Yields

If we think of the price as a present value and the face value as a future value, then we can use the future value formula to solve for the return.

$$FV = Price \times (1 + k)^n \qquad \text{Eq. 1}$$

Where
FV = the face value of the bond
Price = the price of the bond at time 0
k = the return on the bond (yield to maturity)
n = the number of years until maturity

We can solve for the return on the bond by simplifying Eq. 1.

$$k = \left[\frac{FV}{Price}\right]^{1/n} - 1 \qquad \text{Eq. 2}$$

- k = Yield to maturity (or yield)
  - o An estimate of the annual return an investor will earn if they buy a bond and hold it to maturity.

- o Also known as the return.
- Treasury spot rates
  - o The yield on a default-free zero coupon (Treasury or Government of Canada) where the yield is quoted for immediate settlement.
  - o There is almost no risk that the Government of Canada will fail to pay its obligations.

3.3 Yield Example

A two year, zero-coupon bond has a face value of $1,100 and sells for $960.78. What is the yield on the bond? (It is called the two-year "spot" rate, and is denoted k_2.)

ANSWER:

k_2 =

3.4 Term Structure of Interest Rates and the Yield Curve

Maturity Date	Price ($100 face value)	Yield to Maturity
1	$99.009	
2	$96.117	2%
3	$91.514	3%
4	$85.480	4%
5	$78.353	5%

- The table above shows the prices for five different zero coupon bonds with five different maturities. The yields are shown in the right-hand column.
- If the bonds are government bonds with no default risk, then the yields are called "spot rates."
- The collection of yields is called the term structure of interest rates because they are rates for different terms.

What is the yield on the one-year bond?

ANSWER:

k_1 =

Plot the yields from the table above on the graph below.

137

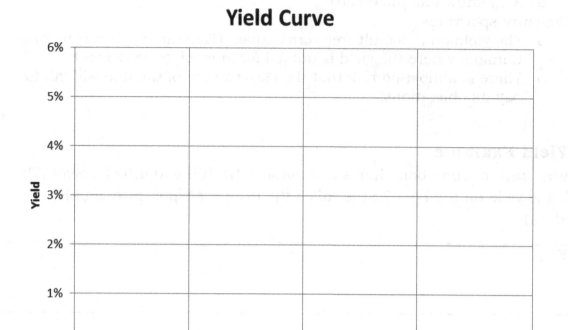

4. Determinants of the Shape of the Yield Curve

Factors that determine position and slope of the spot rate yield curve

- Real interest rates
- Inflation
- Expectations
- Maturity preference
- Default risk
- Liquidity

4.1　Inflation

- The real rate of interest is the rate that would prevail if there was no inflation.
- The nominal rate of interest is the observed rate of interest.
  - o If inflation is zero, then the real rate equals the nominal rate.

The relationship between the nominal rate, the real rate and inflation was derived by an American economist called Irving Fisher. Eq 3 is called the Fisher Equation.

$$(1 + k_n) = (1 + k_r) \times (1 + \pi) \qquad\qquad Eq. 3$$

Where

k_n = the nominal interest rate
k_r = the real interest rate
π = the expected rate of inflation

The real rate of interest is 10% and expected inflation is 5%. What is the nominal rate of interest?

ANSWER:

k_n =

The real rate of interest stays at 10% but expected inflation rises to 6%. What is the new nominal rate of interest?

> **ANSWER:**
>
> $k_n =$

4.2 Inflation in Canada: 1982–2012

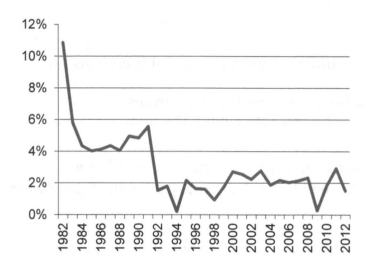

11   What rate of inflation has the Bank of Canada targeted since 1992?
  A)   0%
  B)   1%
  C)   2%
  D)   3%

Assume inflation is consistently 2% every year. A chocolate bar costs $1 today. When will it cost $2? (In how many years?)

> **ANSWER:**
>
> $n =$

5. Expectations

5.1 Expected Future Spot Rates

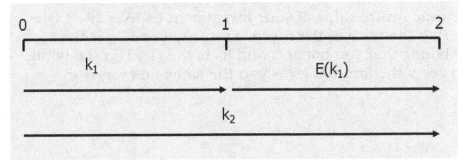

- k_1 is the one-year spot rate.
- Next year there will be a one-year spot rate with maturity at Year 2.
- At Time 0, the spot rate expected to prevail next year is the expected future spot rate, denoted $E(k_1)$.

5.2 Two Year Investment Horizon: Roll-over or Lock-in?

- Consider someone interested in a two-year maturity. They have two investment options:
  o Lock-in for two years (i.e., buy a two-year bond).
  o Roll-over. Invest for one year by buying a one-year bond. Then, roll the money over by buying a one-year bond at Date 1.

5.3 Lock-In

Maturity	Price (FV = $100)	Yield
1	$94.34	6%
2	$87.34	7%

12   The table above shows price and yield information for two zero coupon bonds. Consider investing $87.34 in a two-year zero coupon bond. The yield on the bond is $k_2 = 7\%$. How much will you have at the end?
- A) $96.42
- B) $97.55
- C) $98.20
- D) $100.00
- E) None of the above

13   How many of the two-year bonds did you buy?
      A)   1
      B)   2

14   You can express the future value of your investment as $FV = (P_n \times Q) \times (1 + k_n)^n$ where P_n = the price of the n-year maturity bond; Q is the quantity of the bonds that you bought; and k_n is the yield on the bond. (Hint: Check to see if the formula gives you the same answer as in Question 1.)
      A)   True
      B)   False

Use the equation from the previous question to solve for the future value of your investment in two years if you buy two bonds (i.e., $Q = 2$).

ANSWER:

$FV_2 =$

5.4 Roll-Over

Maturity	Price (FV = $100)	Yield
1	$94.34	6%
2	$87.34	7%

The table above shows price and yield information for two zero coupon bonds. Consider investing $87.34 in a one-year zero coupon bond. How many of those bonds can you afford to buy?

ANSWER:

$Q =$

Consider investing $87.34 in a one-year zero coupon bond. You buy 0.9258 of the bonds at a price of $94.34 each. The yield on the bond is $k_1 = 6\%$. How much will you have at the end of the year? (What is the future value of your investment?)

> **ANSWER:**
>
> $FV_1 =$

Today is Date 1 on the time line. There is a new one-year zero coupon bond (FV = $100) that is priced at $92.58 to yield 8%. You take your proceeds from the last question and buy one of the new one-year zero coupon bonds at Time 1 (ignore the penny). How much money will you have at Time 2?

> **ANSWER:**
>
> $FV_2 =$

5.5 Lock-in v. Roll-over Conclusions

15 In the last set of examples, which investment strategy was better? That is, if you compare investing $87.34 in the lock-in versus the same amount in the roll-over, which gives you more money at Year 2?
   A) Lock-in
   B) Roll-over
   C) Both the same

16 If you invest $1 in the lock-in, then the future value of your investment is given by:
   A) $FV_2 = \$1 \times (1 + k_2)$
   B) $FV_2 = \$1 \times (1 + k_2)^2$
   C) $FV_2 = \$1 \times (1 + k_1) \times (1 + k_2)$

17 If you invest $1 in the roll-over, then the future value of your investment is given by (where $E(k_1)$ is the expected future spot rate in Year 2):
   A) $FV_2 = \$1 \times (1 + k_2)$
   B) $FV_2 = \$1 \times (1 + k_2)^2$
   C) $FV_2 = \$1 \times (1 + k_1) \times (1 + k_2)$
   D) $FV_2 = \$1 \times (1 + k_1) \times (1 + E(k_1))$

5.6 Expectations Theory

- The expectations theory assumes that investors are indifferent between lock-in or roll-over.
  - o This need not be true. There are risks to each.
- If investors are indifferent, then the last example represented an equilibrium because both strategies yielded the same dollar outcome for the investment and the same return on investment.
- The equilibrium condition is that, given expectations, the future value of investing $1 in each strategy is equal:
  - o $1 \times (1 + k_2)^2 = FV_2 = \$1 \times (1 + k_1) \times (1 + E(k_1))$
    OR
  - o $(1 + k_2)^2 = (1 + k_1) \times (1 + E(k_1))$ Eq. 4
- This is a law-of-one price argument. The two strategies are equivalent so they must be priced to give the same return.
- If the returns are different, then investors will adopt the strategy with the higher returns. This will affect prices and returns and restore the equilibrium.

Assume that the expectations theory holds. The yield on a one-year bond is 6% and the expected future spot rate (next year) is 8%. What is the yield on the two-year bond?

ANSWER:

$k_2 =$

---

18   If the yield on a one-year bond is 6% and the yield on a two-year bond is 7%, then what is the shape of the yield curve?
    A)   Upward sloping
    B)   Downward sloping
    C)   Flat

19   Assume that the expectations theory holds. If the yield curve is upward sloping, then future spot rates are expected to be _____ current spot rates.
    A)   Greater than
    B)   Lower than
    C)   The same as

Assume that the expectations theory holds. The yield on a one-year bond is 6% and the yield on a two-year bond is 5.5%. What is the expected future spot rate (next year)?

> **ANSWER:**
>
> $E(k_1) =$

20. Assume that the expectations theory holds. If the yield curve is downward sloping, then future spot rates are expected to be _____ current spot rates.
    A) Greater than
    B) Lower than
    C) The same as

6. Forward Rates

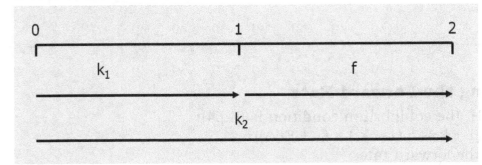

- In the diagram above, the yield on the one-year bond in the second year is denoted f.
- Given, the two spot rate, k_1 and k_2, what rate in the second year (what value for f) equates the future values of investments in the lock-in and the roll-over?
- This is called the forward rate or implied forward rate.

6.1   Solving for the Forward Rate

The future value of the lock-in is:

$$FV_2 = \$1 \times (1 + k_2)^2$$

The future value of the roll-over at f (in the second year) is:

$FV_2 = \$1 \times (1 + k_1) \times (1 + f)$

Solve for f:

$$f = \frac{(1 + k_2)^2}{(1 + k_1)} - 1$$

The one-year spot rate is 2% and the two-year spot rate is 2.5%. What is the forward rate?

ANSWER:
f =

The three-year spot rate is 8% and the two-year spot rate is 7%. What is the forward rate in Year 3?

ANSWER:
f =

6.2 Interpreting the Forward Rate
- Under the EH, the equilibrium condition is (Eq.4):
  - $(1 + k_2)^2 = (1 + k_1) \times (1 + E(k_1))$
- Formula for the forward rate:
  - $(1 + k_2)^2 = (1 + k_1) \times (1 + f)$
- If both are true, then the forward rate can be interpreted as the expected future spot rate: $f = E(k_1)$.

21 You are working at a bank. Your boss asks you for a forecast of next year's interest rate. The easiest source for this is:
   A) Create an open-economy model of the macroeconomy. Use it to forecast rates.
   B) Calculate the forward rate from spot-rate data provided by the Bank of Canada or the Federal Reserve (for free).
   C) Create a time-series model of interest rates and forecast the rate econometrically.

7. The Maturity Preference Theory

- Assumes that investors are not indifferent between lock-in and roll-over.
- Assumes that investors prefer to roll-over.
- If this is true, then to entice investors, long maturity securities must offer higher returns.
- Under this theory, if spot rates satisfy the expectations equilibrium equation (Eq.4):
  - $(1 + k_2)^2 = (1 + k_1) \times (1 + E(k_1))$
    - o Then investors won't buy the two-year bond, they'll choose roll-over.
    - o Thus, issuers of bonds with longer maturities (i.e., the two-year) must offer a higher yield. In other words, k_2 must be big enough so that:
      - $(1 + k_2)^2 > (1 + k_1) \times (1 + E(k_1))$
- Relative to the two-year spot rate implied by the Expectations Theory, k_2 includes a premium in it to entice investors to the long-term.

7.1 Implication #1 of the MPT

- If $(1 + k_2)^2 > (1 + k_1) \times (1 + E(k_1))$, then $f > E(k_1)$
- If the MPT is true, then the forward rate is a little larger than the expected future spot rate because of the premium built into k_2.

  - o You can't interpret the forward rate as a perfect forecast of future rates. It will slightly overestimate future interest rates.
  - o Don't let this dissuade you from using the forward rate as an estimate. The difference is small.

7.2 Implication #2 of the MPT

- The yield curve will be a little steeper than the expectations hypothesis predicts.

Assume that the expectations theory holds. The yield on a one-year bond is 6% and the expected future spot rate (next year) is 6%. What is the yield on the two-year bond?

> **ANSWER:**
>
> $k_2 =$

22   Assume that the expectations theory holds. If the yield on a one-year bond is 6% and the yield on a two-year bond is 6%, then what is the shape of the yield curve?
   A)   Upward sloping
   B)   Downward sloping
   C)   Flat

23   Assume that the maturity preference theory holds. The yield on a one-year bond is 6% and the expected future spot rate (next year) is 6%. What is the yield on the two-year bond?
   A)   Less than 6%
   B)   6%
   C)   A little more than 6%

24   Assume that the MPT holds. If the yield on a one-year bond is 6% and the expected future spot rate is 6%, then what is the shape of the yield curve?
   A)   Upward sloping
   B)   Downward sloping
   C)   Flat

8. Default Risk

- Default means the failure to fulfill an obligation.
- Default is the major risk associated with corporate and foreign government bonds.
- Investors in bonds with a higher probability of default pay lower prices and earn higher yields.
- The difference in yields due to default risk is called the "Default Risk Premium" (DRP).

Figure 7.6 Yield Spread Between Mid-Maturity BBB Corporate and Government of Canada

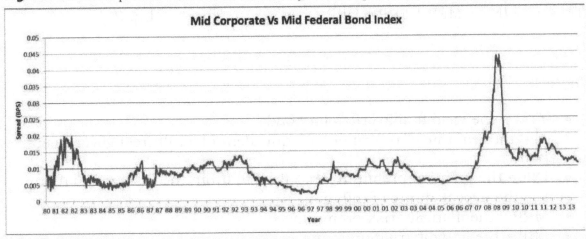

Source: TMX Group.

25   In what period was the default risk premium at its highest?
- A)   The recession of 1981–84
- B)   The recession of 1991–92
- C)   The financial crises of 2008
- D)   Wow!

9. Liquidity

- Liquidity is the ease with which an asset can be converted to cash.
- NYSE listed stocks are liquid assets.
- Real estate is illiquid.
- Liquidity risk premium (LRP) is
  - A component of a bond yield which compensates the bond holder for the potential costs in selling the bond.
  - The difference in yields of illiquid and liquid bonds.

10. Determinants of Yield

$$YTM = k_r + INF + MRP + LRP + DRP \qquad\qquad Eq.\ 2$$

Where

- YTM = the yield to maturity of a bond
- k_r = the real rate of return on an equivalent (default free) government bond
- INF = the inflation premium = $\pi + (k_r \times \pi)$ (from the Fisher Equation)
- π = the expected rate of inflation
- MRP = the maturity risk premium
- LRP = the liquidity risk premium
- DRP = the default risk premium

26   Which of the following is the best expression for the yield on a government T-Bill?
  A) $YTM = k_r$
  B) $YTM = k_r + INF$
  C) $YTM = k_r + INF + MRP$
  D) $YTM = k_r + INF + MRP + LRP$
  E) $YTM = k_r + INF + MRP + LRP + DRP$

Solutions

Yield Example (3.3)

$k_2 = 0.07$
$k_1 = 0.01$

Inflation (4.1, 4.2)

$k_n = 0.155$
$k_n = 0.166$
$n = 35$

Lock-In (5.3)

$FV = (1 \times \$87.34) \times (1.07)^2 = \$100$
$FV = (2 \times \$87.34) \times (1.07)^2 = \$200$

Roll-Over (5.4)

$Q = 0.9258$
$FV_1 = \$92.58$
$FV_2 = \$100$

Expectations Theory (5.6)

$k_2 = 0.07$
$E(k_1) = 0.05$

Forward Rates (6.1)

$f = 0.03$
$f = 0.1003$

Maturity Preference (7.2)

$k_2 = 0.06$

Coupon Bonds (Ch.7, LO3–LO5)

1. Introduction
In this workbook you will:

- Learn the basic concepts and cash flows of coupon bonds
- Learn the relationship between zero coupon bonds and coupon bonds
- Learn about yield to maturity
- Learn how to value annual and semi-annual bonds given their yields
- Learn some bond price properties including:
    - Premiums and discounts
    - How bond prices change over time
    - Interest rate risk
    - How maturity affects interest rate risk

2. Coupon Bond Concepts and Cash Flows

- A coupon bond pays annual (or semi-annual) coupons and a face amount at maturity.
- This time line shows the cash flows for a two-year annual coupon bond.

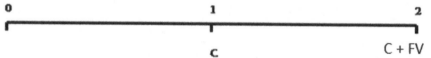

- C = annual coupon
- FV = face value
- C/FV = coupon rate

3. The Relationship Between Zeros and Coupon Bonds

3.1 Price a One-year Zero Coupon Bond

A one-year Government of Canada zero coupon bond has a face value of $10, denoted $C in the figure. The one year spot rate is $k_1 = 1\%$. What is the price of the bond?

ANSWER:

$P_1 =$

3.2 Price a Two-year Zero Coupon Bond

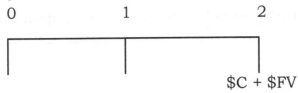

$$\$C + \$FV$$

A two-year Government of Canada zero coupon bond has a face value of $110, denoted ($C + $FV) in the figure. The two year spot rate is $k_2 = 2\%$. What is the price of the bond?

ANSWER:

$P_2 =$

3.3 Coupon Bond Cash Flows

A two-year Government of Canada coupon bond has a face value of $100 and pays annual coupons with a coupon rate of 10%. Enter the cash flows for the bond in the table below.

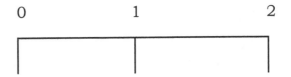

1   Are the cash flows from this two-year coupon bond different from the cash flows you would receive if you owned the two zero coupon bonds from the previous two questions?
     A)   They aren't different.
     B)   They are different.

3.4   Pricing a Coupon Bond

- If the cash flows (and risk) of the coupon bond and the portfolio of zeros are identical, then they are identical securities. By the law of one price, they must trade for the same price.

How much would it cost you to buy the two zero coupon bonds above?

ANSWER:

$P_1 + P_2 =$

- The equation we used to calculate that price is:

$$P_{bond} = \frac{C}{(1+k_1)} + \frac{C+FV}{(1+k_2)^2}$$

- This generalizes for any number of years, n:

$$P_{bond} = \sum_{t=1}^{n} \frac{C_t}{(1+k_t)^t} + \frac{FV}{(1+k_n)^n}$$

- Note that the k_t values are the spot rates for each maturity from the yield curve.

Consider a Government of Canada bond with two years to maturity, a 10% coupon rate ($100 coupons at the end of every 12 months) and a face value of $1,000. What is the price of the bond given these spot rates?

Maturity	Spot Rate
1	6.0%
2	7.0%

ANSWER:

P_{bond} =

4. Yield to Maturity

4.1 Solving for the Yield to Maturity

Consider a Government of Canada bond with two years to maturity, a 10% coupon rate and a face value of $1,000. You pay $1,055.12 for the bond. What is your annual return on the bond?

ANSWER: Find one rate, k_d, that discounts the bond's cash flows so that they equal the price:

$$P_{bond} = \sum_{t=1}^{n} \frac{C_t}{(1+k_d)^t} + \frac{FV}{(1+k_d)^n} \qquad Eq.1$$

In this case P_{bond} = 1,055.12 and n = 2, so

$$1,055.12 = \frac{C}{(1+k_d)} + \frac{C+FV}{(1+k_d)^2} = \frac{100}{(1+k_d)} + \frac{1,100}{(1+k_d)^2}$$

2   The yield to maturity, using trial-and-error, is:
   A)   6.5%
   B)   6.95%
   C)   7.25%

4.2 Facts About Yield to Maturity

- Price and yield are interchangeable:
    - o If we know the price, then we can derive the yield.
    - o If we know the yield, then we can solve for the price.
- YTM is approximately equal to the annual return received by the investor if the bond is held to maturity.
    - o We say "approximately" because we are assuming re-investment at the ytm rate. (Our assumption may be wrong.)
- YTM is a (complicated) average of the spot rates.

4.3 The Reinvestment Rate Assumption

Consider a Government of Canada bond with two years to maturity, a 10% coupon rate and a face value of $1,000. When you receive the first coupon you invest it for one year (until the maturity date of the bond) at 8%. How much money do you have at maturity (in total) from the bond?

ANSWER:

FV =

Consider the bond from the last question. You paid $1,055.12 to buy it at time T = 0. Given your answer to the last question, what is the compound annual return on the investment? (Hint: What annual rate, with two years of compounding, makes the purchase price grow to the FV that you just calculated?)

ANSWER:

k =

3   Is your answer the same as the yield to maturity?
     A)   Yes
     B)   No

Consider a Government of Canada bond with two years to maturity, a 10% coupon rate and a face value of $1,000. When you receive the first coupon you invest it for one year at 6.95%. How much money do you have at maturity (in total) from the bond?

> **ANSWER:**
>
> FV =

Consider the bond from the last question. You paid $1,055.12 to buy it at time T = 0. Given your answer to the last question, what is the compound annual return on the investment?

> **ANSWER:**
>
> k =

4   If you can re-invest your coupons at the yield-to-maturity rate, then your actual return on a bond will be equal to the yield-to-maturity (assuming that you hold to maturity).
A)   True
B)   False

4.4   Yield to Maturity Self-Test

Check out the yield to maturity self-test on page 7.4.7 in CFO.

It's Time to Do a Self-Test

19. Practise computing a coupon bond's yield-to-maturity. Answer

5. Coupon Bond Pricing Given Yield

- To solve for the yield to maturity, we used Eq.1 given the price.
- We can also use Eq. 1 to solve for the price if we are given the yield.
  - o In this case, it is simplest to treat the coupons as an ordinary annuity.
  - o We can do this because we are using the same interest rate (the yield) to discount every coupon.
- The formula for pricing a bond given the yield is:

$$P_{bond} = C \times \text{PVIFA}_{n,k_d} + \frac{FV}{(1 + k_d)^n}$$

$$\text{PVIFA} = (1/k) \times [1 - (1 + k)^{-n}]$$

Today is September 28, 2001. Ranger Oil issued a bond today with 15 years to maturity, annual coupons of $80 and a face value of $1,000. The yield to maturity is 12%. What is the bond worth today?

ANSWER:

P_{bond} =

5.1 Bond Pricing Self-Test

Check out the bond pricing self-test on page 7.4.10 in CFO.

It's Time to Do a Self-Test

20. Practise computing a coupon bond price. Answer

5.2　Semi-Annual Coupon Bonds Cash Flows

0		1	...	n

$C/2　　　　　　$C/2　　　　　　　　　　$C/2 + $FV

- A semi-annual coupon is half of the annual coupon = C/2.
  - o　It is paid each 6 months.
- Number of periods = 2n
- Semi-annual yield = $k_d/2$

5.3　Semi-Annual Coupon Bond Pricing

$$P_{bond} = \frac{C}{2} \times PVIFA_{2n, k_d/2} + \frac{FV}{\left(1 + k_d/2\right)^{2n}}$$

Today is September 28, 2001. Ranger Oil issued a bond today with 15 years to maturity and a face value of $1,000. The annual coupon of $80 is paid in two parts: $40 on September 28 and $40 on March 28. What is the bond worth today if the yield is 12%?

ANSWER:
P_{semi} =

5.1　Semi-Annual Bond Pricing Self-Test

Check out the semi-annual bond pricing self-test on page 7.4.14 in CFO.

It's Time to Do a Self-Test

21. Practise computing a coupon bond price.　`Answer`

6. Coupon Bond Price Properties

6.1 Premiums and Discounts

- A bond trades at a premium when its price is above face value.
- A bond trades at a discount when its price is below face value.

5   Consider the annual Ranger Oil bond from the last section. Did it trade
     at a premium or a discount?
     A)   Premium
     B)   Discount

6   Consider the Ranger Oil bond from the last section. What was the
     relationship between its coupon rate and its yield?
     A)   Coupon rate > yield
     B)   Coupon rate < yield
     C)   Coupon rate = yield

7   A bond trades at a premium when its coupon rate is _____ its yield
     to maturity.
     A)   Above
     B)   Below

8   A bond trades at a discount when its coupon rate is _____ its yield
     to maturity.
     A)   Above
     B)   Below

6.2 Bond Price Changes Over Time

Consider a Government of Canada bond. When it was issued it had two years
to maturity, a 10% coupon rate ($100 coupons at the end of every 12 months)
and a face value of $1,000, and it sold for a price of $1,055.12. The yield on the
bond was 6.95%. Now one year has passed. There is one coupon remaining in
one year (the first coupon was paid yesterday). The yield is still 6.95%.
Calculate the price of the bond today and the percentage change since issue.

Assume that you bought the Government of Canada bond from the last question when it was issued for \$1,055.12. After the first coupon, you sold it for the price that you calculated in the last question. What are the coupon yield and the total return (AKA holding period return) on this investment?

Coupon Yield = $\$C/P_0$
Total Return = $(\$C + P_1 - P_0)/P_0$

ANSWER:

Coupon Yield =

Total Return =

What is the sum of the percentage change in price (over the first year) and the coupon yield?

ANSWER:

Coupon Yield + $\%\Delta P$ =

9 Consider holding a coupon bond for one year. If interest rates don't change, then the sum of the coupon yield and the capital gain yield is equal to the yield to maturity.
 A) True
 B) False

10 If a medium maturity coupon bond is issued at a premium, then over its first year, its price will _____ (assuming that interest rates don't change).
 A) Rise
 B) Fall
 C) Remain unchanged

11   If a medium maturity coupon bond is issued at a discount, then over its
      first year, its price will _____ (assuming that interest rates don't
      change).
      A)   Rise
      B)   Fall
      C)   Remain unchanged

6.3   Bond Price Changes Over Time Explore It

Check out the "Bond Price Changes over Time" Explore It on page 7.5.17 of
CFO.

6.4   Bond Prices and Interest Rates Move Inversely

- This is true for zero coupon bonds and coupon bonds, but it is easier to
  compute zero coupon bond prices, so we will show it with zeros.

Consider a Zero coupon bond with 10 years to maturity and a face value of
$100. The yield is 10%. What is the bond's price?

ANSWER:

$P_0 =$

Consider a Zero coupon bond with 10 years to maturity and a face value of
$100. The yield is 5%. What is the bond's price?

ANSWER:

$P_0 =$

Plot the bond prices against yields on the following graph.

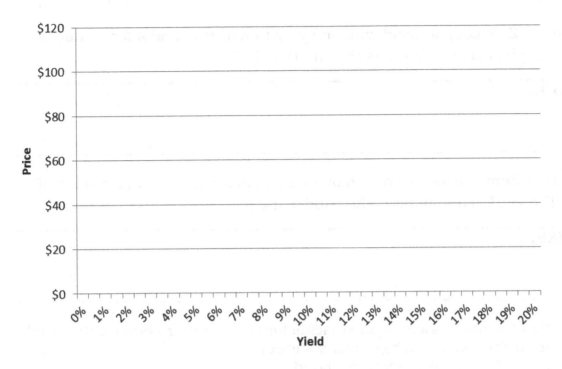

12   What is the slope of the relationship between bond prices and yields?
    A)   Downward sloping (negative)
    B)   Upward sloping (positive)

6.5   Bond Price and Interest Rate Explore It

Check out the bond price and interest rate Explore It on page 7.5.5 of CFO.

6.6   Definition: Interest Rate Risk

- Interest rate risk is the risk of capital loss on a bond investment.
    - o   If interest rises, bond prices fall.
- This only applies to investors who intend to sell the bond before maturity.

6.7 Longer Maturity Bonds Have More Interest Rate Risk

Consider a Zero coupon bond with one year to maturity and a face value of $100. The yield is 10%. What is the bond's price?

ANSWER:

$P_0 =$

Consider a Zero coupon bond with one year to maturity and a face value of $100. The yield is 5%. What is the bond's price?

ANSWER:

$P_0 =$

---

13. Plot the bond prices against yields for the one-year bond on the graph from Section 6.4. Which line is steeper?
    A) The one-year maturity bond
    B) The 10-year maturity bond

14. Calculate the percentage change in price for the 10-year bond when yields fall from 10% to 5% and then repeat the calculation for the one-year bond. Which one is larger?
    A) The one-year maturity bond
    B) The 10-year maturity bond

15. You are friends with the Governor of the Bank of Canada. He admits that the Bank of Canada is going to lower interest rates. This will come as a complete surprise to the market. You want to profit from this knowledge. What is your best investment strategy?
    A) Buy short maturity bonds
    B) Buy long maturity bonds
    C) Short sell short maturity bonds
    D) Short sell long maturity bonds

Solutions

The Relationship Between Zeros and Coupon Bonds (3.1, 3.2, 3.4)

$Price = $9.901

$Price = $105.73

$P_1 + P_2 = 115.63

$P_{bond} = $1,055.12$

Yield to Maturity (4.1, 4.3)

ytm = 6.95%

FV = $1,208

k = 0.07

FV = $1,206.95

k = 0.0695

Coupon Bond Price (5, 5.2)

$P_{bond} = 727.57

$P_{semi} = 724.70

Bond Price Changes over Time (6.2, 6.4)

$P_{bond} = $1,028.518$

$\%\Delta P = -0.02521$

Coupon Yield = 0.094776

Total Return = 0.0695

Coupon Yield + $\%\Delta P$ = 0.0695

$P_0 = 38.55

$P_0 = 61.39

$P_0 = 90.909

$P_0 = 95.238

$\%\Delta P_{10} = 60\%$

$\%\Delta P_1 = 5\%$

Stocks (Ch.8, LO1–LO3)

1. Introduction

In this workbook you will:

- Learn about stocks and short selling
- Learn how to calculate the intrinsic value of preferred shares using the no-growth dividend discount model
- Learn how to calculate the intrinsic value of common shares using the one-year holding period valuation model
- Learn how to calculate the intrinsic value of common shares using the constant growth dividend valuation model
- Learn how to calculate the intrinsic value of common shares using the non-constant growth dividend valuation model

2. Introduction to Stocks

The instructor will provide a brief introduction and show these videos:

What is a stock?	Search YouTube for: "Thrasher University: What is a stock?"
What is short selling?	Search YouTube for: "Thrasher University: What is short selling?"
What is intrinsic value?	Search YouTube for: "Warren Buffett How to Value a Stock"

3. Intrinsic and Market Value

Definition:

Intrinsic value is the actual or true value of a stock based on the present value of the cash flows derived from its business.

Investors use a variety of analytical techniques to estimate the intrinsic value of stocks, such as:

1. Dividend Discount Models
   a. No growth
   b. Constant growth
   c. Non-constant growth
2. Total Payout Model
3. Relative Valuation Models
   a. P/E
   b. M/B
   c. etc.
4. Discounted Cash Flow (DCF) Valuation

Definition:

Market value is the consensus value of all potential traders as manifested by the last traded price for the stock.

- Differences between market value and intrinsic value create potentially profitable trading opportunities.

1 If the market value of a stock is less than the intrinsic value, then you should _____.
   A) Buy
   B) Sell
   C) Hold

2 If the market value of a stock is greater than the intrinsic value, then you should _____.
   A) Buy
   B) Sell
   C) Hold

4. Preferred Shares

- Preferred stock has some characteristics of debt and some characteristics of equity.
- It typically has no maturity date and no voting rights.
- Preferred shares have a face value (AKA par value) that is an amount the preferred shareholder receives if the company is liquidated.
- The preferred shareholder receives preference over common stock if the firm is liquidated.
- These shares pay a regular dividend:
  - Preferred dividends have preference over common dividends.
    - A company can't pay common shareholders until preferred shareholders are paid.
  - Dividend is expressed in dollar terms (e.g., $0.85 per year) or as a percentage of par value.
- For plain vanilla preferred, we model the dividends as a level perpetuity:

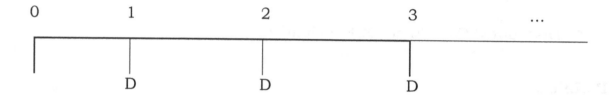

The intrinsic value of the share is equal to the present value of the dividends:

$$P_{Preferred} = \frac{D}{k}$$

Where

$P_{Preferred}$ = the estimated "fair" price for a share (intrinsic value)

D = the periodic dividend

k = the required return of preferred shareholders (their discount rate)

If preferred shareholders require a 12.5% return and the preferred stock pays annual dividends of $1.50 (starting in one year), then what is the fair market price for a share?

ANSWER:

$P_{Preferred}$ =

National Carbon preferred shares pay a 7% annual dividend on a $100 par value. The current market price of the shares is $41.67. What return will you earn if you buy one share and hold it in perpetuity?

> **ANSWER:**
>
> k =

5. Common Shares

- Common shares have no par value. If the company is liquidated, the shareholders are the residual claimants.
- Dividends are variable and are paid at the discretion of the board.
- Most companies have a single class of common shares with one vote.
- Some companies have dual classes of shares, such as Canadian Tire Corp.

Share	TSX Ticker	Shares Outstanding	Ownership Share of Executives and Directors
Common Shares	CTC	3.4M	61%
Class A Non-voting	CTC.A	76.56M	1.1%

3   If there is a vote on a shareholder resolution at Canadian Tire's annual general meeting, then who is going to win the vote?
   A)   The executives and directors
   B)   The outside shareholders
   C)   Large pension and mutual funds
   D)   Ontario Teachers' Pension Plan

5.1   Valuation with One-year Holding Period

Assume that you plan to hold a stock for one year and then sell it for a price of P_1. You expect to receive one dividend at the end of the year (D_1). How much will you pay for the stock today if your required return is k%?

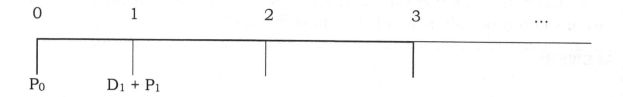

$$P_0 = \frac{D_1 + P_1}{(1 + k)}$$

Where

P_0 = the estimated "fair" price at time 0 for a share (intrinsic value)

How much will you pay for a common share today if you expect to sell it in one year for $60 and you expect to receive a dividend of $0.16 in one year? You require a return of 12%.

ANSWER:
P_0 =

4   If an investor is going to hold for one year, then the most important determinant of the value today is not the dividend but the stock price next year.
   A)   True
   B)   False

5.2   One-Period Valuation Self-Test
Check out the one-period valuation self-test on page 8.3.5 of CFO.

It's Time to Do a Self-Test

5. Practise computing the share price using the one-period valuation model. **Answer**

5.3   What Will the Buyer Pay at Time 1?
Assume that the buyer also has a one-year holding period. She will buy right after the Year 1 dividend. Assume that the company pays annual dividends. Her time line is:

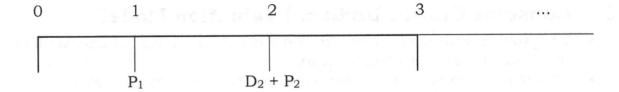

Her fair price is:

$$P_1 = \frac{D_2 + P_2}{(1+k)}$$

Substitute this into the pricing equation for period 0:

$$P_0 = \frac{D_1}{(1+k)} + \frac{D_2 + P_2}{(1+k)^2}$$

5.4 The Generalized Dividend Valuation Model

Repeat the above exercise for n future investors and the formula for the fair stock price at Time 0 is:

$$P_0 = \frac{D_1}{(1+k)} + \frac{D_2}{(1+k)^2} + \cdots + \frac{D_n + P_n}{(1+k)^n}$$

If n is large, then the last term is nearly zero.

5   If an investor is going to hold for one year, then the most important determinant of the value today is the future dividends and not the stock price next year.
      A)   True (That last question was a trick.)
      B)   False

6   If a company's articles of incorporation prohibit it from ever paying a dividend, what is the fair price for its common shares? (Assume that the company will continue operations for at least 100 years and won't be taken over.)

We can re-write the generalized dividend discount model as:

$$P_0 = \sum_{t=1}^{\infty} \frac{D_t}{(1+k)^t}$$

171

6. Constant Growth Dividend Valuation Model

- The problem with the generalized model is that you have to forecast all of the dividends into the distant future.
- Let's make a simplifying assumption: assume dividends grow at a constant rate forever.

$$D_t = D_{t-1} \times (1 + g)$$

Where

D_t = dividend in period t

D_{t-1} = dividend in period t – 1

g = dividend growth rate

Yesterday the company paid a dividend of $1. The dividend is expect to grow at g = 8% per annum. How big will the dividend be in two years?

ANSWER:

D_2 =

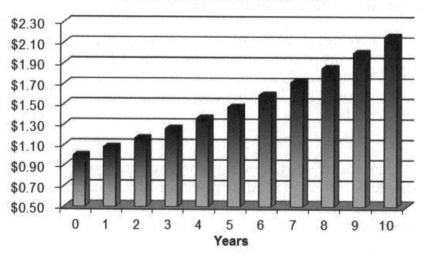

172

6.1 End-of-period (AKA New Year's Eve) Timing

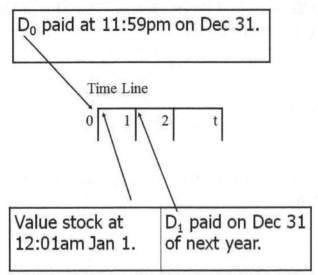

7   If you buy the stock at 12:01 a.m. January 1, how long will it be until the next dividend (D_1)?

    A)   0
    B)   1 year

8   If you buy the stock at 12:01 a.m. January 1, do you receive the D_0?
    A)   No
    B)   Yes

6.2   Time Line of Constant Growth Dividends

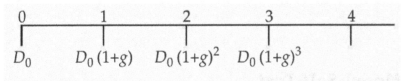

Where

   D_0 = the last dividend paid (at time zero)

   g = the growth rate in dividends

6.3 Constant Growth Pricing Formula

If you buy the stock at Time 0 (and do not receive D_0), the present value of the dividends you receive (in perpetuity) is:

$$P_0 = \frac{D_0 \times (1 + g)}{k - g} = \frac{D_1}{k - g} \qquad \text{Eq. 8.6}$$

9 With the constant growth model we must assume $g < k$. If $g > k$, then the stock price is _____.
   A) Negative
   B) \$0
   C) Infinity

Pan American Airlines pays annual dividends on December 31. Today is January 1 and the next dividend is expected to be \$3. Dividends are expected to be paid in perpetuity and will grow at the rate of 8% per annum. Investors expect a return of 15% on Pan Am shares. What is the fair price for Pan Am?

ANSWER:

$P_0 =$

6.4 Constant Growth Model Explore It

Check out the constant growth model Explore It on page 8.3.7 of CFO.

6.5 Constant Growth Model Self-Test

Check out the constant growth model self-test on page 8.3.12 of CFO.

10. Practise computing the price of a share. `Answer`

6.6 Solve for Stockholders' Required Return

Take the second version of Eq.8.6 (with D_1 in the numerator) and solve for k as a function of P_0, D_1 and g.

ANSWER:

k =

If Ben & Jerry Inc.'s current dividend, D_0, is $2.00, its expected dividend growth rate is a constant 10% and the current price is $44, what is the required return of investors for Ben & Jerry's stock?

ANSWER:

k =

6.7 Price Changes Under Constant Growth

Time Line

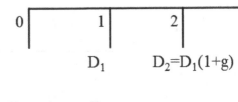

Dividends D_1 $D_2=D_1(1+g)$

Price P_0 P_1

The proportionate change in price from Time 0 to Time 1 is:

$$\frac{P_1 - P_0}{P_0} = \frac{P_1}{P_0} - 1$$

We know from Eq.8.6 that:

$$P_0 = \frac{D_1}{k - g}$$

What is the equation for P_1?

> **ANSWER:**
>
> $P_1 =$

Substitute the two expressions for P_0 and P_1 in the expression for the proportionate change in stock price. Simplify. What is it equal to?

> **ANSWER:**
>
> $[P_1/P_0] - 1 =$

10   Under the constant growth dividend model, the stock price grows at the same rate as the dividends.
   A)   True
   B)   False

7. Non-constant Growth

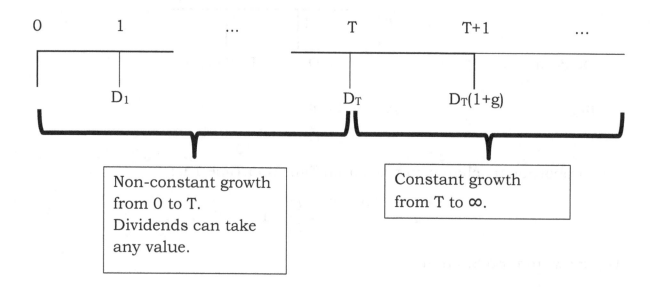

176

● Three-step method to find PV of dividends (fair price):

1. Determine the dividend expected at the end of each year during the non-constant growth period.
2. Estimate the constant growth rate and use it to price the dividend stream that begins after the non-constant growth period.
3. Find the present value of the non-constant dividends and add the sum to the present value of the price found in Step 2.

At the time of writing, Google shares trade for $520. Is that above or below its intrinsic value? Google doesn't pay a dividend right now, but it will probably start paying in three years. Earnings per share are $20 now, so in three years they will probably double to $40. Google will probably adopt a payout rate of 75%, so its first dividend will be $30. Google shareholders require a 9% rate of return. It is expected that Google's dividends will grow at an annual rate of 3% in perpetuity after they start. What is the present value of an infinite series of growing dividends that starts in Year 3? (Find the present value as of Year 2.)

ANSWER:

$PV_2 =$

What is the present value of your answer to the previous question as of Year 0? (In other words, discount your last answer two years at 9%.) That is your estimate of the fair price of Google today.

ANSWER:

$P_0 =$

N.B. We didn't need to do Step 1 in this problem because Google's dividends were $0 in Years 1 and 2.

What dividend does Google need to pay in Year 3 in order for your answer to the last question to equal the market price of $520? That is, keep everything in the last question the same but solve for a dividend so that the fair price for Google is $520.

● **ANSWER:**

$D_3 =$

7.1 Super-normal Growth

Super-normal growth is a variation of a non-constant growth problem where the growth rate in the non-constant period is constant and faster than in the constant growth period. You still attack these problems with the same three-step process.

Ivaco Inc.'s dividends are forecast to increase over the next three years at 12% due to the introduction of their new line of industrial fasteners. The last dividend (yesterday) was $2.00 per share. After this period of growth, Ivaco's dividends are expected to grow at their long run rate of 10%. Investors have historically required a 15% rate of return on Ivaco's stock. Dividends are paid annually on December 31. It is January 1. What are the dividends over the next four years? (Round your answers to pennies.)

ANSWER:

$D_1 =$

$D_2 =$

$D_3 =$

$D_4 =$

Ivaco's dividend in Year 4 is its first in the constant growth period. What is the present value of the constant growth period dividends as of Year 3?

ANSWER:

$PV_3 =$

What is the present value of your answer to the previous question as of Year 0? (In other words, discount your last answer three years.)

ANSWER:

$PV_0 =$

What is the present value of Ivaco's first three super-normal dividends as of Year 0?

ANSWER:
$PV_0 =$

What is the fair price for Ivaco's shares? (Hint: Sum the super-normal dividends and the constant growth dividends.)

ANSWER:
$P_0 =$

7.2 Super-normal Growth Model Explore It

Check out the super-normal growth model Explore It on page 8.3.20 of CFO.

7.3 Super-normal Growth Model Self-Test

Check out the super-normal growth model self-test on page 8.3.21 of CFO.

14. Practise computing the share price with nonconstant growth. `Answer`

Solutions

<u>Preferred Shares</u> (4)

$P_{Preferred}$ = \$12
k = 0.168

<u>Common Shares</u> (5.1)

P_0 = \$53.71

<u>Constant Growth</u> (6, 6.3, 6.6, 6.7)

D_2 = \$1.1664
P_0 = \$42.86

$k = D_1/P_0 + g$
k = 0.15
$P_1 = D_2/(k - g)$
$[P_1/P_0] - 1 = g$

<u>Non-Constant Growth</u> (7, 7.1)

PV_2 = \$500
P_0 = \$420.84
D_3 = \$37.069
D_1 = \$2.24; D_2 = \$2.51; D_3 = \$2.81; D_4 = \$3.09
PV_3 = 61.80
PV_0 = 40.63
PV_0 = 5.60
P_0 = 46.33

Stocks (Ch.8, LO3)

1. Introduction

In this workbook you will:

- Learn about the history of share repurchases in Canada and the U.S.
- Learn the basics about how share repurchases work
- Learn how to use the total payout model to value shares
- Learn the P/E relative valuation model
- Learn the M/B relative valuation model

2. Share Repurchase History

Figure 1. Total Dollar Value of Cash Dividends and Repurchases by U.S. Listed Companies

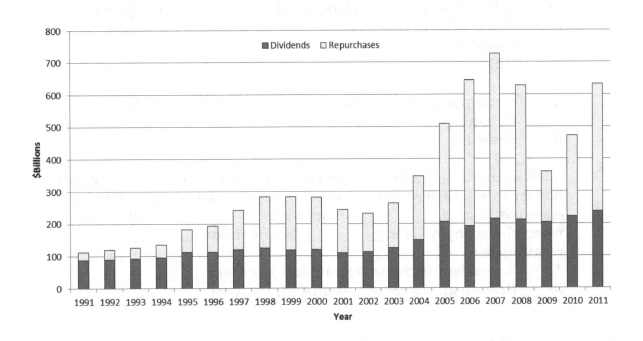

Figure 2. Total Dollar Value of Cash Dividends and Repurchases by Canadian Listed Companies

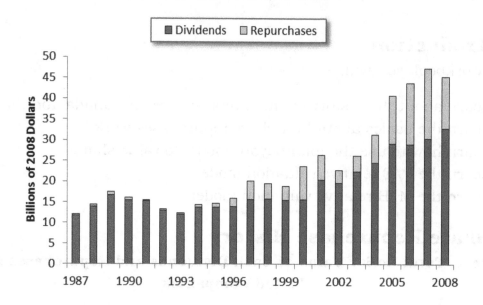

1   Looking at the most recent data, in which country are repurchases a larger share of total payouts?
  A)   Canada
  B)   U.S.

2   In both countries, repurchases are a _____ trend.
  A)   Declining
  B)   Growing

3   Look at the U.S. graph. (This is also true for Canada but it is a little harder to see.) There were recessions in 2001 and 2008. When the economy is in _____, companies _____ repurchases; but when the economy is in _____, companies _____ repurchases.
  A)   Recession, increase, expansion, decrease
  B)   Recession, decrease, expansion, increase

3.   Share Repurchase Facts

- Share repurchasing is an alternative way to distribute cash to shareholders.
- It is especially good for firms with clienteles that prefer capital gains.
- Repurchased shares are cancelled (no longer outstanding).

There are three kinds of repurchases:

- Open market repurchase
  - Most popular type in Canada and the U.S.
  - In Canada this is called a normal course issuer bid.
  - The company's broker is given cash and instructed to buy shares at the market price.
  - In Canada you can't buy more than 5% per year. In the U.S. there is no limit, but companies buy an average of about 8% and it takes them almost three years to do it.
- Fixed-price offer
  - In Canada this called a substantial issuer bid.
  - A company makes a tender offer for its own shares.
  - A company buys a percentage (@20%) at premium to the pre-announcement market price.
- Dutch auction
  - This is a type of auction in which the auctioneer begins with a high asking price which is lowered until a bidder is willing to accept the auctioneer's price.
  - For stocks, the company announces range of acceptable prices and invites shareholders to submit sale offers with a price within the range.
  - The sale offers are ranked by price from lowest to highest.
  - The company accepts all of the lowest priced offers up to the quantity it has targeted. All accepted offers receive the price of the marginal offer.

	U.S.			Canada
	Fixed Price	Dutch Auction	Open Market	Open Market
Proportion Sought	21.4%	17.3%	7.8%	5.0%
Tender Premium	20.9%	3%–16%	0%	0%
Announcement Period Return	12.5%	8.2%	2.3%	0.73%

	Number of Repurchases			
	U.S.			Canada
	Dutch Auctions	Fixed-Price	Open Market	Open Market
1987	9	42	132	224
1988	21	32	276	154
1989	22	49	499	143
1990	10	41	778	187
1991	4	51	282	106
1992	7	37	447	93
1993	5	51	461	80
1994	10	52	824	135
1995	8	40	851	188
1996	22	37	1,111	180
1997	30	35	967	214
1998	20	13	1,537	298
1999	19	21	1,212	327
2000	10	13	597	
2001	7	11	485	
2002	6	7	337	
2003	12	9	351	
2004	8	5	451	
2005	18	5	520	
2006	17	3	508	
2007			785	

U.S. data from Grullon and Ikenberry (2000). Canadian data from Canadian Financial Markets Research Centre database and Toronto Stock Exchange Daily Record.

4   Which type of repurchase is most common?
   A)   Open market
   B)   Fixed-price
   C)   Dutch auction

5   Which type of repurchase offers the largest premium over the pre-announcement price?
   A)   Open market
   B)   Fixed-price
   C)   Dutch auction

6   Which type of repurchase targets the largest percentage of shares outstanding?
   A)   Open market
   B)   Fixed-price
   C)   Dutch auction

3.1   Share Repurchase Mechanics

Cash Inc. has one asset: $100. The company is all equity financed with 100 shares outstanding. There are 10 shareholders who each hold 10 shares. Cash Inc. announces a stock repurchase. It will buy one share from each shareholder. (This symmetry is unnecessary but makes every shareholder identical.)

What is the fair value of each share before the repurchase?

> **ANSWER:**
>
> $P_B =$

How many shares will be outstanding after the repurchase?

> **ANSWER:**
>
> $N_A = N_B - N_R =$

What is each shareholder's proportionate ownership share of the company after the repurchase?

> **ANSWER:**
>
> Share =

What is the stock price after the repurchase if the company pays $1 for each repurchased share?

ANSWER:

P_A =

Consider a shareholder with 10 shares before the repurchase. The shareholder sells one share into the repurchase at $1 and keeps the remainder. What is the shareholder's change in wealth?

ANSWER:

ΔW =

---

7   When a company buys back shares at a price equal to fair value ($P_R = P_B$), then the price remains unchanged after the repurchase and no wealth is transferred.
   A)   True
   B)   False

4.   Total Payout Model

Definition:

Total Payouts = Total dollars paid to shareholders in a year
Total Payouts = $Dividends + $Repurchases

Where
$Dividends = the value of dividends paid in a year
$Repurchases = the value of shares repurchased in a year

4.1   Generalized Total Payout Model
- The value of owning all of the shares in a company is equal to the present value of all of the payouts received in perpetuity.

$$E_0 = \sum_{t=1}^{\infty} \frac{TP_t}{(1+k)^t}$$

186

Where

E_0 = the value of the company's equity (in aggregate)

TP_t = Total payouts in year t

k = the shareholder' required return

4.2   Constant Growth Total Payout Model

- The problem with the generalized model is that you have to forecast all of the payouts into the distant future.
- Let's make a simplifying assumption: assume payouts grow at a constant rate forever.

$$TP_t = TP_{t-1} \times (1 + g)$$

Where

TP_t = Total payouts in period t

TP_{t-1} = Total payouts in period t – 1

g = dividend growth rate

4.3   Time Line of Constant Growth Payouts

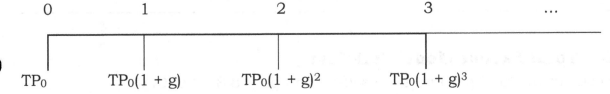

0	1	2	3	...
TP_0	$TP_0(1 + g)$	$TP_0(1 + g)^2$	$TP_0(1 + g)^3$	

4.4   Constant Growth Pricing Formula

If you buy all of a company's shares at Time 0 (and do not receive TP_0), then the present value of the payouts you receive (in perpetuity) is:

$$E_0 = \frac{TP_0 \times (1 + g)}{k - g} = \frac{TP_1}{k - g}$$

8   With the constant growth model we must assume g < k. If g > k, then the value of equity is _____.

   A)   Negative

   B) $0

   C)   Infinity

Notice that the growth equation gives the value of equity in aggregate. To get the stock price, just divide by the number of shares outstanding:

$$P_0 = \frac{E_0}{N}$$

Where

P = the stock price
N = the number of shares outstanding

In the year to May 31 (yesterday), Nike issued $412.9M of dividends and repurchased $904.7M worth of shares. Assume that today is June 1 and that all payouts occur on May 31 of each year. Assume that Nike's payouts are expected to rise by 4% each year in perpetuity. Nike has 487M shares outstanding. Assume that investors require an 8% rate of return on Nike. What is the total payout model estimate of Nike's fair share price?

ANSWER:

P_0 =

4.5 Total Payout Model Self-Test

Check out the total payout model self-test on page 8.3.29 of CFO.

It's Time to Do a Self-Test

15. Practise calculating a share price using the total payout model. Answer

5. Relative Valuation Methods

5.1 Price-Earnings Valuation Method

The price-earnings ratio is defined as:

$$P/_E = \frac{P_0}{EPS_{0,1}}$$

Where
P_0 = the stock price today
EPS_0 = earnings per share (trailing—that is for the last reporting period ending

yesterday)

EPS_1 = earnings per share (forecast for the end of the current period)

Ignore EPS timing (it is either one or the other) and multiply both sides by EPS:

$$P/_E \times EPS = \frac{P_0}{EPS} \times EPS$$

$$P/_E \times EPS = P_0$$

- So, today's price is equal to the P/E ratio multiplied by EPS.
- You can't use the own company's P/E or you get P = P.
- Treat P/E like a physical constant (e.g., speed of light).
    o The P/E constant
    o Obtain the P/E constant from other equivalent companies.
        ▪ That's why we call this relative valuation.

The P/E constant for Nike is 18.8. What is the fair price for Nike if its EPS = $3?

ANSWER:
P_0 =

9   If Nike's shares are trading for $65, then you should _____.
    A)   Buy
    B)   Sell
    C)   Hold

5.2   A Second Approach to P/E Valuation

The P/E constant for Nike is 18.8. Nike has EPS of $3 and currently trades for $65. What is Nike's current P/E ratio?

ANSWER:
P/E =

10   If Nike's P/E ratio is larger than its P/E constant, then the shares are
_____ and you should _____.
A)   Overvalued, buy
B)   Overvalued, sell
C)   Undervalued, buy
D)   Undervalued, sell
E)   Fairly valued, hold

5.3   Selecting Equivalent Companies for P/E Constant

- Question: How do you construct a P/E constant?
- Answer: Average the P/E ratios for equivalent companies.
- Question: What companies are equivalent?
- Answer: Ones with the same characteristics.
- Question: What characteristics?

Recall the constant growth dividend discount model:

$$P_0 = \frac{D_1}{k - g}$$

If a company has earnings per share of $5 and has a payout rate of 50%, what is the dividend?

ANSWER:

D =

We can express the dividend, D, as:

D = EPS × p

Where

p = the payout rate

Substitute this into the numerator of the constant growth pricing model:

$$P_0 = \frac{p \times EPS_1}{k - g}$$

Divide both sides by EPS_1:

$$\frac{P_0}{EPS_1} = \frac{p}{k - g}$$

- If all of the assumptions of the constant growth dividend model hold, then the P/E ratio is equal to the payout ratio dividend by $k - g$.
- If you are choosing equivalent firms to build a P/E constant, then try to find firms in the same business with the same payout rate, growth and risk
  - o Why risk? Because the required return, k, is positively related to risk.

You are trying to value Blackberry, the Waterloo-based smartphone company. You are using the P/E valuation model. Blackberry has earnings-per-share of $0.25. You need a P/E constant. To get it, you will average the P/E ratios of other smartphone companies. Should you include Apple in that group of comparable companies? Assume that Apple has the same payout rate as Blackberry and the same risk.

> **ANSWER:**

5.4   Market-to-Book Model

Below is the right-hand side of the Fritz Electrics' balance sheet. Use this information to answer the questions that follow.

Right-hand side of Balance Sheet

Current Liabilities

Short-term debt	535,000
Accruals	1,568,880
Total current liabilities	2,103,880
Long-term debt	560,000
Share Capital	1,000,000

Retained earnings	2,893,920
Owner's equity	3,893,920
TOTAL	6,557,800

What is the book value of equity for Fritz?

ANSWER:

If Fritz has 1,000,000 shares outstanding, then what is the book value per share for Fritz?

ANSWER:

11   If a company is liquidated and all of its assets are sold for their book (depreciated) value, what are the proceeds from the sale?
A)   Total fixed assets
B)   Total assets
C)   Total owner's equity
D)   Total liabilities

12   If the money from the liquidation from the previous question is used to pay all liabilities and debts of the company, how much is left over?
A)   Total fixed assets
B)   Total assets
C)   Total owner's equity
D)   Total liabilities

13   If the proceeds from the previous question are divided equally amongst the outstanding shares, the result is:
A)   Earnings per share
B)   Book value per share
C)   Total assets per share

● If Fritz's shares are trading for $5, what is the market-to-book ratio for Fritz?

ANSWER:

- The market-to-book ratio is the ratio of the market price and the book value per share.
- The market price is the present value of all future cash flows expected to be paid to shareholders from the operation of the company.
- The book-value-per-share is the liquidation value of a share from selling the company's stuff.
- Those numbers should rarely be equal and the market-to-book ratio should rarely equal one.

If Fritz's shares are trading for $3, what is the market-to-book ratio for Fritz?

ANSWER:

● M/B =

Assume that Fritz's shares are trading for $3. Outline a trading strategy to take advantage of this. What is your profit assuming zero transaction costs?

ANSWER:

Profit =

---

14   Microsoft has a M/B ratio of 6.4 and Ford Motor Corp. has a M/B of 1.1. Does this mean that Microsoft is overvalued?
   A)   Yes
   B)   No (Hint: Think about the left hand side of their balance sheets.)

5.5   Market-to-book Valuation Method

● The market-to-book ratio is defined as:

$$M/B = \frac{P}{BVPS}$$

Where

BVPS = book value per share

Multiply both sides by BVPS:

$$M/B \times BVPS = \frac{P}{BVPS} \times BVPS$$
$$P = M/B \times BVPS$$

- So, today's price is equal to the M/B ratio multiplied by BVPS.
- You can't use the own company's M/B or you get P = P.
- Treat M/B like a physical constant (e.g., speed of light).
    - The M/B constant
    - Obtain the M/B constant from other equivalent companies.
        - That's why we call this relative valuation.

The M/B constant for the athletics and apparel industry is 3. What is the fair price for Nike?

Selected Financial Information
Nike

EPS	$3	Cash	$3,630M
Debt	$545M	EBITDA	$2,770M
Equity	$9,087M	Shares	487M

ANSWER:

P₀ =

15   If Nike's shares are trading for $65, then you should _____.

A)   Buy
B)   Sell
C)   Hold

Solutions

<u>Share Repurchase Mechanics</u> (3.1)

P_B = $1
N_A = 90
Share = 0.1 or 10%
P_A = $1
ΔW = $W_A - W_B$ = $0

<u>Total Payout Model</u> (4.4)

P_0 = $70.34

<u>P/E</u> (5.1, 5.2, 5.3)

P_0 = $56.40
P/EPS = 21.67
D = $2.50

No. Don't include Apple. Even if Apple has the same payout and risk, it is growing at a very fast rate and Blackberry is growing very slowly.

<u>M/B</u> (6.4, 6.5)

Book Equity = $3,893,920
Book Value per share = $3.89
Market-to-book ratio = 1.28

Market-to-book ratio = 0.899

Buy all of the shares of the company for $3.5 million. Convene a board meeting and liquidate the company: proceeds = $3.893 million.

Profit = 0.393 million.

P_0 = $55.98

Capital Budgeting Techniques (Ch.9)

1. Introduction

1.1 Learning Objectives

In this workbook you will:

- Learn about payback period
- Learn about NPV
- Learn about IRR
- Learn about NPV Profiles
- Learn about problems using IRR to rank mutually exclusive projects
- Learn about the profitability index
- Learn about capital rationing

1.2 Introductory Video

Watch the Explain It video on page 10.2.13 of CFO which describes the capital budgeting process behind the Boeing Dreamliner project.

2. Payback Period

2.1 Definition

The payback is simply the number of years it takes to recover the initial investment given a particular sales (cash flow) forecast.

2.2 Question

A project requires an investment of $1,000 today and will generate cash flows of $600 at the end of each of the next two years (see time line). How many years will it take to get your $1,000 back? Assume that the Year 2 cash flow is paid out smoothly through the year to compute a fraction. To estimate the fraction, divide the remaining balance (at the beginning of the year) by the cash inflow received during the year.

A Quick Question

At the start of the year you have $600 of your investment not paid back. During the year you expect to receive cash flows of $800. At what point in the year will you reach full payback?

ANSWER:
Fraction of Year =

Now, Back to the Previous Question

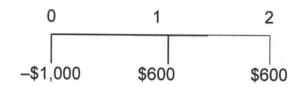

ANSWER:
Payback =

2.3 Question

Rainbow Products is considering purchasing one of two paint-mixing machines to reduce labour costs: Model L or Model S. Both machines cost $1,000 and last for four years. The cash flows from the labour savings are shown in the following table.

Year	Model S	Model L
0	−1,000	−1,000
1	500	100
2	400	200
3	300	500
4	100	600

The payback for Model S is 2.33 years. What is the payback for Model L?

ANSWER:
Payback =

2.4 Comments

- The payback period does not consider all of the cash flows of a project.

198

- The payback period does not consider the time value of money, i.e., the cost of capital.
  - o We can address this criticism by using the discounted payback.

3. Net Present Value

3.1 Definition

Net present value is the present value of all project cash flows when discounted at the investors' required rate of return (WACC).

$$NPV = PV \text{ (Cash Inflows)} - PV \text{ (Cash Outflows)}$$

OR

$$NPV = \sum_{t=1}^{n} \frac{CF_t}{(1+k)^t} - Initial\ Investment$$

The second formula assumes that the investment happens at time zero. Many of our examples will make this assumption. More realistically, the investment is spread out over time and so it must be discounted to the decision date.

3.2 Question

A project requires an investment of $1,000 today and will generate cash flows of $600 at the end of each of the next two years (see time line). The required return of investors is 10%. What is the net present value of the project?

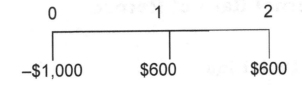

0	1	2
−$1,000	$600	$600

ANSWER:
NPV =

3.3 Question

Rainbow Products is considering purchasing one of two paint-mixing machines to reduce labour costs: Model L or Model S. Both machines cost $1,000 and last for four years. The cash flows from the labour savings are shown in the table in Section 2.3. The cost of capital for Rainbow is 10%. The NPV of Model S is $78.82. What is the NPV of Model L?

ANSWER:
NPV =

3.4 Comments

- If NPV > 0, then the project's cash flows can pay the required return on capital employed, return the principal and leave some profit left over.
- NPV is the present value of the leftover profits.
- The NPV is also the project's contribution to firm value.
- Choosing the project with the highest NPV is consistent with maximizing the firm value and stock price.

3.5 NPV Simulator

Check out the NPV Self-Test on Page 9.3.13 in CFO.

It's Time to Do a Self-Test

4. A firm is considering the purchase of a machine for $3,350,000. The machine is expected to generate net revenues of $1,150,000 for 4 years before it is worn out. If the cost of capital is 14%, what is the NPV? Should the firm buy the machine?

Algebraic Answer Excel Answer Calculator Answer

5. Practise computing the NPV. Answer

4. Internal Rate of Return

4.1 Definition

- Internal rate of return (IRR) is the yield to maturity of the project.
- It represents the rate that discounts all of the cash inflows to equal the initial capital outlay (NPV = 0).
- IRR indicates the highest cost of capital that the project can satisfy.

4.2 Example

Rainbow Products is considering purchasing one of two paint-mixing machines to reduce labour costs: Model L or Model S. Both machines cost $1,000 and last for four years. The cash flows from the labour savings are shown in the table above. What is the IRR for Model S?

$$NPV_S = 0 = \frac{-\$1,000}{(1+k)^0} + \frac{\$500}{(1+k)^1} + \frac{\$400}{(1+k)^2} + \frac{\$300}{(1+k)^3} + \frac{\$100}{(1+k)^4}$$

The solution is k = 14.5%. With k = 14.5% NPV$_S$ = 0.

4.3   Question
What is the IRR of Model L?

ANSWER:
IRR$_L$ =

4.4   Question

16   If the IRR of a project is bigger than the cost of capital (k), is NPV greater than or less than zero?
   A)   NPV > 0
   B)   NPV < 0

Hint:

Consider a one year project with a $100 investment due immediately and $110 cash flow in one year. The cost of capital is 5%. What is the IRR?

ANSWER:
IRR =

What is the NPV?

ANSWER:
NPV =

What is the relationship between the cost of capital and the IRR?

4.5   Comments
   - If the IRR > cost of capital, then NPV > 0 and the project is profitable.
   - The IRR is the highest cost of capital that allows the project to break even (NPV = 0).
   - IRR can lead to bad decisions when choosing between mutually exclusive projects.

4.6 IRR Simulator

Check out the IRR Self-Test on Page 9.3.32 in CFO.

5. Mutually Exclusive Projects: Problems with IRR

5.1 Question

Rainbow Products is considering purchasing one of two paint-mixing machines to reduce labour costs: Model L or Model S. Both machines cost $1,000 and last for four years. The cash flows from the labour savings are shown in the table in Section 2.3. The cost of capital for Rainbow is 10%. The NPV of Model S is $79.

At a cost of capital of 6.72%, the NPV of both projects is $143.

At a cost of capital of 5%, the NPV of Model L is $200. Compute the NPV of Model S when k = 5% and complete the table below.

Cost of Capital (k)	Model S	Model L
5%		**$200**
6.72%	**$143**	**$143**
10%	**$79**	

5.2 Question

Plot the points from the table above onto the following graph. Use one line for each project: Model S and Model L. The graph is called an "NPV Profile."

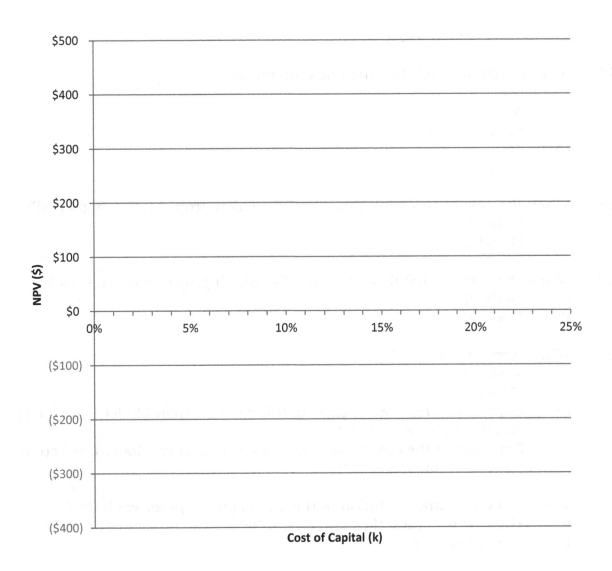

5.3   NPV Profile Explore It

Check out the NPV profile Explore It on page 9.3.17 in CFO.

17   Which is a true statement about the NPV profile?
    A)   The lines are parallel.

B)   The lines intersect.

18   At what cost of capital do the lines intersect?
      A)   5%
      B)   6%
      C)   6.72%
      D)   7%
      E)   10%

19   When the cost of capital is below 6.72%, which project has a higher NPV?
      A)   Model S
      B)   Model L

20   When the cost of capital is above 6.72%, which project has a higher NPV?
      A)   Model S
      B)   Model L

21   Which project is better?
      A)   Model S
      B)   Model L
      C)   Depends on the cost of capital. If k < 6.72% then Model L is better; otherwise Model S is better.
      D)   Depends on the cost of capital. If k > 6.72% then Model L is better; otherwise Model S is better.

22   What is the best interpretation of the x-axis intercept for each line?
      A)   The cost of capital that makes the NPV of the project equal to 0
      B)   The project's IRR

23   If you were to choose between the two mutually exclusive models by picking the project with the highest IRR, which project would you select?
      A)   Model S
      B)   Model L

24   Does the IRR decision-rule (suggested in Question #7) select the best project?

25   What causes the IRR to mis-rank mutually exclusive projects?

6. Profitability Index and Capital Rationing

6.1 Definition

$$PI = \frac{PV(Cash\ inflows)}{PV(Cash\ outflows)}$$

or

$$PI = \frac{PV(Cash\ inflows)}{Initial\ investment}$$

The numerator is the present value of the benefits of taking the project and the denominator is the present value of the cost.

6.2 Question

Recall that:

NPV = PV (Cash Inflows) – PV (Cash Outflows)

Use this expression to replace the numerator of the definition of PI. Then answer the following question.

26   If NPV > 0, is PI greater than or less than 1?
    A)   PI > 1
    B)   PI < 1

6.3 Question

Calculate the PI of each project in the following table.

Project	Investment (Outflow)	NPV	Profitability Index	PI Rank
A	$9M	$1.75M		
B	$10M	$2M		
C	$10M	$1.8M		

Rank the three projects by PI from highest (#1) to lowest (#3). Enter the ranks in the last column.

27   If you only had $20 million to invest, which two projects would you choose if you want the two highest ranked projects by PI?
    A)   A + B
    B)   A + C

C) B + C

28 If you only had $20 million to invest, which two projects would you
    choose if you want the highest combined (sum total) NPV?
    A) A + B
    B) A + C
    C) B + C

29 Assume that you are an NPV maximizer. In situations where capital is
    rationed, should you select projects by ranking them by PI and choosing
    the highest ranked projects?
    A) Yes
    B) No. You should maximize the summed NPV.

6.4   NPV Maximization Self-Test

Check out the NPV Maximization Self-Test on page 9.3.23 in CFO.

10. Practise computing project selection through NPV maximization. Answer

Solutions

<u>Payback Period</u> (2.2, 2.3)

Fraction of Year = 0.75

Payback = 1.67 years
Payback = 3.33 years

<u>Net Present Value</u> (3.2, 3.3)

NPV = $41.32
NPV = $41.66

<u>Internal Rate of Return</u> (4.2, 4.4)

IRR_L = 11.5%

IRR = 10%
NPV = $4.76

<u>Profitability Index and Capital Rationing</u> (6.3)

PI_A = 1.194
PI_B = 1.2
PI_C = 1.18

Depreciation and Expansion (Ch.10, LO1–LO2)

1. Introduction

In this workbook you will:

- Learn about the depreciation tax shield
- Learn how to calculate operating cash flow
- Learn about the CCA depreciation system
- Learn how the sale (salvage) of an asset affects taxes
- Learn how to calculate the initial, operating and terminal cash flows for an expansion project
- Calculate the NPV of an expansion project

2. Depreciation Tax Shield

2.1 Comment

- Under Federal (and Provincial) Corporate Income Tax, depreciation is deductible from net income.
  - o In Canada, this is known as the capital cost allowance (CCA).
  - o In the United States, this is known as the modified accelerated cost recovery system (MACRS).
- The depreciation expense is not a cash flow, but it does affect cash flow by reducing taxes.
  - o This is called the depreciation tax shield.
  - o Depreciation expense = Tax rate × Depreciation expense

2.2 Question

Consider two countries: Bolo and Bozo. Depreciation is tax deductible in Bolo but not in Bozo. In every other respect the two countries are identical. KOT Industries has identical divisions operating in both countries. Complete the income statements for both divisions in the table below. The tax rate is 40% and KOT's depreciation expense is $20 in both countries. What is the difference in taxes between Bolo and Bozo?

KOT Industries
Income Statement

	Bolo	Bozo
Revenues	$100	$100
COGS and SG&A	50	50
Depreciation	20	n.a.
EBIT	30	50
Interest	0	0
Earnings Before Tax	30	50
Taxes (@40%)		
Net Income		

ANSWER:
Difference in Taxes =

2.3   Question

If the depreciation expense is $20 and the tax rate is 40%, what is the depreciation tax shield?

ANSWER:
Depreciation Tax Shield =

3. Operating Cash Flows

3.1   Definition

OCF = Sales – COGS – SG&A – Taxes

Let Costs = COGS + SG&A

So,

OCF = Sales – Costs – Taxes   Eq. 1

Taxes = T × (Sales – Costs – Depr)   Eq. 2

Where

Depr = depreciation expenses
T = corporate tax rate

3.2   Question

30   Substitute Eq. 2 into Eq. 1 and simplify. Which of the following is (are) a correct expression for operating cash flows? (Check them all. It might be more than one.)
A)   = (Sales – Costs – Depr) × (1 – T)
B)   = (Sales – Costs – Depr) × (1 – T) + Depr
C)   = (Sales – Costs) × (1 – T) + Depr × T
D)   = NOPAT + Depr

Definitions:
- EBIT = (Sales – Costs – Depr)
- NOPAT = EBIT × (1 – T)

4. CCA Depreciation

4.1   Definition
- CCA = Capital Cost Allowance
- CCA is the Canada Revenue Agency's depreciation system.
- It is a declining balance depreciation system.

You can calculate depreciation expense as:

$$Depr_t = dr × UCC_{t-1}$$

Where

dr = depreciation rate

UCC_{t-1} = undepreciated capital cost at the end of the previous year (year $t – 1$)

4.2   Question
A $300,000 machine falls into Class 39 with a 25% depreciation rate. The Year 1 CCA depreciation expense is:

$$Depr_1 = 0.25 \times UCC_0$$

ANSWER:
$Depr_1 =$
Hint: UCC_0 is the purchase price of the machine.

At year-end, the undepreciated balance (undepreciated capital cost or UCC or book value) is:

$$UCC_1 = UCC_0 - Depr_1 = \$300,000 - \$75,000 = \$225,000$$

What is the Year 2 CCA depreciation expense?

ANSWER:
$Depr_2 =$

4.3   Definition

- Half Year Rule:
  - o To make allowance for different purchase timing through the year, the CCA system only permits half of the regular depreciation expense in the first year.
  - o Use dr/2 in the first year, not dr.
- Asset pools:
  - o If there are a number of assets in any given class, then those assets are pooled and treated as one.
  - o This affects treatment of assets when they are sold.

4.4   Question

The Garcia Corp purchased a $300,000 machine which falls into Class 39 with a 25% depreciation rate. The machine is used for four years and then sold. Calculate the depreciation expense in each year and the ending UCC.

	Year 1	Year 2	Year 3	Year 4
UCC_{t-1}	$300,000			
CCA Rate (dr)	0.125	0.25	0.25	0.25
Depr				
UCC_t				

5. Tax Impact of Salvage

5.1   Definition

- The proceeds from selling an asset are not taxable. The income tax system taxes income from a business.
- There is a tax impact if the salvage value (sale price) is different from the ending UCC.
- There are two systems:
    - o The asset class is closed because the last asset in the class is sold.
        - ▪ This usually occurs when the business is closed.
    - o The asset class remains open.
- Our default assumption is that the asset class stays open.
    - o When an asset is sold, subtract the sale price from the balance in the pooled asset class regardless of whether UCC > Salvage or UCC < Salvage.

Present value from tax shields gained (lost) due to salvage is given by:

$$PV\ Tax\ Shields_n = \frac{T \times dr \times (UCC_n - S)}{k + dr}$$

5.2   Example

What is the PV of tax shields if an asset sold for S = $110,742?

UCC of asset, UCC_n = $110,742
dr = 25%
T = 40%
k = 10%

ANSWER:
PV Tax Shields =

What is the PV of tax shields if an asset sold for S = $75,000?

UCC of asset, UCC_n = $110,742
dr = 25%
T = 40%
k = 10%

ANSWER:
PV Tax Shields =

6. Expansion Project Cash Flows

6.1   Initial Cash Flows

–	Initial purchase price of new asset
–	Installation/shipping cost of new asset
–	Increase in net working capital
=	Initial cash flow

6.2   Question

To produce its new product, Grapeful Soda, the Garcia Corp. will have to purchase machinery with a cost of $300,000. Garcia's inventories will have to be increased by $10,000 at the time of the initial investment. What are the initial cash flows for the project?

ANSWER:
Initial cash flows =

6.3   Operating Cash Flow Self-Test

Check out the operating cash flow self-test on page 10.2.10 of CFO.

It's Time to Do a Self-Test

6.4   Operating Cash Flows for Garcia Corp.

The Garcia Corp expects to sell 200,000 cartons of Grapeful Soda in each of the next four years at a price of $2.00 per carton, but $1.50 per carton will be needed to cover fixed and variable operating costs. Use the depreciation expenses calculated above to compute the operating cash flows in each year. The tax rate is 40%

	1	2	3	4

Revenues	$400,000	$400,000	$400,000	$400,000
Operating Costs	300,000	300,000	300,000	300,000
Depreciation	37,500			
EBIT	62,500			
Less: Taxes	25,000			
NOPAT	37,500			
Plus: Depreciation	37,500			
OCF	75,000			

6.5   Net Salvage

Net salvage = Salvage + PV of Tax Shields

If the Garcia Corp. sells its machinery at the end of four years for $110,742, what is net salvage?

ANSWER:
Net Salvage =

6.6   Terminal Year Cash Flows

+	OCF
+	Net Salvage
+	Decrease in net working capital
=	Terminal year cash flow

What are the terminal year cash flows for the Grapeful Soda project?

ANSWER:
Terminal Year Cash Flows =

6.7   Project Cash Flows

What are the initial, operating and terminal cash flows for the Grapeful Project?

Year	Cash Flow Type	$ Cash Flow
0	Initial	
1	Operating	
2	Operating	
3	Operating	
4	Terminal	

6.8   NPV

What is the NPV of the Grapeful Soda project if the cost of capital is 10%?

ANSWER:
NPV =

Solutions

Depreciation Tax Shield (2.2, 2.3)

Difference in Taxes = $8
Depreciation Tax Shield = $8

CCA Depreciation (4.2, 4.4)

$Depr_1$ = $75,000
$Depr_2$ = $56,250

	Year 1	Year 2	Year 3	Year 4
Starting UCC	300,000	262,500	196,875	147,656
CCA Rate	0.1250	0.2500	0.2500	0.2500
Depreciation Expense	37,500	65,625	49,219	36,914
Ending UCC	262,500	196,875	147,656	110,742

Tax Impact of Salvage (5.2)

PV Tax Shields = $0

PV Tax Shields = $10,212

Expansion Project Cash Flows (6.2, 6.4, 6.5, 6.7, 6.8)
Initial Cash Flows = −$310,000

	1	2	3	4
Revenues	400,000	400,000	400,000	400,000
Operating Costs	300,000	300,000	300,000	300,000
Depreciation	37,500	65,625	49,219	36,914
EBIT	62,500	34,375	50,781	63,086
Taxes	25,000	13,750	20,313	25,234
NOPAT	37,500	20,625	30,469	37,852

+ Depreciation	37,500	65,625	49,219	36,914
OCF	75,000	86,250	79,688	74,766

Net Salvage = $110,742 + $0

Terminal Cash Flows = $74,766 + $110,742 + $10,000 = $195,508

Year	Cash Flow Type	$ Cash Flow
0	Initial	–310,000
1	Operating	75,000
2	Operating	86,250
3	Operating	79,688
4	Terminal	195,508

NPV = $22,868

Replacement and Refinements (Ch.10, LO3–LO4)

1. Introduction

In this workbook you will:

- Learn about replacement project cash flows (initial, operating and terminal)
- Do a replacement project example
- Learn about refinements to capital budgeting (such as sunk costs, externalities and opportunity costs)
- Learn how to compare projects with unequal lives using the equivalent annual annuity approach and the replacement chain approach.

2. Replacement Project Initial Cash Flows

2.1 Definition

–	Initial purchase price of new asset
+	Proceeds from Sale of Old Asset
–	Increase in net working capital
=	Initial cash flow

2.2 Tax Effects

- There are no immediate tax effects from replacing an asset at the time of replacement. The cost of a new asset is added to the CCA pool. The proceeds from selling the old asset are deducted from the pool.
- In other words, add incremental capital cost, ΔC, to the pool.

Definition:

Incremental capital cost or $\Delta C = C_0 - S_0$

Where

C_0 = cost of new machine

S_0 = salvage value of old machine on replacement date

2.3   Question

A $12,000 machine is purchased to replace an old machine that can be sold today for $1,000. Both machines are in Class 39 with a 25% depreciation rate. The company must increase inventory by $1,000. What are the initial cash flows associated with this replacement project?

ANSWER:
Initial Cash Flows =

---

3. Replacement Project Operating Cash Flows

3.1   Definition

$\Delta OCF = [\Delta Revenues - \Delta Operating\ Expenses - \Delta Depr] \times (1 - T) + \Delta Depr$

Where

Δ = change or incremental amount

3.2   Incremental Depreciation (ΔDepr)

Incremental depreciation is calculated by depreciating the incremental capital cost as if it were a new asset.

This implicitly applies the half-year rule to the sale of the old asset, which is correct under the CCA system.

3.3   Question

A $12,000 machine is purchased to replace an old machine that can be sold today for $1,000. Both machines are in Class 39 with a 25% depreciation rate. The new machine is used for two years and then sold. Calculate the incremental depreciation expense in each year and the ending UCC.

	Year 1	Year 2
ΔUCC_{t-1}	$11,000	
CCA Rate (dr)	0.125	0.25
ΔDepr		
ΔUCC_t		

3.4 Operating Cash Flow Self-Test

Check out the operating cash flow self-test on page 10.3.9 of CFO.

It's Time to Do a Self-Test

8. Practise computing the annual operating cash flows for a replacement project. [Answer]

4. Replacement Project Terminal Cash Flows

4.1 Definition

+	Operating cash flows
+	Salvage value of new asset
−	Salvage value of old asset
+	PV of tax shields from selling new asset
−	PV of tax shields from selling old asset
+	Decrease in net working capital
=	Terminal cash flows

4.2 Tax Impact of Salvage

Incremental salvage or $\Delta S = S^{New} - S^{Old}$

Where
S^{New} = salvage value of new asset in the terminal year
S^{Old} = salvage value of old asset in the terminal year

The PV of tax shields gained from selling the new machine is:

$$PV\ Tax\ Shields_{New} = \frac{T \times dr \times (UCC^N - S^N)}{k + dr}$$

Where
UCC^N = UCC of new asset in the terminal year
S^N = salvage value of new asset in the terminal year

The foregone PV of tax shields that could have been gained from selling the old machine is:

$$PV\ Tax\ Shields_{New} = \frac{T \times dr \times (UCC^O - S^O)}{k + dr}$$

Where

UCC^O = UCC of old asset in the terminal year

S^O = salvage value of old asset in the terminal year

The incremental PV of tax shields is:

= PV Tax Shields$_{New}$ – PV Tax Shields$_{Old}$

OR

$$Incremental\ PV\ Tax\ Shields = \frac{T \times dr \times (\Delta UCC - \Delta S)}{k + dr}$$

Where

ΔUCC = incremental UCC (from incremental depreciation schedule)

ΔS = incremental salvage

4.3   Example

The Fritz Electric Company replaced an old machine five years ago with a new one. They sold the new machine today for $300,000. If Fritz had kept the old machine, it could have been sold for $100,000 today. The incremental UCC is $220,000. The tax rate is 35%. The depreciation rate for the machines is 30% and Fritz's cost of capital is 9%. What is the incremental PV of tax shields associated with selling the new machine?

ANSWER:
Incremental PV Tax Shields =

4.4   Terminal Cash Flow Self-Test

Check out the terminal cash flow self-test on page 10.3.12 of CFO.

It's Time to Do a Self-Test

9. Practise calculating the terminal cash flows for a replacement project. Answer

5. Replacement Project Example

5.1 Question

To satisfy the demand for smooth felt, the Rumpel Felt Company purchased a felt press last year. The machine had an expected life of three years at the time of purchase and an estimated salvage value of $200 at the end of the three years. The machine was depreciated at 25%. The division manager reports that a new felt press that makes even smoother felt can be purchased for $12,000 (including installation). The new felt press will expand sales from $10,000 to $15,000 a year because the new fashion is for smoother felt. Further, it will reduce labour and raw materials usage sufficiently to cut operating costs from $7,000 to $5,000. (Note that incremental operating costs are negative.) The new machine has an estimated salvage value of $2,000 at the end of two years. The new machine requires an increase in felt inventory of $1,000. The old machine's current market value is $1,000. Taxes are 40%, and the firm's cost of capital is 10%. Should Rumpel buy the new machine?

5.2 Incremental Initial Cash Flows

ANSWER:
Initial cash flows =

5.3 Incremental Depreciation Schedule

	Year 1	Year 2
ΔUCC_{t-1}	$11,000	
CCA Rate (dr)	0.125	0.25
$\Delta Depr$		
ΔUCC_t		

5.4   Incremental Operating Cash Flows

	1	2	
Revenues	$5,000	$5,000	
Operating Costs	–$2,000	–$2,000	**N.B. –ve incremental operating costs**
Depreciation			
EBIT			
Less: Taxes			
NOPAT			
Plus: Depreciation			
OCF			

5.5   Incremental Net Salvage

ΔNet salvage = ΔSalvage + ΔPV of Tax Shields

ANSWER:
ΔSalvage =

ANSWER:
ΔPV of Tax Shields =

5.6   Terminal Year Cash Flows

+	OCF
+	Net Salvage
+	Decrease in net working capital
=	Terminal year cash flow

What are the terminal year cash flows for the Rumpel Felt project?

ANSWER:
Terminal Year Cash Flows =

5.7   Project Cash Flows

What are the initial, operating and terminal cash flows for the Rumpel Felt project?

Year	Cash Flow Type	$ Cash Flow
0	Initial	
1	Operating	
2	Terminal	

5.8   NPV

What is the NPV of the Rumpel Felt project if the cost of capital is 10%?

ANSWER:
NPV =

6. Capital Budgeting Refinements

Garcia Corp. is currently evaluating a new carbonated grape juice product called Grapeful Soda. Grapeful is superior to competing grape products like Grape Nehi. Production facilities for the Grapeful product would be set up in an unused section of Garcia's main plant. Machinery with an estimated cost of $300,000 will be purchased to manufacture the soda. Garcia's inventories would have to be increased by $10,000 at the time of the initial investment.

The machinery has a CCA depreciation rate of 25%. The machinery is expected to have a salvage value of $110,742 after four years of use.

Garcia's management expects to sell 200,000 bottles of the new product in each of the next four years at a price of $2.00 per bottle, but $1.50 per bottle would be needed to cover fixed and variable operating costs. Garcia's tax rate is 40% and the overall cost of capital is 10%.

Donna Jean and Bob, recent business school graduates who are now working at Garcia as financial analysts, must analyze this project and then present their findings to the company's executive committee. They have calculated that the NPV of the project is $22,868, as shown in the following analysis. Answer the following questions about their analysis.

		Depreciation Schedule:			
		Year 1	Year 2	Year 3	Year 4
UCC_t–1		300,000	262,500	196,875	147,656
Depreciation Rate		0.125	0.25	0.25	0.25
Depreciation Exp.		37,500	65,625	49,219	36,914
UCC_t		262,500	196,875	147,656	110,742
	0	1	2	3	4
Revenues	-	400,000	400,000	400,000	400,000
Operating Costs	-	300,000	300,000	300,000	300,000
Depreciation	-	37,500	65,625	49,219	36,914
Pre-Tax Income	-	62,500	34,375	50,781	63,086
Taxes	-	25,000	13,750	20,313	25,234
NOPAT	-	37,500	20,625	30,469	37,852
Add: Depreciation	-	37,500	65,625	49,219	36,914
OCF	-	75,000	86,250	79,688	74,766
Investment	(300,000)				-
Net Work Cap	(10,000)				10,000
PV of Tax Shields	-	-	-	-	0
Salvage	-	-	-	-	110,742
Net Cash Flows	(310,000)	75,000	86,250	79,688	195,508

6.1 Refinement #1

The section of the plant that will be used for production has been unused for several years. Last year Garcia spent $100,000 to renovate that section of the main plant. Bob believes that the renovation expense should be charged to the Grapeful project. He argues that if the renovations had not taken place, the firm would have had to spend the $100,000 to prepare the site for the Grapeful project. Is Bob correct? What is your revised NPV estimate?

> **ANSWER:**
> Is Bob correct?
> Revised NPV =

6.2   Refinement #2

Garcia's sales manager is concerned that the Grapeful project will cut into the firm's sales of other grape beverages. (This type of effect is called cannibalization.) The sales manager estimates that grape concentrate sales will fall by 5% if Grapeful Soda is introduced. Donna Jean talked to both the sales and production managers, and she concluded that the new project will lower grape concentrate sales by $20,000 (of course, if there are less sales than there are lower costs). Production costs for grape concentrate would fall by $10,000 per year (pre-tax). Thus, the net pre-tax loss is: –$20,000 + $10,000 = –$10,000. What is the NPV of the project if Donna Jean and Bob include this consideration in their analysis? (Ignore the previous question and adjust the original NPV estimate.)

ANSWER:
Revised NPV =

6.3   Refinement #3

The section of the plant where the production would occur has been unused for several years. A local wine company, Lesh Wines, has offered to lease the space to make organic red wine. Lesh is offering to pay $1,100 per month to rent the space. What is the NPV of the project if Donna Jean and Bob include this consideration in their analysis? (Ignore the previous questions and adjust the original NPV estimate.)

ANSWER:
Revised NPV =

7. Comparing Projects with Unequal Lives

7.1   Question

Suppose a firm has access to the following two projects. These projects are mutually exclusive and future replacement is expected.

Year	Cash Flows Project L	Project S
0	–$52,000	–$40,000
1	15,000	18,000
2	15,000	18,000
3	15,000	18,000
4	15,000	
5	15,000	

The NPV of Project L is $6,344.77. What is the NPV of Project S if the cost of capital is 9%? Which project has higher NPV?

ANSWER:

NPV_S =

7.2   Question: NPV/year

What is the NPV per year for Projects L and S?

ANSWER:

$NPV_L/5$ =

ANSWER:

$NPV_S/3$ =

Which project has a higher NPV per year?

7.3   Definition: Equivalent Annual Annuity

Equivalent Annual Annuity, EAA, is the solution to:

$$NPV = EAA \times PVIFA_{k,n}$$

OR

$$EAA = NPV/PVIFA_{k,n}$$

Where
n = life of the project
NPV = NPV of the project
k = WACC

- If the NPV were an annuity, EAA is the dollar amount that you would get per year.
- This is like smoothing the NPV out over the project's life.
- EAA is similar to NPV per year, but it takes into account the time value of money.

7.4   Question: EAA

What is the equivalent annual annuity for Projects L and S?

ANSWER:
$EAA_L =$

ANSWER:
$EAA_S =$

Which project has a higher EAA?

7.5   Which Light Bulb?

You are shopping for a new light bulb. You have two choices: incandescent (Philips DuraMax) or LED. The LED lasts longer than the incandescent, uses less electricity, produces less light (in lumens) but costs more. Since the two bulbs have different lives, you should select the bulb with the higher effective annual annuity. Data on the two bulbs is provided in the table below.

	Philips DuraMax 60w	Philips LED 50w
Cost	$1.62	$18.00
Light output (lumens)	830	470
Bulb Life (in hours)	1,460	24,820
Service Life* (years)	1	17
Watts used per hour	60	8
Kilowatts per hour (kWh)	0.06	0.008
*Assuming 4 hours per day for 365 days per year or 1,460 hours per year.		

Since the light output is unequal, the two bulbs generate different amounts of benefits. To balance the comparison, assume that you buy 1 Duramax or 1.766 LEDs (830/470 = 1.766). That way the two bundles generate the same amount of light and have the same benefit. Now we only have to compare the NPV of the costs.

The NPV of a bulb is equal to:

$$NPV_{Bulb} = -\$Price - \sum_{t=1}^{n} \frac{\$Cost}{(1+k)^t}$$

Where
$Cost = annual cost of electricity to operate the bulb
n = service life (in years) of the bulb (DuraMax = 1 year, LED = 17 years)
k = your cost of capital (k = 5%)

To evaluate the costs, we must make some usage assumptions. Assume that the bulbs are used for four hours per day every day or 1,460 hours per year. Assume that the usage occurs in a lump sum at the end of every year (to make the discounting easier).

COSTS:

The cost of operating a light bulb is the cost of the electricity it uses. Assume that the cost of electricity is $0.11/kWh. The annual cost of powering a bulb is:

$Cost = #kWh per hour × #hours per year × $0.11/kWh

For 1 LED the $Cost is:

$Cost (LED) = 0.008 × 1,460 × 0.11 = $1.285

What is the annual cost for the DuraMax bulb?

ANSWER:	
$Cost (DuraMax)	
$Cost (LED)	$1.285

What is the annual cost for 1.7566 LED bulbs?

ANSWER:
$Cost for 1.7566 (LED)

NPV:

What is the NPV of each bulb bundle?

ANSWER:
$NPV (DuraMax)
$NPV (LED)

EAA:

What is the EAA of each bulb bundle?

ANSWER:
$EAA (DuraMax)
$EAA (LED)

7.6   Sensitivity Analysis

The big unknown in this analysis is the service life of the LED bulb. If it breaks early, then it may be better to buy a series of incandescent bulbs. The following graph shows the EAA for each bulb at different values for the service life of the LED. The incandescent is constant at one year.

EAA of Light Bulbs and Life of the LED Bulb

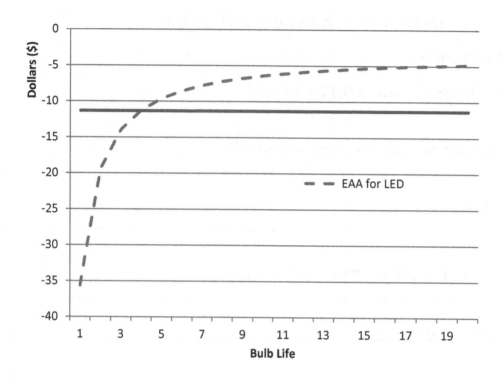

If the LED lasts more than four years, which bulb is superior?

ANSWER:
Better bulb =

7.7   Replacement Chain

- The EAA approach does not allow for the impact of inflation or changes in technology.
- If there are changes in project cash flows in the future, we must use the "replacement chain method."
- In this method, repeat one or both projects until both projects run for the same length of time, and then compare the NPV of the extended projects.

7.8   Replacement Chain Example

- Karkus Kold Kuts Inc. is submitting a bid to the government to produce sandwich meats for cabinet meetings for four years. Ted Karkus, the CEO, has two technology options to complete the work under the contract:

    - Machine A has an installed cost of $50,000 but is expected to generate operating cash flows of $20,000 a year for four years.

After four years, the machine has no salvage value. Ignore any tax impact of salvage.

- Machine B has only a two year lifetime and its installed cost is $30,000. For the two years it is expected to produce operating cash flows of $20,000 a year. When it is replaced after two years at a cost of $30,000, the firm expects to generate operating cash flows of $22,000 a year for two years because of improved efficiency due to the new model of machine. Both versions of machine B have no salvage value and ignore the tax impact of salvage.

- Should the firm submit a bid for the contract? If yes, should it plan to use machine A or machine B? The cost of capital at Karkus is 10%. Assume that the purchase of the machines occurs at the beginning of the year but operating cash flows occur at the end of the year.

Year	Machine A			Machine B		
	Outflows	Inflows	Net	Outflows	Inflows	Net
0	–$50,000		–$50,000	–$30,000		–$30,000
1		$20,000	$20,000		$20,000	$20,000
2		$20,000	$20,000	–$30,000	$20,000	–$10,000
3		$20,000	$20,000		$22,000	$22,000
4		$20,000	$20,000		$22,000	$22,000

What is the NPV for the replacement chains for Machines A and B?

> **ANSWER:**
> $NPV_A =$

> **ANSWER:**
> $NPV_B =$

Which replacement chain has a higher NPV?

Solutions

Replacement Project Initial Cash Flows (2.3)

Initial Cash Flows = –$12,000 + $1,000 – $1,000 = –$12,000

Replacement Project Operating Cash Flows (3.3)

	Year 1	Year 2
ΔUCC_{t-1}	$11,000	9,625

233

CCA Rate (dr)	0.125	0.25
ΔDepr	1,375	2,406.25
ΔUCC$_t$	9,625	7,218.75

Replacement Project Terminal Cash Flows (4.3)

Incremental PV of Tax Shields = $5,384.62

Replacement Project Example (5.2, 5.3, 5.4, 5.5, 5.6, 5.7, 5.8)

Initial Cash Flows = –$12,000 + $1,000 – $1,000 = $12,000

	Year 1	**Year 2**
ΔUCC$_{t-1}$	$11,000	9,625
CCA Rate (dr)	0.125	0.25
ΔDepr	1,375	2,406.25
ΔUCC$_t$	9,625	7,218.75

OPERATING CASH FLOWS	Year 0	Year 1	Year 2
Revenues		5,000.00	5,000.00
Costs		–2,000.00	–2,000.00
EBITDA		7,000.00	7,000.00
Depreciation		1,375.00	2,406.25
EBIT		5,625.00	4,593.75
Taxes		2,250.00	1,837.50
NOPAT		3,375.00	2,756.25
Depreciation		1,375.00	2,406.25
OCF		4,750.00	5,162.50

Incremental Salvage = $2,000 – $200 = $1,800
Incremental PV of Tax Shields = $1,548.21
Net salvage = $1,800 + $1,548.21 = $3,348.21

Terminal Cash Flows = $5,162.50 + $3,348.21 + $1,000 = $9,510.71

Year	Cash Flow Type	$ Cash Flow
0	Initial	–12,000
1	Operating	4,750

234

$NPV_{RUMPEL} = \$178.28$

Capital Budgeting Refinements (6.1, 6.2, 6.3)

Bob is incorrect. $100,000 is a sunk cost. Ignore it. NPV = $22,868

Annual Operating Cash Flow due to Reduced Sales = –$6,000
$PV_{OCF\ Due\ to\ Lost\ Sales} = -\$19,019$
NPV = $22,868 – $19,109 = $3,848

Annual Operating Cash Flow due to Lease = $7,920
$PV_{OCF\ Due\ to\ Lease} = \$25,105$
This is an opportunity cost, so subtract from initial NPV estimate:
NPV = $22,868 – $25,105 = –$2,238. Don't make Grapeful Soda, lease to Lesh.

Comparing Projects with Unequal Lives (7.1, 7.2, 7.4, 7.5, 7.8)

$NPV_S = \$5,563.30$

$NPV_L/5 = \$1,269$

$NPV_S/3 = \$1,854$

$EAA_L = \$1,631$

$EAA_S = \$2,198$

$Cost (DuraMax) = 0.06 × 1,460 × 0.11 = $9.636
$Cost for 1.7566 LEDs = 1.7566 × 1.28 = $2.2689
$NPV_{DuraMax} = -\$10.79$
$NPV_{LED} = -\$57.37$
$EAA_{DuraMax} = -\$11.33$
$EAA_{LED} = -\$5.09$

$NPV_A = \$13,397.31$

$NPV_B = \$11,472.58$

Cost of Capital (Ch.11)

1. Introduction

In this workbook you will:

- Learn the meaning and definition of the weighted average cost of capital
- Learn to calculate the cost of debt
- Understand why we use the after-tax cost of debt
- Learn to calculate the cost of equity (three different ways)
- Learn how to calculate capital structure weights

2. Cost of Capital

2.1   Definition

The cost of capital (COC) is the hurdle rate for capital budgeting decisions.

- Capital: Non-spontaneous funds used to finance assets (e.g., equity and debt)
- Hurdle: The return on the project must exceed the return required by providers of capital.

2.2   Question

IMAGINARY CORP BALANCE SHEET

Assets		Liabilities & Owners Equity	
		Debt (Bonds)	25
		Owner's Equity	75
Total Assets	100	Total Liabs & O.E.	100

Assume that the balance sheet for Imaginary Corp. is in market values and that you own all of its securities (debt and equity). You require a return of 8% on the bonds (k_D = 8%) and 25% on the stocks (k_E = 25%). What is the required return on your portfolio if the debt and equity are the only two securities that you own? Recall that the return on a portfolio is given by:

$$k_p = w_D k_D + w_E k_E$$

Where the w's are the portfolio weights.

ANSWER:
$k_p =$

2.3   Definition: Weighted Average Cost of Capital

The weighted average cost of capital (WACC) is the weighted average of the required returns on the company's sources of capital. The weights are the company's optimal (target) capital structure weights.

$$k_{WACC} = w_D k_D (1 - T) + w_E k_E + w_P k_P$$

Where

w_D = proportion of debt financing in optimal capital structure

w_E = proportion of common equity financing in optimal capital structure

w_P = proportion of preferred equity in optimal capital structure

k_P = cost of preferred equity (required return of shareholders)

$k_D(1 - T)$ = the after-tax cost of debt

k_E = the cost of common equity

2.4   Question

The pre-tax cost of debt is 11%, preferred stock costs 14%, and equity costs 15%. What is the weighted average cost of capital assuming a tax rate of 40% and a target capital structure of 40% debt, 20% preferred stock and 40% equity?

ANSWER:
$k_{WACC} =$

---

3. Cost Of Debt

- Cost of debt is the interest rate on debt. It represents the return that lenders want to earn.
    - Cost of debt is new debt, not old debt. It is the rate on debt issued today.
    - For loans, the cost of debt = the interest rate on a loan initiated today.
    - For bonds, the cost of debt = yield to maturity on an issue of new debt.
        - You may think that the cost of debt is the coupon rate, since the company pays the coupons. For new debt, the coupon

rate and yield are typically equal. Issuers set the coupon rate to equal the yield so that the bond is priced at face value when it is issued. As a result, the coupon rate ($C/FV) = the yield to maturity.

3.1 Question

The Loose Wheel Motor Corp. is issuing a 20-year bond with annual coupons. The face value of each bond is $1,000. The investment banker advises that corporate bonds with similar maturity and risk currently trade with a yield to maturity of 6%. Loose Wheel wants the bonds to sell at a price of $1,000 when they are issued. What coupon rate should the company offer on the bond?

> **ANSWER:**
> $C/FV =

3.2 Question: Yield to Maturity

The Loose Wheel Motor Corp. has bonds outstanding with one year remaining to maturity. The bonds pay annual coupons at a rate of 5%. The face value of each bond is $1,000 and they are trading for $975. What is the yield to maturity on the bonds?

Hint: The yield to maturity is k_d, the solution to:

$$P_{bond} = C \times \text{PVIFA}_{n,k_d} + \frac{FV}{(1 + k_d)^n}$$

OR, equivalently, the solution to:

$$P_{bond} = \sum_{t=1}^{n} \frac{C_t}{(1 + k_d)^t} + \frac{FV}{(1 + k_d)^n}$$

> **ANSWER:**
> k_d =

3.3 The After-tax Cost of Debt

We use the after-tax cost of debt in WACC instead of k_d. Why? Because it incorporates the interest tax shield and allows us to omit interest (and interest tax deductibility) from the cash flow estimates in capital budgeting and corporate valuation.

After tax cost of debt = $k_d \times (1 - T)$

Where

T = corporate tax rate

3.4 Question

The Loose Wheel Motor Corp. has bonds with a yield of 5%. The corporate tax rate is 40%. What is Loose Wheel's after-tax cost of debt?

> **ANSWER:**
> $k_d \times (1 - T) =$

3.5 Definition: Interest Tax Shield

- Taxes are reduced due to interest deductibility.
- The amount of the reduction = T × $Interest Expense
- This is called the interest tax shield.

3.6 Interest Tax Shield and Capital Budgeting

There are two ways to incorporate the interest tax shield into capital budgeting: Method #1: Include the interest expense in the tax calculation (in OCF) and discount at before-tax WACC; or Method #2: ignore interest in the tax calculation (in OCF) and discount at after-tax WACC. The two methods produce the same answer, as you will see below. We use Method #2.

Consider a company with annual (perpetual) EBIT of $217 per year.

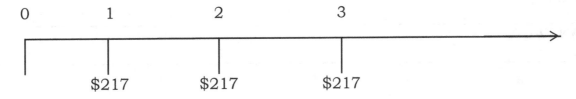

The company is worth $2,000 today. Equity is worth $1,000 and stockholders require a return of 10%. Debt (bonds) is also worth $1,000. The bonds have a face value of $1,000, an annual coupon of $50 and bondholders require a yield of 5%. The bonds are perpetuities.

What is the before-tax cost of debt for KOT?

> **ANSWER:**
> $k_d =$

METHOD #1:

Complete the operating cash flow calculation for KOT Industries under Method #1 below.

KOT Industries Method #1 Operating Cash Flows	
EBIT	$217
– Interest	
Earnings Before Tax	
– Taxes (@40%)	
Net Income	
OCF = Net Income + Interest	

What is the WACC for KOT Industries using the before-tax cost of debt?

ANSWER: WACC =

What is the present value of KOT's operating cash flows using the WACC above? (Assume that the cash flows are a perpetuity starting one year from today.)

ANSWER: V_{KOT} =

METHOD #2:

Complete the operating cash flow calculation for KOT Industries under Method #2 below.

KOT Industries Method #2 Operating Cash Flows	
EBIT	$217
Interest	n.a.
Earnings Before Tax	

Taxes (@40%)	
Net Income	
OCF = Net Income	

What is the WACC for KOT Industries using the after-tax cost of debt?

ANSWER:
WACC =

What is the present value of KOT's operating cash flows using the WACC above? (Assume that the cash flows are a perpetuity starting one year from today.)

ANSWER:
V_{KOT} =

4. Cost Of Equity

- There are three possible approaches to calculate k_E:

  1. CAPM (preferred method)
  2. Dividend discount model
  3. Company's bond yield + equity risk premium

4.1   Capital Asset Pricing Model (CAPM)

- Expected (equilibrium) return is given by:

  - $E(k_i) = k_F + \beta_i \times [E(k_M) - k_F]$

  - k_F = risk-free rate = return on T-Bills or short-maturity government bonds

  - B_i = company beta (Obtain from GlobeInvestor.com or yahoo finance.)

  - $[E(k_M) - k_F]$ = 6.5% (1900 – 2000 average from Dimson, Marsh and Staunton)

4.2   Question

You are calculating the cost of equity for the Gap, Inc., a chain of retail clothing stores. The risk-free rate is 5%, the expected return on the market is 12% and the Gap's beta is 1.3. What is the expected return on the Gap?

> **ANSWER:**
> $E(k_i) =$

4.3   Dividend Discount Model

- If a company pays dividends that grow at a constant rate, then we can use the stock market price to infer the discount rate used by the market to price the stock. In other words, we can solve for shareholders' required rate of return.
- Under the constant growth model, the stock price is:

$$P_0 = \frac{D_1}{k_E - g}$$

- Re-arrange the constant growth model to solve for k_E:

> **ANSWER:**
> $k_E =$

4.4   Question

What is the return on equity if $D_1 = \$1$, $P_0 = \$10$ and $g = 4\%$?

> **ANSWER:**
> $k_E =$

4.5   Bond Yield + Premium

- Add a premium to the company's bond yield.
- Problem: How big should the premium be?
    - There is no theory to guide us.

Which should be greater, in equilibrium, k_D or k_E? Why?

31   Which claimholder is exposed to more risk?
    A)   Bondholder
    B)   Stockholder

32   In equilibrium, if risk and return are related, who should earn a higher return?
    A)   Bondholder

B) Stockholder

33 Which should be larger in equilibrium?
A) k_D
B) k_E

The benefit of the bond yield plus premium approach is that it reminds us that the cost of equity must always be larger than the cost of debt.

5. Capital Structure Weights

- Total Capital (V) = Debt (D) + Equity (E)

- $w_E = E/V$

- $w_D = D/V$

If D = $80 and E = $120, what are:

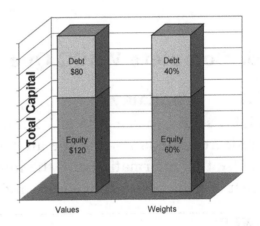

5.1 Definition:
- Proportions (weights) of debt and equity are based on the current market value of all the firm's outstanding securities.

- Market value of equity, E, = Price × shares outstanding.
- The market value of debt, D, is the market value of bonds and loans.
- If the market values are difficult to obtain, then we commonly use book value.
    o This is usually the case for debt.
- This is assumed to be the company's optimal capital structure.
- If the optimal weights are known and are different from the market weights, then use the optimal weights.

5.2　Question

Vandalay Industries has 1 million shares of common outstanding with a market price of $12 per share. The firm's outstanding bonds have ten years to maturity, a face value of $5 million and a coupon rate of 10%, and sell for $985. What are the capital structure weights for equity and debt?

ANSWER:

E =

D =

V =

w_E =

w_D =

---

6. Complete WACC Questions

6.1　Vandalay

Vandalay's stock has a beta of 1.2 and the company is in the 40% tax bracket. The risk-free rate is 7% and the analysts' expected return for the market is 14%. Use this information and the information in the last section to solve for the cost of debt, the cost of equity and Vandalay's WACC.

ANSWER:

k_E =

k_D =

k_W =

6.2　Wayne Enterprises

Selected financial information for Wayne Enterprises is provided in the table below. Calculate the company's WACC.

Hint: the preferred shares are a third security in the portfolio. You will need to calculate the required return on preferred shares and a third capital structure weight.

In this case, V = E + D + P, where P is the value of preferred shares.

Recall that the price of a preferred share is given by:

$$P_{Preferred} = \frac{D}{k_P}$$

Use this to solve for the required return, k_P.

Selected Financial Information for Wayne Enterprises
Long-term Debt $10M Face Value Coupon rate = 3.5% Annual Coupons Time to maturity = 10 years YTM = 5% Tax rate = 35%
Preferred Shares 1.0M shares outstanding par value = $5 per share 8% dividend rate (annual) Equivalent preferred shares yield 6%
Common Shares Shares outstanding = 5M Market price = $25 per share Beta = 0.8; T-Bill rate = 3% Expected return on the market = E(km) = 9%

ANSWER:
k_E =
k_D =
k_P =
w_E =
w_D =
w_P =
k_W =

6.3   Wayne Enterprises (Again)

Use the cost of capital Explore It on page 11.2.4 (in CFO) to compute Wayne's WACC.

246

Solutions

<u>Cost of Capital</u> (2.2, 2.4)

k_p = 0.2075

k_{WACC} = 0.114

<u>Cost of Debt</u> (3.1, 3.2, 3.4, 3.6)

C/FV = yield = 6%

k_D = 7.69%

$k_D \times (1 - T)$ = 3%

k_D = 5%
WACC = 7.5%
V_{KOT} = 2,000
WACC = 6.5%
V_{KOT} = 2,000

<u>Cost of Equity</u> (4.2, 4.3, 4.4)

$E(k)$ = 0.141

$$k_E = \frac{D_1}{P_0} + g$$

k_E = 0.14

<u>Capital Structure Weights</u> (5.2)

V = 200
w_E = 0.6
w_D = 0.4

E = 12M
D = 4.925M
V = 16.925

w_E = 0.70901
w_D = 0.29099

<u>Complete WACC Questions</u> (6.1, 6.2)

k_D = 10.247%
k_D = 15.4%
k_W = 12.71%

k_E = 0.078
k_D = 0.05
k_P = 0.06

w_E =0.8896
w_D = 0.0629
w_P = 0.0474
k_W = 0.0743

Capital Structure (Ch.12)

1. Introduction
In this workbook you will:

- Learn the definition of leverage
- Learn how to measure operating and financial leverage
- Learn how financial leverage affects EPS
- Learn about EBIT-EPS Analysis
- Learn about M&M Propositions I & II without taxes
- Learn about M&M Propositions I & II with taxes

2. Leverage

2.1 Definition: Leverage
- Financial leverage is the addition of debt to the capital structure.
- The use of financial leverage increases the risk to common stockholders by concentrating the business risk over a smaller number of investors.

2.2 Definition: Business Risk
- Business risk is measured by the standard deviation of EBIT.
    - o Business risk increases as operating leverage $\uparrow$.
- It is influenced by:
    - o Sensitivity of sales to economic conditions
    - o Industrial structure
        - In competitive markets, a firm can't control product price. In monopolistic markets, a firm has some price-setting power.
    - o Input price variability (i.e., oil or commodity prices)
    - o The firm's capital budgeting decisions (project choices)

2.3 Definition: Financial Risk
- Financial risk is measured by the standard deviation of EPS.
- Probability of bankruptcy:
    - o no chance of bankruptcy = no financial risk
- Financial risk increases as D/E ratio $\uparrow$.
- It may increase or decrease a firm's value (that is what this topic is all about).

2.4 Definition: Operating Leverage
- Operating leverage measures responsiveness of EBIT to changes in sales.

- Companies with high operating leverage are those with high fixed costs.
    - When fixed costs are covered, additional sales are (almost) all profit.
    - When fixed costs aren't covered, then there are losses.

$$DOL = \frac{\text{Percentage change in EBIT}}{\text{Percentage change in Sales}} = \frac{\% \, \Delta EBIT}{\% \, \Delta Sales}$$

2.5 Definition: Financial Leverage
- Financial leverage measures the responsiveness of EPS to changes in EBIT.
- Companies with high financial leverage are those with high fixed borrowing costs (interest).

$$DFL = \frac{\text{Percentage change in EPS}}{\text{Percentage change in EBIT}} = \frac{\% \, \Delta EPS}{\% \, \Delta EBIT}$$

2.6 Definition: Total Leverage
$$DTL = DOL \times DFL$$

$$DTL = \frac{\%\Delta EBIT}{\%\Delta Sales} \times \frac{\%\Delta EPS}{\%EBIT} = \frac{\%\Delta EPS}{\%\Delta Sales}$$

2.7 Question: DOL & DFL

Complete the following table to compare Microsoft and American Railcar. Then answer the questions that follow. American Railcar makes tankers, gondola cars and hoppers. Tankers are currently very popular for hauling oil. Carl Icahn owns 55% of the company.

Selected Financial Information American Railcar and Microsoft			
American Railcar Industries Inc. ($000,000s)		Microsoft ($000,000,000s)	
Year 1	Year 2	Year 1	Year 2

Sales	$519.4	$711.7	$73.7	$ 77.8
EBIT	32.7	121.4	21.8	26.8
Net Income	4.3	63.8	17.0	21.9
Shares Out	21.4	21.4	8.3	8.3
EPS	$ 0.20	$ 2.99	$ 2.05	$ 2.63
PP&E	194.2	376.2	8.3	10.0
Total Assets	703.8	809.8	121.3	142.4
Debt (Long-term)	275.0	272.2	10.7	12.6
Equity	310.2	369.5	66.4	78.9
PP&E/Total Assets	28%	46%	7%	7%
Debt-to-equity	0.89	0.74	0.16	0.16

34   Which company has a larger amount of fixed assets (PP&E as a
     proportion of total assets)?
     A)   American Railcar
     B)   Microsoft

35   Which company has a more debt (relative to equity)?
     A)   American Railcar
     B)   Microsoft

Complete the following table. (Compare the two years for each company.)

	American Railcar Industries Inc.	Microsoft
%Change in Sales	37%	6%
%Change in EBIT	271%	
%Change in EPS		28%

Use the figures above to complete the following table.

	American Railcar Industries Inc.	Microsoft
DOL	7.3	
DFL		1.2
DTL	38.0	

36   Which company has a larger degree of operating leverage?
     A)   American railcar
     B)   Microsoft

251

37   Which company has a larger degree of financial leverage?
    A)   American railcar
    B)   Microsoft

3. The Effect of Financial Leverage on EPS

Fritz Electric wants to expand into PC repair for manufacturers like Dell and HP. Fritz needs $10 million to build the repair depot. Fritz has been approached by two investment bankers with plans for financing the business. Al Lequity proposes 100% equity financing. He suggests that Fritz sell 400,000 shares at $25 per share. Len Derr proposes that half the project be financed with debt (bonds) and half with equity. Len proposes selling 200,000 shares at $25 per share and issuing 5,000 bonds, each with a face value of $1,000. The bonds will have a coupon of 8%. The yield on equivalently risky bonds is 8%.

Details of the two proposals are summarized below. Answer the questions that follow to help Fritz understand the implications of the two financing plans.

	All Equity Plan	Half-and-Half Plan
Assets	$10M	$10M
Debt	$0	$5M
Equity	$10M	$5M
Debt-to-equity ratio	0	1
Shares Outstanding	400,000	200,000
Share Price	$25	$25
Interest rate on Debt	0%	8%

The table below provides estimates of the business's EBIT under different states of nature.

EBIT Forecasts for Fritz Electric PC Repair			
	BAD	NORMAL	GOOD
$EBIT	$600,000	$1,200,000	$1,800,000

Use the following table to compute the EPS for each state of nature under the All Equity Plan. The tax rate is 0%.

EPS Forecast
All Equity Plan

	BAD	NORMAL	GOOD
$EBIT	$600,000	$1,200,000	$1,800,000
Less: $Interest	$0	$0	$0
Pre-Tax Income	$600,000	$1,200,000	$1,800,000
Less: Taxes (@0%)	$0	$0	$0
Net Income	$600,000		
#Shares Out	400,000	400,000	400,000
EPS	$1.50		

Use the following table to compute the EPS for each state of nature under the half-and-half financing Plan. The tax rate is 0%. Recall that the interest rate is 8%.

EPS Forecast
50% Debt/50% Equity Plan

	BAD	NORMAL	GOOD
$EBIT	$600,000	$1,200,000	$1,800,000
Less: $Interest	400,000	400,000	400,000
Pre-Tax Income	200,000		1,400,000
Less: Taxes (@0%)	$0	$0	$0
Net Income	200,000		
#Shares Out	200,000		
EPS	$1		

38 In a normal economy, which capital structure produces a higher EPS?
   A) All equity
   B) 50% debt/50% equity

39 In a bad economy, which capital structure produces a higher EPS?
   A) All equity
   B) 50% debt/50% equity

40 In a good economy, which capital structure produces a higher EPS?
   A) All equity
   B) 50% debt/50% equity

41 Which capital structure produces more volatility in EPS across the states of nature?
   A) All equity
   B) 50% debt/50% equity

3.1 EBIT-EPS Analysis

Copy your answers from the last section into the following table.

EBIT v EPS Under 100% Equity and 50% Debt Fritz Electric PC Repair		
EBIT	100% Equity	50%-50%
$600,000	$1.50	$1
$1,200,000		
$1,800,000		

Plot the points on the following graph.

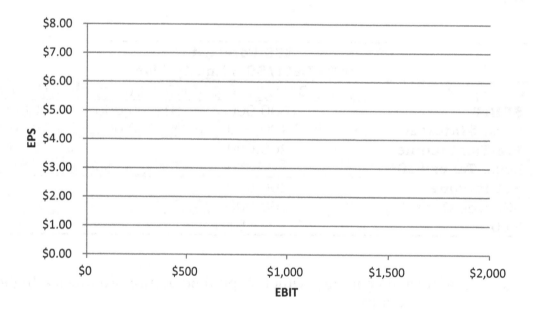

42   Which line is steeper?
   A)   All equity
   B)   50% debt/50% equity

At approximately what level of EBIT do the two lines cross?

ANSWER:
EBIT =

The intersection point is called the EBIT-EPS indifference point. At that level of EBIT, shareholders like either capital structure equally.

43 If EBIT is greater than the indifferent point value, which capital structure do shareholders prefer?
    A) All equity
    B) 50% debt/50% equity

44 If EBIT is smaller than the indifferent point value, which capital structure do shareholders prefer?
    A) All equity
    B) 50% debt/50% equity

3.2 EBIT-EPS Analysis Self-Test

Check out the EBIT-EPS self-test on Page 12.2.8 in CFO.

It's Time to Do a Self-Test

3. Try EBIT-EPS analysis. [Answer]

4. Capital Structure Notation and Model

4.1 Presentation: Introduction

The instructor will introduce the M&M model (with a fixed dollar amount of debt).

4.2 FCF in an M&M World

Recall that

FCF = OCF – CAPEX – Inv. in Net Working Capital   Eq.1

OCF = EBIT × (1 – T) + Depr   Eq. 2

Assume the following:

- The company makes no investments in net working capital.
    - Inv. in Net Working Capital = $0
- CAPEX is always equal to depreciation.
    - CAPEX = Depr
- The tax rate is zero.
    - T = 0

Derive an expression for free cash flow under these assumptions. (Hint: Substitute Eq. 2 into Eq. 1 and then make the assumptions in the list.)

4.3 Company Value in an M&M World

Consider a company with annual (perpetual) EBIT.

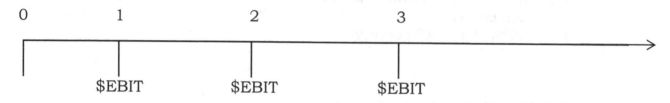

The DCF value of the company at Time 0 is the present value of the perpetuity:

$$V_0 = \frac{EBIT}{k_w}$$

This is perfectly general for any capital structure (i.e., any capital structure weights, w_E and w_D).

4.4 DCF Value (No Tax)

The Huck Glove Company forecasts EBIT of $10 million annually in perpetuity. Huck's WACC is 8%. What is the value of the Huck Glove Company? (Assume the next cash flow is in one year.)

ANSWER:

V_0 =

4.5 Value of an Unlevered M&M Firm (No Tax)

- An unlevered firm has no debt.
- The value of the unlevered firm is denoted V_U.
- The required return of shareholders in the unlevered firm is denoted k_U.

The DCF value of the unlevered firm at Time 0 is:

$$V_U = \frac{EBIT}{k_U}$$

4.6 Value of Unlevered M&M Firm (No Tax)

The Rumpel Felt Company forecasts EBIT of $10 million annually in perpetuity. Rumpel is all equity financed. Rumpel stockholders require a return of 11%. What is the value of the Rumpel Felt Company?

What is the value of the equity in the Rumpel Felt Company?

4.7 Debt at a Levered M&M Firm (No Tax)

Fritz Electric is partially debt financed. The company has bonds outstanding with a face value denoted D. The bonds are perpetuities, so they pay an annual coupon forever. The yield on the debt is k_D and that is also the coupon rate. Assume that the first coupon is paid in one year's time.

45   When the coupon rate is equal to the yield to maturity, then the market value of a bond is equal to the face value.
    A)   True
    B)   False

The face value of the debt is D and the coupon rate is k_D, so the total amount of coupons paid annually is:

$$\$coupons = D * k_D$$

If the face value of debt is D = \$1,000 and the coupon rate is k_D = 5%, what is the dollar amount of coupons (interest on the debt) paid annually?

4.8 Equity at a Levered M&M Firm (No Tax)

This year, Fritz Electric expects earnings before interest and taxes of \$EBIT. It will pay interest on its bonds of $D * k_D$.

46   If taxes are zero, then Net Income = (EBIT – k_DD).
    A)   True
    B)   False

Fritz Electric is expecting EBIT of $500 at the end of the year. It has bonds outstanding with a face value of $1,000. The bonds pay a 5% coupon. Fritz has a 100% payout ratio, so all of Net Income is paid out as a dividend to shareholders. What are total dividends going to be at the end of the year?

ANSWER:

Dividends =

The market value of equity is the present value of the dividends when discounted at the (levered) firm's shareholders' required return (denoted k_E).

$$E_L = \frac{EBIT - k_D D}{k_E}$$

What is the value of Fritz's equity if the stockholders require a return of 10%?

ANSWER:

E =

4.9 The Value of a Levered M&M Firm (No Tax)

The value of the levered firm is equal to the sum of the value of its debt and equity:

$V_L = E_L + D$

What is the value, V, of Fritz Electric?

ANSWER:

V =

What are the capital structure weights for Fritz?

w_E =

w_D =

What is Fritz's WACC? (Recall: k_D = 5%, k_E = 10% and T = 0.)

k_{WACC} =

What is the value of Fritz?

$$V_0 = \frac{EBIT}{k_w}$$

V =	

5. M&M Proposition I (No Tax)

5.1 Presentation on M&M Proposition I

The instructor will present Prop I.

5.2 Proof of Prop I (Part 1: The Violation)

Consider two identical companies that will last one year and then generate a one-time lump sum of cash which depends on the economy as follows.

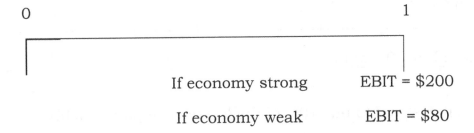

0   1

If economy strong   EBIT = $200

If economy weak   EBIT = $80

The only difference between the two is that one is all equity financed (unlevered) and the other is levered. The following table presents some information about the securities of the two companies. Both the debt and equity generate a one-time cash flow for the owners at Time 1.

		Unlevered	Levered
Face Value of Debt	D	$0	$50
Coupon rate (= YTM)	k_D	0%	10%
Market Value of Equity	E_U / E_L	$100	$40

What is the market value of the unlevered firm?

ANSWER:
V_U =

What is the market value of the levered firm?

ANSWER:

$$V_L =$$

This is a violation of M&M Proposition I, because $V_U \neq V_L$.

5.3 Proof of Prop I (Part 2: Arbitrage)
- Principle: Buy low and sell high.
- Buy 10% of L's equity and debt.
- Short sell 10% of U's equity.

What does it cost you to buy 10% of the levered company's equity? (Refer to the table above for market values.) Express purchases as negative values and receipts as positive.

ANSWER:
Cash flow to buy 10% of E_L =

What does it cost you to buy 10% of the levered company's debt?

ANSWER:
Cash flow to buy 10% of D =

What do you receive if you short sell 10% of the unlevered company's equity?

ANSWER:
Cash flow from short selling 10% of E_U (V_U) =

What is your net cash flow at Year 0?

ANSWER:
Net Cash Flow =

What are your cash flows from the long and short positions at Year 1 for either a weak or strong economy? Complete the following table.

	Cash Flows to Investor at End of Year		
Position		**Weak Economy**	**Strong Economy**
Long E_L	$0.1 \times [EBIT - D \times (1 + k_D)]$		
Long D	$0.1 \times D \times (1 + k_D)$		
Short E_U	$-0.1 \times EBIT$		

260

47 Do you have any net obligation at the end of the year in either economy?
   A) Yes
   B) No

48 An arbitrage trade involves no investment or risk and generates an immediate profit. Are the trades described above an arbitrage trade?
   A) Yes
   B) No

5.4 Example: M&M Prop I. The Recapitalization

The instructor will demonstrate the M&M Prop I self-test on Page 12.3.6 in CFO.

It's Time to Do a Self-Test

4. Practice computing M&M Proposition 1. Answer

5.5 Example: M&M Prop I. The Recapitalization

The Broken Glass Toy Co. (BGT) generates an annual EBIT of $150 million. The EBIT occurs annually at the end of the year and we are currently at the beginning of a year. Analysts expect BGT to continue generating the same amount of EBIT in perpetuity. BGT shareholders require a return of 5%.

What is the value of BGT?

ANSWER:
$V_U =$

BGT is going to borrow $200 million by issuing perpetual bonds with an annual coupon of 10%. The investment banker has found that bonds with similar risk have a yield of 10%. The proceeds from the bond issue will be used to repurchase (and retire) shares.

What is the value of BGT after the bond issue and share repurchase?

ANSWER:
$V_L =$

What is the value of BGT's equity after the bond issue and share repurchase?

ANSWER:

$E_L =$

5.6 Conclusion

49 According to M&M Proposition I (no taxes), can a firm change its market value by splitting its cash flows into different proportions of dividends and interest?

    A)   Yes

    B)   No

6. M&M Proposition II (No Tax)

6.1 WACC Unaffected by Leverage

For an unlevered firm, we know that:

$$V_U = \frac{EBIT}{k_W^U}$$

- Basic DCF valuation equation
- k_W is the WACC

So,

$$k_W^U = \frac{EBIT}{V_U}$$ Rearrange

For an unlevered firm, we also know that:

$$k_W^U = k_U$$ • Because there is no debt. ($w_D = D/V = 0$)

For a levered firm, we know that:

$$k_W^L = \frac{EBIT}{V_L}$$

Since $V_U = V_L$ (by Proposition I), it is true that:

$$k_W^L = \frac{EBIT}{V_L} = \frac{EBIT}{V_U} = k_W^U = k_U$$

WACC is constant regardless of capital structure (when there are no taxes).

6.2 Proposition II

We know that the levered firm's WACC is:

$$k_W^L = \frac{D}{V}k_D + \frac{E}{V}k_E$$

Or, given that $k_W = k_U$:

$$k_U = \frac{D}{V}k_D + \frac{E}{V}k_E$$

Solve for k_E. Make use of the fact that $\frac{V}{E} = \frac{E+D}{E} = 1 + \frac{D}{E}$.

ANSWER:
$k_E =$

---

50   The expected rate of return on the common stock of a levered company, k_E, _____ in direct proportion to the debt/equity ratio.
    A)   Increases
    B)   Decreases

51   According to M&M (with no taxes), the WACC rises as leverage increases.
    A)   True
    B)   False

6.3 M&M Prop I. Recapitalization via a Repurchase

Check out the M&M Prop II Explore It on Page 12.3.9 in CFO.

  Proposition 2 is shown graphically in the Explore It and described in the Explain It video. The Explore It also graphs the WACC. Notice that the WACC is constant regardless of the level of debt. As leverage increases, the rising cost of equity offsets the lower cost of debt and causes the WACC to remain constant. The next self-test gives you a chance to practice Proposition 2.

6.4 Recapitalization Example

The Broken Glass Toy Co. (BGT) generates an annual EBIT of $150 million. The EBIT occurs annually at the end of the year and we are currently at the beginning of a year. Analysts expect BGT to continue generating the same amount of EBIT in perpetuity.

BGT has debt with a market value (and face value) of $200 million. The bonds are perpetuities with an annual coupon of 10%. The company's shares trade for $2 and there are 400 million outstanding.

What is the value of BGT?

ANSWER:
$V =$

What is the required return of unlevered shareholders for BGT?

ANSWER:
$k_U =$

What is the required return of shareholders at BGT?

ANSWER:
$k_E =$

What is BGT's WACC?

ANSWER:
$k_W =$

RECAPITALIZATION: BGT borrows an additional $100 million and uses the money to buy back 50 million shares at $2 per share.

What is the value of BGT after the recapitalization?

> **ANSWER:**
> V =

What is the required return of shareholders at BGT after the recapitalization?

> **ANSWER:**
> k_E =

What is BGT's WACC after the repurchase?

> **ANSWER:**
> k_W =

What is the stock price after the repurchase?

> **ANSWER:**
> P =

6.5 Conclusion

52   According to M&M Proposition I and II (no taxes,) is the market value of the firm (or its WACC) affected by its capital structure?
A)   Yes
B)   No

7. M&M Proposition I (with Tax)

7.1 Presentation on M&M Proposition I

The instructor will present Prop I.

$$V_L = \frac{EBIT(1-T)}{k_U} + TD$$

7.2 M&M Prop I. The Recapitalization

Reefer Trucking Inc. is an all equity firm that generates EBIT of $3 million per year. The cost of equity capital $k_U = 16\%$, and its marginal tax rate, T, is 35%.

What is the market value of Reefer Trucking?

ANSWER:
$V_U =$

If Reefer now issues $4 million of perpetual bonds with an annual coupon of 9%, what is the market value of the firm? (Assume debt is used to repurchase stock.)

ANSWER:
$V_L =$

What is the market value of the firm's equity?

ANSWER:
$E_L =$

7.3 The Recapitalization cont.

This is a continuation of the Reefer Trucking Inc. example. Reefer had 1 million shares outstanding before the recapitalization.

What was the stock price before?

ANSWER:
$P =$

When Reefer borrowed $4M to repurchase shares, it paid $12.1875 per share. How many shares were left outstanding after the repurchase?

ANSWER:
Shares Outstanding$_{AFTER} =$

What was the stock price after the repurchase?

ANSWER:
$P_{AFT} =$

53   Knowing what you know now, if you had been a shareholder, would you have sold any shares to the company when they announced the repurchase at $12.1875 per share?

A)   Yes

B)   No

BONUS QUESTION: What price should the company have offered to buy back shares such that it equalled the post-repurchase price?

ANSWER:

P_{REPO} =

7.4 Self-Test in CFO (p. 12.3.16)

It's Time to Do a Self-Test

7. Practice computing M&M Proposition 1. Answer

8. M&M Proposition II (with Tax)

8.1 Explore It in CFO (p. 12.3.17)

M&M Proposition 2: Debt and Required Return (with Taxes)

M&M Proposition 2 with taxes is similar to Proposition 2 without taxes. The cost of equity is an increasing function of leverage.

$$k_E = k_U + (k_U - k_D)(1 - T)\frac{D}{E} \qquad \text{Eq. 12.13}$$

8.2 Self-Test in CFO (p. 12.3.16)

It's Time to Do a Self-Test

8. Practice computing M&M Proposition 2. [Answer]

8.3 Example: Leverage and WACC with Taxes

Brick Aviation Inc. has no debt but can borrow at 8% if it needs to. The company's WACC is 15%. The tax rate is 35%.

What is the required return of the company's shareholders?

> **ANSWER:**
> $k_U =$

If the company borrows such that its debt-to-value (D/V) ratio is 25%, what will its debt-to-equity ratio be?

> **ANSWER:**
> $D/E =$

If the company borrows such that its debt-to-value (D/V) ratio is 25%, what will its cost of equity be?

> **ANSWER:**
> $k_E =$

If the company borrows such that its debt-to-value (D/V) ratio is 50%, what will its cost of equity be?

> **ANSWER:**
> $k_E =$

8.4 Conclusion

54 According to M&M Proposition I and II (with taxes), the market value of the firm _____ as the amount of debt increases.
  A) Increases
  B) Decreases

55 According to M&M Proposition I and II (with taxes), the WACC _____ as the amount of debt increases.
  A) Increases
  B) Decreases

56 If you are a CFO who wants to maximize the market value of your company, what is the optimal D/V ratio according to M&M Proposition I and II (with taxes)?
  A) It doesn't matter
  B) D/V = 1

Solutions

Leverage (2.7)

	American Railcar	Microsoft
%Change in Sales	37%	6%
%Change in EBIT	271%	23%
%Change in EPS	1395%	28%

	American Railcar	Microsoft
DOL	7.3	4.1
DFL	5.1	1.2
DTL	38.0	5.0

The Effect of Financial Leverage on EPS (3, 3.1)

Under All equity Plan			
	BAD	NORMAL	GOOD
$EBIT	$600,000	$1,200,000	$1,800,000
$Interest	$0	$0	$0
Pre-Tax Income	$600,000	$1,200,000	$1,800,000
Taxes (@0%)	$0	$0	$0
Net Income	$600,000	$1,200,000	$1,800,000
#Shares Out	400,000	400,000	400,000
EPS	$1.50	$3.00	$4.50

Under 50% Debt/50% Equity Plan			
	BAD	NORMAL	GOOD
$EBIT	$600,000	$1,200,000	$1,800,000
Less: $Interest	400,000	400,000	400,000
Pre-Tax Income	200,000	800,000	1,400,000
Less: Taxes (@0%)	$0	$0	$0
Net Income	200,000	800,000	1,400,000
#Shares Out	200,000	200,000	200,000
EPS	$1	$4	$7

EBIT v EPS		
EBIT	100% Equity	50%-50%

$600,000	$1.50	$1
$1,200,000	$3	$4
$1,800,000	$4.5	$7

EBIT-EPS indifference point is at EBIT = $800,000

Capital Structure Notation and Model (4.2, 4.4, 4.6, 4.7, 4.8, 4.9)

FCF = EBIT

Huck Glove DCF Value:
$V_0 = \$125M$

Rumpel Felt Unlevered Value:
$V_U = \$90.91$
$E_U = \$90.91$

Since the yield equals the coupon rate, the market value of the bonds equals the face value. So, market value is also D.

Fritz Electric:
$coupons = \$1,000 \times 0.05 = \$50$
Net Income = $EBIT – D * k_D$
Dividends = Net Income = $450
$E_L = \$4,500$
$V = \$5,500$

$w_E = 0.8182$
$w_D = 0.182$
$k_W = 9.09\%$
$V = EBIT/k_W = 500/0.0909 = \$5,500$

M&M Prop I (5.2, 5.3, 5.5)
$V_U = \$100$
$V_L = \$90$

$-0.1 \times E_L = -\$4$
$-0.1 \times D = -\$5$
$0.1 \times V_U = \$10$
Net = $-\$4 – \$5 + \$10 = \$1$

Cash Flows to Investor at End of Year		
	Weak	Strong

271

Position		Economy	Economy
Long E_L	$0.1 \times [EBIT - D \times (1 + k_D)]$	2.5	14.5
Long D	$0.1 \times D \times (1 + k_D)$	5.5	5.5
Short E_U	$-0.1 \times EBIT$	-8	-20
NET		0	0

Broken Glass Toy Co.:
$V_U = \$150/0.05 = \$3,000$
$V_L = V_U = \$3,000$
$E_L = \$2,800$

M&M Prop II (6.2, 6.4)

$$k_E = k_U + [k_U - k_D]\frac{D}{E}$$

Broken Glass Toy Co.:
$V_L = \$1,000$
$k_U = 0.15$
$k_E = 0.1625$
$k_W = k_U = 0.15$ by Prop II

After Recap, V = \$1,000 by Proposition I.
D = \$200 + \$100, so $E_L = V - D = 1,000 - 300 = 700$
$k_E = 0.1714$ by Proposition II
$k_W = 15\%$ by Proposition II

Number shares = 400 − 50 = 350
Price = $E_L/350 = 700/350 = \$2$

M&M Prop I (with Tax) (7.2, 7.3)

Reefer Trucking:
$V_U = 3(1 - 0.35)/0.16 = 12.1875M$
$V_L = V_U + TD = 12.1875 + 4 \times 0.35 = 13.5875M$
$E_L = V_L - D = 13.5875 - 4 = 9.5875$

$P = E_U/100 = 12.1875/1 = \$12.19$

Shares Purchased = \$4M/12.1875 = 328,205
$Shares_{AFTER}$ = 1M − 328,205 = 671,795
$Price_{AFT} = E_L/671,795 = 9.5875/0.671795 = \$14.27$

$P_{REPO} = \$13.5875$

Hint:
Shares Purchased = $4M/Price_{AFT}$

<u>M&M Prop II (with Tax)</u> (8.3)

k_U = 15%
D/E = 0.3333
k_E = 0.1652
k_E = 0.1955

Dividends & Repurchases (Ch.13)

1. Introduction

In this workbook you will

- Learn about the pattern of repurchases and dividends over time
- Learn about dividend dates
- Learn how dividends affect the stock price and shareholder wealth
- Learn about tax clienteles
- Learn about dividend policy
- Learn some facts about repurchases
- Learn how a repurchase affects the stock price and shareholder wealth
- Learn about signalling with dividends and repurchases
- Learn how dividends (and repurchases) affect management incentives
- Learn about stock splits

2. Repurchases & Dividends

2.1 Aggregate Repurchases & Dividends in U.S.

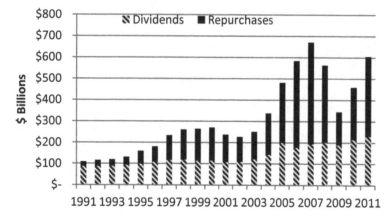

2.2   Aggregate Repurchases & Dividends in Canada

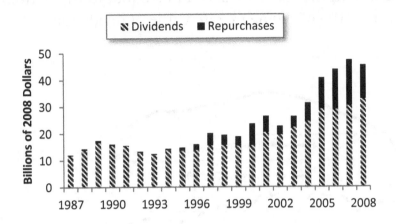

2.3   Questions

57   In which country are repurchases bigger than dividends?
A)   United States
B)   Canada

58   What is the trend for repurchases in both countries?
A)   More popular over time
B)   Less popular over time

59   In 2000 and 2008 there were recessions in the United States. Which of the following best describes the pattern of dividends and repurchases between 1991 and 2011 in the U.S.?
A)   Dividends steadily increase. Repurchases vary with the business cycle (i.e., the decline in recessions).
B)   Repurchases are steady. Dividends vary with the business cycle.

2.4   Who Pays Dividends?

The following graph shows the percentage of public companies that do not pay dividends (ignoring repurchases) in the United States. In other words, it shows the ratio of the number of companies that pay a dividend over the total number of public companies. The graph also shows the percentage of aggregate dividends paid by the most generous 10% of dividend paying firms (i.e., the dollar amount of dividends paid by the top 10% of companies over the total

275

amount of dividends paid in the year). If every dividend paying firm is equally generous with its dividends, then the top 10% should be equal to the bottom 10% and both should pay out 10% of the aggregate value of dividends.

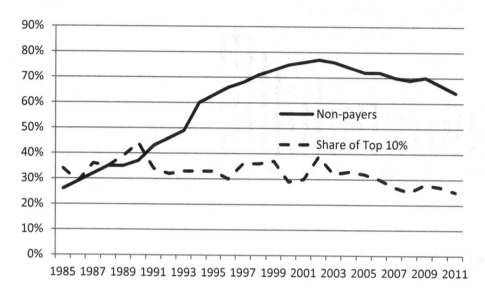

60   In 2011, most U.S. companies paid dividends.
      A)   True
      B)   False

61   Over the last 25 years, the percentage of non-paying firms has risen.
      A)   True
      B)   False

62   Which of the following is a correct statement about the concentration of dividends amongst firms that pay dividends?
      A)   Dividends are pretty equally distributed across firms.
      B)   Dividends are quite concentrated with the top 10% of firms accounting for one third of all dividends.

3. Dividend Dates

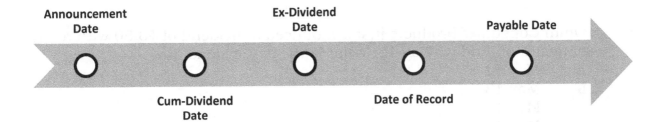

Announcement Date	Date dividend is publicly announced.
Cum-Dividend Date	Three business days before the day of record. This is the last day on which an investor can buy the stock and receive the forthcoming dividend.
Ex-Date	Two business days prior to the day of record. This is the first day on which the buyer will not be entitled to receive the forthcoming dividend.
Date of Record	The day on which the list of dividend recipients is created. Registered owners on the date of record receive the dividend.
Payable Date	The date the dividend is transferred to shareholders.

Definition:

Settlement is the process by which registered ownership of a stock (or security) is transferred from the seller to the buyer (and cash is transferred from the buyer to the seller).

63 How long is the settlement delay for stock transactions in Canada and the United States? (Hint: Google it.)
- A)   1 day
- B)   2 days
- C)   3 days
- D)   4 days

64   The cum-dividend day is three days before the date of record because of
      the three-day settlement delay for stocks.
      A)   True
      B)   False

65   Omni Consumer Products just announced a dividend of $0.50 with a day
      of record on Friday, May 15. What is the ex-dividend day?
      A)   May 12
      B)   May 13
      C)   May 14
      D)   May 15

66   Cyberdyne Systems just announced a dividend of $0.25 with a day of
      record on Monday December 28. What is the cum-dividend day? (Hint:
      What happens on December 25? Is it a business day?)
      A)   Dec 21
      B)   Dec 22
      C)   Dec 23
      D)   Dec 24

4. M&M Dividend Irrelevance

4.1   Pricing Model

Consider a company with some cash and an annual (perpetual) FCF.

The DCF value of the company at Time 0 is the sum of the cash and the
present value of the perpetuity:

$$V_0 = \text{cash} + \frac{FCF}{k_w} \qquad \text{Eq. 1}$$

If the firm is all equity financed, then

$$V = E = P \times N$$
Where
E = the value of equity
P = the stock price
N = the number of shares outstanding

Using Eq.1, we can express the stock price as:

$$P = \left[\frac{1}{N} \times \frac{FCF}{k_w}\right] + \frac{cash}{N}$$

4.2   Impact of Dividend on Stock Price

67   If all of the cash is paid out as a dividend, then the dividend per share is D = cash/N.
    A)   True
    B)   False

68   If all of the cash is paid out as a dividend, then the stock price after the dividend is $P = \left[\frac{1}{N} \times \frac{FCF}{k_w}\right]$.
    A)   True
    B)   False

4.3   Dividend Example

Karkas Cold Cuts Inc. has $10 of cash. Analysts expect the company to generate $5 of free cash flow at the end of the current year. The same amount of free cash is expected annually in perpetuity. The Karkas' cost of capital is 10% and there are 100 shares outstanding. What is the fair stock price for Karkas?

ANSWER:
P =

Karkas is considering a cash dividend of $0.10 per share. If it pays the dividend, what will the value of the company be after the dividend?

ANSWER:
V_A =

Karkas is considering a cash dividend of $0.10 per share. If it pays the dividend, what will the stock price be after the dividend?

ANSWER:
P_A =

69   When a company pays a dividend, the stock price falls by the amount of
      the dividend.
      A)   True
      B)   False

70   When a company pays a dividend, the stock price falls by the amount of
      the dividend on the morning of the ex-dividend day.
      A)   True
      B)   False

71   If you owned 10 shares of Karkas before the dividend was announced,
      what is your wealth before the dividend and after the dividend, and how
      does it change?
      A) $W_B = \$6$; $W_A = \$5$; $\Delta W = -\$1$
      B) $W_B = \$6$; $W_A = \$6$; $\Delta W = \$0$
      C) $W_B = \$6$; $W_A = \$7$; $\Delta W = \$1$

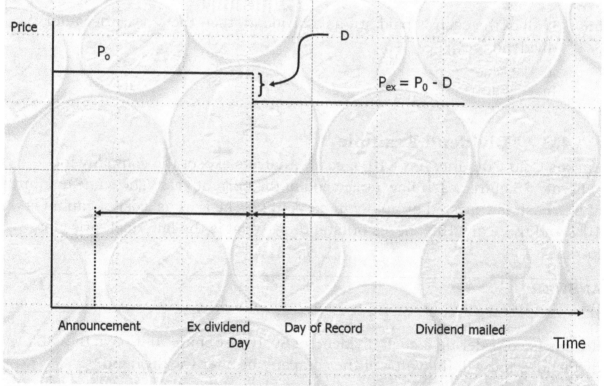

72   If you look at the graph of the stock price above, does it look like you
      could profit from the stock price decline by short-selling the stock before
      the ex-dividend day and then buying it back on (or after) the ex-day?
      A)   Yes
      B)   No

73 When you short-sell a stock, you first have to borrow the stock from someone.
   A)   True
   B)   False

74 If you borrow the stock and short sell and then the company announces a dividend, then who will receive the dividend?
   A)   You (the short-seller)
   B)   The original owner who loaned you the stock
   C)   The person who took the long-side of the trade when you shorted

75 If you borrow the stock and then the company announces a dividend, will the lender of the stock expect to receive the dividend?
   A)   Yes
   B)   No. The lender will be happy to forgo receiving the dividend as part of the loan agreement to you (the short-seller).

76 If you borrow the stock and then the company announces a dividend and the lender of the stock expects to receive the dividend, who will pay the dividend?
   A)   The company will issue two dividends.
   B)   You (the short-seller) will have to pay.

77 What is the profit from short-selling around a dividend of $D?
   A)   < –$D
   B)   – $D
   C) $0
   D)   + $D
   E)   > $D

4.4   Another Dividend Example

PAN AM Airlines earns an FCF of $10M and has $4M in cash that it wants to pay out as a dividend. There are 0.6M shares outstanding. The current price is $90 and PAN AM wants to pay a special dividend of $6.67. PAN AM is all equity financed and its WACC is $k_w = 20\%$. What is the value of the company before the dividend?

ANSWER:
$V_B =$

What will the value of the company be after the dividend?

281

ANSWER:
$V_A =$

What will the stock price be after the dividend?

ANSWER:
$P_A =$

5. Taxes and Clienteles

The following table shows marginal tax rates for 2013 for Ontario.

		Ordinary Income	Capital Gains	Canadian Dividends
A	$43,561–69,958	31.15%	15.58%	13.43%
B	$69,958–79,448	32.98	16.49	14.19
C	$79,448–82,420	35.39	17.70	17.52
D	$82,420–87,123	39.41	19.70	19.88
E	$87,123–135,054	43.41	21.70	25.40
F	$135,054 <	46.41	23.20	29.54

A marginal tax rate is the percentage of tax paid on the last dollar of income earned (or an additional dollar of income).

78   Assume that there two ways to receive the same amount of income from a corporation: as a capital gain or as a dividend. If investors want to maximize their after-tax income, which ones will prefer dividends?
A)   A & B
B)   C & D
C)   E & F

79   Assume that there two ways to receive income: as a capital gain or as a dividend. If investors want to maximize their after-tax income, ones will prefer capital gains?
A)   A & B
B)   C & D
C)   E & F

80   Assume that there two ways to receive income: as a capital gain or as a
      dividend. If investors want to maximize their after-tax income, which
      ones don't care whether it is dividends or capital gains?
      A)   A & B
      B)   C & D
      C)   E & F
      D)   C & D plus investors in a TFSA or RRSP

5.1   Tax Clienteles

- Investors have different effective tax rates on dividends.
- Different investors prefer different combinations of dividends and repurchases.
- Groups with common preferences are called tax "clienteles."
- Companies might attract a higher valuation if they change their payout policy to satisfy an under-serviced clientele.
    - Why would there be an under-serviced clientele?
        - Should there be in an efficient market?
        - What if there is a change in tax rates?

5.2   Tax Clientele Example

Last week Lucky Strike Inc. was worth $100M and its shares traded for $10 (there are 10 million shares outstanding). Lucky is an all-equity firm. Yesterday Lucky management announced that the company won $20 million in the lottery and the stock price rose to $12. Lucky is trying to decide whether to distribute the cash. It can issue a $2 dividend or leave the cash in the company. Use this information to answer the following questions.

You own 100 shares. Your marginal tax rate is 15% on dividends is 15% and 25% on capital gains. Assume that the company pays the dividend and then you sell your shares. What is your after-tax wealth? (Hint: Wealth = value of shares plus dividend minus tax liability.)

ANSWER:
$W_A =$

You own 100 shares. Your marginal tax rate is 15% on dividends and 25% on capital gains. Assume that the company does not pay the dividend and you sell your shares. What is your after-tax wealth? (Hint: Wealth = value of shares minus tax liability.)

ANSWER:

$$W_A =$$

81 Reflecting on your last two answers, if your marginal tax rate is 15% on dividends and 25% on capital gains, what do you want the company to do?
- A) Keep the cash in the company.
- B) Issue the dividend.

You own 100 shares. Your marginal tax rate is 25% on dividends and 15% on capital gains. Assume that the company pays the dividend and then you sell your shares. What is your after-tax wealth? (Hint: Wealth = value of shares plus dividend minus tax liability.)

ANSWER:
$$W_A =$$

You own 100 shares. Your marginal tax rate is 15% on dividends and 15% on capital gains. Assume that the company does not pay the dividend and you sell your shares. What is your after-tax wealth? (Hint: Wealth = value of shares minus tax liability.)

ANSWER:
$$W_A =$$

82 Reflecting on your last two answers, if your marginal tax rate is 25% on dividends and 15% on capital gains, what do you want the company to do?
- A) Keep the cash in the company.
- B) Issue the dividend.

6. Dividend Policy: How Should Firms Set Their Dividend?

6.1   Stable Dividends

- Stable dividends is the most common policy.
- Dividends = f(future sustainable earnings)
- Sustainable earnings = earnings after the removal of non-recurring revenue or expense.

- Sustainable earnings = earnings that are a good predictor of future earnings.
- Dividends only rise if earnings rise to a "sustainably" higher level.

6.2 Example of Stable Dividends: Pitney Bowes

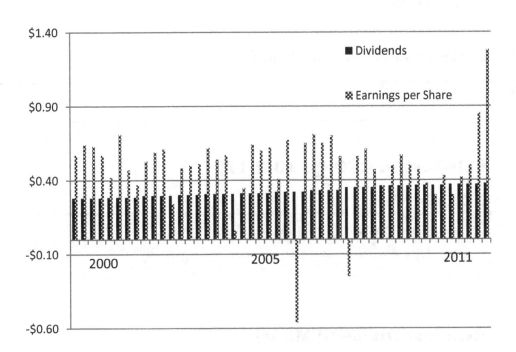

6.3 Lintner's Target Payout Model

- Lintner (1956) surveyed managers and found they:
    o had a target payout ratio based on long-term sustainable earnings;
    o focussed more on dividend changes rather than on levels; and
    o were reluctant to implement a temporary increase.
- His model incorporates all of these characteristics and produces stable dividends.

$$D_{t+1} = D_t + \Delta EPS \times \text{Target Payout} \times \lambda$$

Where
D_t (D_{t+1}) = dividend in the current period t (the next period t + 1)
EPS_t = earnings per share in period t
$\Delta EPS = EPS_{t+1} - EPS_t$ = change in EPS
Target Payout = target payout ratio
λ = adjustment factor

285

6.4   Lintner Model Example

Consider the following data for Pitney Bowes:

- Div Q4 2010 = $0.365
- EPS Q4 2010 = $0.60
- E(EPS) Q1 2011 = $0.65
- Payout = 0.6
- λ = 0.005

What is Pitney Bowes' forecasted dividend for Q1 2011?

ANSWER:

D_{t+1} =

6.5   Self-Test in CFO (p. 13.2.17)

It's Time to Do a Self-Test

12. Practice setting dividends with the Target Payout model. [Answer]

13. Practice setting dividends with the Residual Dividend model. [Answer]

6.6   Residual Dividend Model

- STEP 1: Find the retained earnings needed for the capital budget.
- STEP 2: Pay out any leftover earnings (the residual) as dividends.

$$D_t = \frac{\text{Net Income}_t - \omega_E \times \$\text{Investments}_t}{\text{Shares Outstanding}}$$

Where

D_t = dividend per share

$\$\text{Investments}_t$ = investments in fixed and net working capital during period t

ω_E = target capital structure weight for equity

$\omega_E \times \$\text{Investments}_t$ = portion of capital budget financed by equity

$\text{Net Income}_t - \omega_E \times \$\text{Investments}_t$ = total dividends

6.7   Residual Dividend Example

Consider the following data for Crumple Auto Body Parts Inc.:

286

- Expects net income of $600,000.
- Plans to investment $800,000 into business.
- Equity-to-value ratio is 0.6.
- Has 600,000 shares outstanding.

What amount of Crumple's capital budget will be funded by equity?

> **ANSWER:**
> $\omega_E \times \$Investments_t =$

What is Crumple's dividend?

> **ANSWER:**
> $D_t =$

6.8   Conclusions about Residual Model

- Advantage:
    - o Minimizes trips to capital markets and thus new issue costs.
- Disadvantage:
    - o Results in variable dividends, which sends conflicting signals.
- The residual model doesn't appeal to any specific clientele.
- Net Income is NOT equal to cash available to fund capital expenditures because depreciation is a non-cash charge.
- Conclusion – Consider residual policy when setting long-term target payout, but don't follow it rigidly from year to year.

6.9   Self-Test in CFO (p. 13.2.17)

It's Time to Do a Self-Test

12. Practice setting dividends with the Target Payout model. `Answer`

13. Practice setting dividends with the Residual Dividend model. `Answer`

7. Share Repurchase Facts

- Share repurchasing is an alternative way to distribute cash to shareholders.
- It is especially good for firms with clienteles that prefer capital gains.
- Repurchased shares are cancelled (no longer outstanding),

There are three kinds of repurchases:

- Open market repurchase
    - Most popular type in Canada and U.S.
    - In Canada, this is called a normal course issuer bid.
    - The company's broker is given cash and instructed to buy shares at the market price.
    - In Canada, you can't buy more than 5% per year. In the U.S. there is no limit, but companies buy an average of about 8% and it takes them almost three years to do it.
- Fixed-price offer
    - In Canada, this is called a substantial issuer bid.
    - The company makes a tender offer for its own shares.
    - The company offers to buy a large proportion of shares at premium to the pre-announcement market price.
- Dutch auction
    - A type of auction in which the auctioneer begins with a high asking price which is lowered until a bidder is willing to accept the auctioneer's price.
    - For stocks, the company announces a range of acceptable prices and invites shareholders to submit sale offers with a price within the range.
    - The sale offers are ranked by price from lowest to highest.
    - The company accepts all of the lowest priced offers up to the quantity it had targeted. All accepted offers receive the price of the marginal offer.

	Selected Statistics for Repurchases			
	U.S.			Canada
	Fixed Price	Dutch Auction	Open Market	Open Market
Proportion Sought	21.4%	17.3%	7.8%	5.0%
Tender Premium	20.9%	3%–16%	0%	0%

Announcement Period Return	12.5%	8.2%	2.3%	0.73%

	Number of Repurchases			
	U.S.			Canada
	Dutch Auctions	Fixed-Price	Open Market	Open Market
1987	9	42	132	224
1988	21	32	276	154
1989	22	49	499	143
1990	10	41	778	187
1991	4	51	282	106
1992	7	37	447	93
1993	5	51	461	80
1994	10	52	824	135
1995	8	40	851	188
1996	22	37	1,111	180
1997	30	35	967	214
1998	20	13	1,537	298
1999	19	21	1,212	327
2000	10	13	597	
2001	7	11	485	
2002	6	7	337	
2003	12	9	351	
2004	8	5	451	
2005	18	5	520	
2006	17	3	508	
2007			785	

U.S. data from Grullon and Ikenberry (2000). Canadian data from Canadian Financial Markets Research Centre database and Toronto Stock Exchange Daily Record.

83 Which type of repurchase is most common?
   A)   Open market
   B)   Fixed-price
   C)   Dutch auction

84 Which type of repurchase offers the largest premium over the pre-announcement price?
   A)   Open market
   B)   Fixed-price
   C)   Dutch auction

85 Which type of repurchase targets the largest percentage of shares outstanding?
   A)   Open market
   B)   Fixed-price

C) Dutch auction

8. Repurchase Irrelevance

8.1 Pricing Model

Consider a company with some cash and an annual (perpetual) FCF.

The value of the company (before the repurchase) is the sum of the cash and the present value of the perpetuity:

$$V_B = cash + \frac{FCF}{k_w} \quad \text{Eq. 1}$$

If the firm is all equity financed, then

$V_B = E_B = P_B \times N_B$
Where
E_B = value of equity before
P_B = stock price before
N_B = number of shares outstanding before

If all of the cash is used in the repurchase, then the company will choose the repurchase quantity, N_R, and price, P_R, so that:

$cash = P_R \times N_R$

The value of the equity after the repurchase, E_A, is equal to the value before minus the money used in the repurchase:

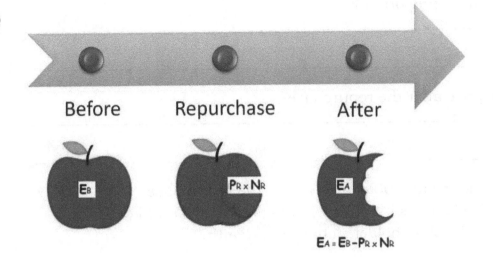

Before   Repurchase   After

E_B

$P_R \times N_R$

E_A

$E_A = E_B - P_R \times N_R$

$E_A = E_B - \text{cash}$

$P_A \times N_A = P_B \times N_B - P_R \times N_R$ Eq. 2

Let the repurchase proportion be denoted f.

$f = N_R / N_B$

We can express Eq. 2 as:

$$P_A = P_B \frac{1}{1-f} - P_R \frac{f}{1-f}$$

8.2   The Impact of a Premium Repurchase

PAN AM Airlines earns FCF of $10M and has $4M in cash that it wants to use to repurchase stock. There are 0.6M shares outstanding. The current price is $90 and PAN AM wants to pay $100 dollars a share to repurchase 40,000 shares. PAN AM is all equity financed and its WACC is 20%.

What is the value of the company before the repurchase?

> **ANSWER:**
> $V_B =$

What is the value of the company after the repurchase?

> **ANSWER:**
> $V_A =$

What is the repurchase proportion?

ANSWER:
f =

What is the stock price after the repurchase?

ANSWER:
P_A =

Consider a shareholder with 100 shares before the repurchase. The shareholder sells 6.67 shares into the repurchase at $100 and keeps the remainder. What is the shareholder's change in wealth?

ANSWER:
ΔW =

Consider a shareholder with 100 shares before the repurchase. The shareholder does not sell any shares after the repurchase is announced. What is the shareholder's change in wealth?

ANSWER:
ΔW =

8.3   The Impact of a "Fair" Repurchase

Now assume that the company repurchased 44,444 shares at a price of $90. What is the value of the company after the repurchase?

ANSWER:
V_A =

What is the repurchase proportion?

ANSWER:
f =

What is the stock price after the repurchase?

ANSWER:
P_A =

Consider a shareholder with 100 shares before the repurchase. The shareholder sells 7.4 shares at $90 after the repurchase is announced and keeps the remainder. What is the shareholder's change in wealth?

> **ANSWER:**
> $\Delta W =$

Consider a shareholder with 100 shares before the repurchase. The shareholder does not sell any shares after the repurchase is announced. What is the shareholder's change in wealth?

> **ANSWER:**
> $\Delta W =$

8.4 The Impact of a Discount Repurchase

Now assume that the company repurchased 50,000 shares at a price of $80. What is the value of the company after the repurchase?

> **ANSWER:**
> $V_A =$

What is the repurchase proportion?

> **ANSWER:**
> $f =$

What is the stock price after the repurchase?

> **ANSWER:**
> $P_A =$

Consider a shareholder with 100 shares before the repurchase. The shareholder sells 8.3 shares at $80 after the repurchase is announced and keeps the remainder. What is the shareholder's change in wealth?

> **ANSWER:**
> $\Delta W =$

293

Consider a shareholder with 100 shares before the repurchase. The shareholder does not sell any shares after the repurchase is announced. What is the shareholder's change in wealth?

> **ANSWER:**
> $\Delta W =$

8.5 Conclusions

86 When a company buys back shares at a price above the fair value ($P_R > P_B$), the price falls after the repurchase is complete and wealth is transferred from those who do not tender shares to those who do.
A) True
B) False

87 When a company buys back shares at a price equal to fair value ($P_R = P_B$), the price remains unchanged after the repurchase and no wealth is transferred.
A) True
B) False

88 When a company buys back shares at a price below fair value ($P_R < P_B$), the price rises after the repurchase is complete and wealth is transferred from those who tender shares to those who do not.
A) True
B) False

89 If you sell the same proportion of shares as the company buys back, your wealth is unaffected by a repurchase.
A) True
B) False

- NOTE: All of these conclusions are based on the assumption of no change in the underlying value of the company.
- The underlying value could change because of a change in leverage (for debt-financed repurchases), or because of a change in investor expectations (Signaling).

8.6 Advantages of Repurchases
- Repurchases are an alternative to changing dividend policy.

o The "one time only" feature of repurchases doesn't raise expectations.
- If some investors don't sell during a repurchase, then they defer their capital gain and lower the effective tax rate.
- Recapitalization – increase leverage
- Reduced free cash flow and agency costs.
- Offset dilution due to ESOP.
- Signals "our stock is undervalued" and that is why we are buying it.

9. Information Signalling

- See: Michael Spence, "Job Market Signaling," *Quarterly Journal of Economics* (1973).
- Information signalling occurs if managers have better information about future earnings than the market (asymmetric information).
- Dividends and repurchases are a way for managers to convey their beliefs about future earnings.
- The market interprets an increase in dividends (or a repurchase) as signalling higher long-term sustainable earnings.
- Significant market abnormal reaction to dividend changes and stock repurchases is evidence of information signalling.

9.1   Dividend Signalling

- Why believe the signal?
- Why is it costly for a low-earnings firm to announce a high dividend in order to attract a high valuation?
    o Miller and Rock (JF 1985). Cost of a dividend is the cost of raising additional capital (when the firm needs it later).
    o Good quality firms (with high level of sustainable earnings) can raise capital at a lower cost (required return) than bad quality firms.

- Evidence is summarized by Li & Lie, JFE (2006).
- Indicates market reaction to U.S. dividend changes.
- Measured the announcement period stock return from the day before to the day after.

		Dividend Decreases			Dividend Increases	
Year	Nobs	Div Change	Announc. Ret	Nobs	Div Change	Announc. Ret

1990	54	–0.0188	–0.015	445	0.0017	0.0076
1991	87	–0.0107	–0.0266	352	0.0014	0.0031
1992	83	–0.0073	–0.0329	381	0.001	0.0066
1993	62	–0.0086	–0.0039	408	0.0013	0.0069
1994	34	–0.0113	0.0035	486	0.0015	0.0094
1995	53	–0.0082	–0.0198	500	0.001	0.007
1996	45	–0.0065	–0.0087	481	0.0009	0.0062
1997	49	–0.0081	–0.0268	386	0.001	0.0093
1998	45	–0.0239	–0.0165	291	0.0014	0.0047
1999	53	–0.0087	–0.0166	301	0.0011	0.0025
2000	37	–0.0122	–0.0068	252	0.0011	0.0103

90 What is the ratio of dividend increases to decreases?
   A)   Somewhere between 5–1 and 10–1.
   B)   Increases are about 10% of decreases.

91 When a company announces cuts in its dividend, what happens to the stock price?
   A)   Rises
   B)   Falls

92 When a company announces increases in its dividend, what happens to the stock price?
   A)   Rises
   B)   Falls

10. Agency

- Michael Jensen, "Agency Costs of Free Cash Flow, Corporate Finance, and Takeover." AER (1986).
- Principal–agent problem: Managers waste corporate capital on negative NPV projects:
  o Inefficient investment (perquisite consumption)
  o Overinvestment (empire building)
  o Or, they just don't work hard: Effort exertion
- Dividends (and interest payments) reduce free cash flow and so reduce managerial waste.
- It forces management to run a tight ship and forces managers to face the scrutiny of capital markets when new project financing is needed.

10.1 Question

FatCats Inc. is at a mature point in the life cycle. Its core business doesn't grow anymore, but it generates $1B of annual free cash flow (FCF), which is expected to continue in perpetuity. FatCats also has $4B of cash ($C). The time line of cash flows is shown below. The cost of capital is 10% and there are 1 billion shares outstanding.

What is the fair stock price for FatCats?

ANSWER:
P =

FatCats Inc. hires a new CEO, Dennis Kozlowski. Mr. Kozlowski's management decisions reduce the annual free cash flow by 25%. He buys a fleet of Gulfstreams, puts Tiger Woods on contract, sponsors annual golf tournaments, buys a mid-town Manhattan HQ, buys a corporate yacht and corporate art, etc.

What is the fair market price of the shares given the reduced free cash flow described above?

ANSWER:
P =

Kirk Kerkorian buys a 10% share (100M shares) in FatCats Inc. He is elected to the board of directors. He persuades the company to pay a $2/share dividend ($2B). This cuts the cash supply to $2B. Michael Jensen's free cash flow hypothesis argues that the reduced financial slack in the company scares Mr. Kozlowski into reducing his wasteful ways. Assume that the 25% waste is eliminated and the annual free cash flow returns to $1B.

What happens to the stock price after the dividend (i.e., on ex-dividend day)?

ANSWER:
P =

What is the change in wealth for Kirk Kerkorian?

ANSWER:
ΔW =

---

11. Stock Splits and Stock Dividends

11.1 Definition
- Stock dividends are when a firm issues new shares in lieu of paying a cash dividend.
    - o If the stock dividend is 10%, you get 10 shares for each 100 shares owned.
- Stock splits refer to a stock dividend that exceeds 25%.

$$\text{Split Ratio} = \frac{\text{Shares Outstanding After}}{\text{Shares Outstanding Before}}$$

Table 13.7 Split Ratios and Shares Outstanding

Split	Shares Outstanding Before	Shares Outstanding After	Split Ratio	New Shares Issued
4-for-3	100	133	1.33	33
3-for-2	100	150	1.50	50
2-for-1	100	200	2	100
3-for-1	100	300	3	200

11.2 Splits
Initech Inc. has 100 shares outstanding. It has announced a 2-for-1 stock split. Every shareholder will receive one additional share so that it will have 200 shares outstanding after the split. What is the split ratio?

ANSWER:
S =

Cyberdyne Systems Inc. has 200 shares outstanding. It has announced a stock split with a split ratio of 3. How many shares will be outstanding after the split? What is the split called?

> **ANSWER:**
> Shares Out$_{After}$ =

Wayne Enterprises has 300 shares outstanding. It has announced a 3-for-2 split. What is the split ratio and how many shares will be outstanding after the split?

> **ANSWER:**
> S =
> Shares Out$_{After}$ =

GloboChem has 1,000 shares outstanding. It has announced a 1-for-5 split. What is the split ratio and how many shares will be outstanding after the split?

> **ANSWER:**
> S =
> Shares Out$_{After}$ =

11.3   Price Impact of a Split

$$P_A = \frac{P_B}{S}$$

Where
P_B = price before split
P_A = price after split

Initech Inc. has 100 shares outstanding, which are trading for $90. Initech's CFO believes that the $90 stock price makes the stock too expensive for the retail investor, since buying a board lot requires an investment of $9,000. To lower the price, Initech announces a 2-for-1 stock split. What is the price after the split?

> **ANSWER:**
> P$_A$ =

11.4 Conclusions

- The number of shares outstanding increases.
- The share price falls proportionately to keep each investor's wealth unchanged (unless the stock dividend or split conveys information or is accompanied by another event like higher dividends).
- Why split?
  - Splits/stock dividends can change price to an "optimal range."

Solutions

<u>Dividend Dates</u> (3)

9   Ex day = May 13

10   Cum day = December 22

<u>M&M Dividend Irrelevance</u> (4.3, 4.4)

Karkas Cold Cuts:

Pre-dividend value: $V = E = \$60$
Pre-dividend stock price: $P_B = \$0.6$

$V_A = \$50$
$P_A = \$0.5$

Pan-Am:

Pre-dividend value: $V_B = 54$
Cost of dividend: $0.6 * 6.67 = \$4M$
Value of firm after dividend: $V_A = 50$
Price after dividend: $P_A = \$83.3$

<u>Taxes</u> (5.2)

If $T_D = 0.15$ and $T_G = 0.25$

After-tax wealth after dividend:
$W_A = 100xP_A + 100 \times \$2 - (100 \times \$2 \times T_D + 100 \times (P_A - P_B) \times T_G)$
$W_A = \$1,000 + \$200 - (\$30 + 0) = \$1,170$

After-tax wealth from no dividend:
$W_A = 100 \times P_A - (100 \times (P_A - P_B) \times T_G)$
$W_A = \$1,200 - (\$50) = \$1,150$

Want to receive dividend.

<u>If $T_D = 0.25$ and $T_G = 0.15$</u>

After-tax wealth after dividend:
$W_A = 100 \times P_A + 100 \times \$2 - (100 \times \$2 \times T_D + 100 \times (P_A - P_B) \times T_G)$
$W_A = \$1,000 + \$200 - (\$50 + 0) = \$1,150$

- After-tax wealth from no dividend:
  $W_A = 100 \times P_A - (100 \times (P_A - P_B) \times T_G)$
  $W_A = \$1,200 - (\$30) = \$1,170$

Want no dividend.

Dividend Policy (6.4, 6.7)

Pitney Bowes:

$D_{t+1} = 0.36515$

Crumple Auto Body:

$\omega_E \times \$Investments_t = \$480,000$
$D_t = \$0.20$

Repurchase Irrelevance (8.2, 8.3, 8.4)

Premium Repurchase:

Pre-repurchase value: $V_B = \$54$
Cost of repurchase: $P_R \times N_R = \$4M$
- Value of firm after repurchase: $V_B = \$50$
Shares outstanding after: $N_A = 560,000$
$f = 6.67\%$
Price after repurchase: $P_A = \$89.29$

Shareholder sells 6.67% of holdings:
$W_B = \$9,000$
$W_A = \$9,000$
$\Delta W = \$0$

Shareholder keeps shares (does not participate in repurchase):
$W_B = \$9,000$
$W_A = \$8,929$
$\Delta W = -\$71$

Fair Price Repurchase:

Cost of repurchase: $P_R \times N_R = \$4M$
Value of firm after repurchase: $V_A = FCF/k = \$50$
$f = N_R/N_B = 7.41\%$
- Price after repurchase: $P_A = \$90$

Shareholder sells 7.4% of holdings:
$W_B = \$9,000$
$W_A = \$9,000$
$\Delta W = \$0$

Shareholder keeps shares (does not participate in repurchase):
$W_B = \$9,000$
$W_A = \$9,000$
$\Delta W = \$0$

Discount Repurchase:

Cost of repurchase: $P_R \times N_R = \$4M$
Value of firm after repurchase: $V_A = \$50$
$f = 8.33\%$
Price after repurchase: $P_A = \$90.91$

Shareholder sells 8.3% of holdings:
$W_B = \$9,000$
$W_A = \$9,000$
$\Delta W = \$0$

Shareholder keeps shares (does not participate in repurchase):
$W_B = \$9,000$
$W_A = \$9,091$
$\Delta W = +\$91$

Agency (10.1)

$V = E = \$14B$; $P = \$14$ per share

$V = E = \$11.5B$; $P = \$11.5$ per share

$V_{ex} = E_{ex} = \$12B$; $P_{ex} = \$12$ per share

Kirk Kirkorian's Wealth:

Cost of buying 100M @ \$11.5 = \$1.15B
Receives dividend of $\$2 \times 100M = \$200M$
Shares after dividend worth $100M \times \$12 = \$1.2B$
Total wealth after dividend = \$1.4B
Change in wealth = $1.4 - 1.15 = 0.25B$ or 21.74%

<u>Stock Splits and Stock Dividends</u> (11.2, 11.3)

$S = 200/100 = 2$
Shares Out$_{After}$ = 600. A 3-for-1 split.

Shares Out$_{After}$ = $3/2 \times 300 = 450$
$S = 450/300 = 1.5$

Shares Out$_{After}$ = $1/5 \times 1,000 = 200$
$S = 200/1000 = 0.2$

$P_A = P_B/S = \$90/2 = \$45$

Sales Forecasting and Cash Budget (Ch.14, LO1–LO2)

1. Introduction

In this workbook you will:

- Learn how to forecast sales
- Prepare a cash inflow forecast
- Prepare a cash outflow forecast
- Prepare a cash budget

2.   Introduction to Cash Budgeting

93   Companies forecast cash needs to ensure the company:
   A)   Can meet on-going obligations such as payroll, tax remittances and supplier invoices.
   B)   Has sufficient funds so that it can invest in attractive investment opportunities when they arise.

94   Companies that run out of cash:
   A)   Are penalized by the CRA for late tax remittances.
   B)   Lose suppliers due to late invoice payment.
   C)   Lose employees due to bounced payroll cheques.
   D)   Lose their business due to missed interest and principal payments (AKA bankruptcy).

95   Cash budgeting is important for:
   A)   Growing business.
   B)   Seasonal business.
   C)   Businesses where running out of cash is a problem.

Cash budgets begin with a sales forecast.

3.   Introduction to Sales Forecasting

3.1   Simple Sales Forecasting

$Sales_t = P_t \times Q_t$

Where

P_t = price of the product in period t
Q_t = quantity sold in period t

To forecast sales, forecast P and Q.

3.2   Simple Sales Forecast Example

Village Farms is a North American greenhouse producer of tomatoes. Village Farms is listed on the Toronto Stock Exchange under ticker VFF. VFF uses technologically advanced greenhouses to improve quality and taste. VFF operates four greenhouses: three in Texas and one in British Columbia. The combined area under cultivation is 220 acres. Last year, VFF harvested 115 million pounds of tomatoes for a yield of 522,727 pounds per acre. VFF sold its output at an average price of $1.1647 per pound for total revenues of $133.9 million.

Until this year, Mexican farmers have been selling field tomatoes as "greenhouse" produced. This supply has reduced prices. At the end of last year, Mexico and the U.S. signed "The Suspension Agreement" under which only truly greenhouse-grown tomatoes can be sold as such. The agreement is expected to increase greenhouse tomato prices by 32% next year.

If VFF's greenhouse capacity and yield is unchanged, what will its sales revenues be next year?

ANSWER:
$Sales_{t+1}$ =

VFF is working on a new technology called Greenhouse Advanced Technology System (GATES) which will increase yields to 880,000lbs/acre. If VFF can implement GATES in all of its greenhouses next year, what will its sales revenues be next year?

3.3   Sales Forecast with Market Share

In some situations the firm's price or output is hard to forecast, but there is an industry sales forecast or quantity forecast available. In those situations, we can use a market-share-based approach to forecasting.

If price can be forecasted, then

Sales$_{t+1}$ = P$_{t+1}$ × (s$_{t+1}$ × IQ$_{t+1}$)

Where
Sales$_{t+1}$ = forecasted sales revenues
P$_{t+1}$ = forecasted price of the product in period t + 1
s$_{t+1}$ = market share (of output quantity) in period t + 1
IQ$_{t+1}$ = industry quantity sold in period t + 1

If price cannot be forecasted, then

Sales$_{t+1}$ = (s$_{t+1}$ × IS$_{t+1}$)

Where
Sales$_{t+1}$ = forecasted sales revenues
s$_{t+1}$ = market share (of sales revenue) in period t + 1
IS$_{t+1}$ = industry total sales revenues in period t + 1

3.4   Forecast Exercise with Market Share

According to Gartner, Samsung's worldwide market share of the smartphone market was 32% for the third quarter of the current year. There were approximately 850 million smartphones sold this year. Analysts expect sales to rise by 5% next year. If Samsung sells its average smartphone for US$250 (wholesale) and if it holds its market share steady next year, what are forecasted sales for next year?

ANSWER:
Sales$_{t+1}$ =

3.5   Retail Forecasting

$Sales_t = \#Stores_t \times Area_t \times \$Sales\ per\ Square\ Foot_t$

Where

$\#Stores_t$ = number of stores owned by the company in Year t

$Area_t$ = average area of a store in Year t

$\$Sales\ per\ Square\ Foot_t$ = average annual revenue per square foot in Year t

3.6   Question

Lululemon athletica (NASDAQ:LULU) is a yoga-inspired athletic apparel company. Data for the last two fiscal years is provided in the table below.

Selected Financial Information Lululemon Athletica			
	Year t – 1	Year t	Year t + 1
Number of stores	174	211	
Area	2,834 sq feet	2,834 sq feet	2,834 sq feet
Sales per square foot	$1,657	$1,823	
Sales (Net revenue for corporate-owned stores)	$816.925 M	$1,090.181M	

In the year ended February 3, Year t Lululemon had sales of $1.09 billion through its 211 corporate-owned stores in the U.S., Canada and Australia. The average size of a Lululemon store is 2,834 square feet. Thus, sales per square foot were $1,823 in Year t, up just over 10% from Year t – 1.

Lululemon plans to add 30 stores in Year t + 1. Assume that it gets one-half of a year of sales from the new stores. Assume that same-store sales growth is 5% in Year t + 1 (both for existing and new stores). Forecast revenues from corporate-owned stores for Year t + 1.

ANSWER:

$Sales_{t+1}$ =

3.7   Another Forecasting Question

Cortex Business Solutions operates a trading partner network that allows firms to digitize their customer invoicing. Cortex focuses exclusively on the North American Oil & Gas firms, which are called "buyers." When a buyer signs onto the network, all of its suppliers are included in the network. Cortex generates recurring revenue primarily through a fee charged for each supplier invoice processed through the network.

Sales are forecasted on the basis of transactions processed through the network, or "Billable Transactions." Thus,

Sales = Billable Transactions × Price

Last year, the average price was $2.18 per transaction.

To forecast billable transactions, we model them as follows:

Billable transactions = #Buyers × #Suppliers per Buyer × #Transactions
Where
#Buyers = number of oil and gas companies using the network
#Suppliers per buyer = average number of suppliers a buyer brings to the network
#Transactions = average number of transactions a supplier does with their buyer

Last year there were 75 buyers on the network, each buyer had an average of 110 suppliers and the average supplier processed 553 invoices.

What were sales revenues last year? If the number of buyers rises by 10% next year and the price per billable rises by 3%, what will sales be next year? Assume that the average number of suppliers and transactions per supplier stay constant.

4.   Cash Budget
- Develop a sales and production scenario with an explicit set of assumptions.
    - Forecast sales, costs and equipment/capital needs.
- Determine the cash inflows expected from operations.
- Calculate the cash outflows expected to arise from operations.

- Estimate other outflows (e.g., taxes and interest).
- Determine the expected financing needed or surplus available.

4.1   Budgeting Cash Inflows

Key Sales Assumptions

- Monthly sales of 10,000 units
- Based on contract with distributor
- Wholesale price of $1.58 (per unit) to distributor
- First month of sales is February
    - Business started on January 1.
    - January was spent preparing for production.
- Accounts Receivable:
    - 50% of sales is collected within one month following the sale and the other 50% is collected two months following the sale.

What are sales revenues in each month? Complete the sales revenue row in the table below.

	January	**February**	**March**	**April**
Sales Revenues	$0			
Collections from Sales Last Month	$0	$0		
Collections from Sales 2 Months Ago	$0	$0	$0	
Total Collections	$0	$0		

How much is collected from the distributor in March?

ANSWER:
March Collections from Sales Last Month =

How much is collected from the distributor in April?

ANSWER:
April Collections from Sales Last Month =
April Collections from Sales Two Months Ago =
April Total Collections =

96   What are accounts receivable at the end of April?

A) $0
B) $7,900
C) $15,800
D) $23,700

4.2   Purchasing and Payments to Suppliers

Key Purchasing and Payment Assumptions

- Raw materials cost $1 per unit.
- Purchases are made one month before sales.
- The supplier is paid one month after the purchase.

What are purchases in each month? Complete the purchases row in the table below.

	January	February	March	April
Sales Revenues	$0	$15,800	$15,800	$15,800
Raw Mats Purchases				
Payments to Suppliers	$0			

How much is paid to the supplier in March?

ANSWER:
March Payments to Supplier =

How much is paid to the supplier in April?

ANSWER:
April Payments to Supplier =

97   What is the inventory of raw materials at the end of April?
    A) $0
    B) $7,900
    C) $10,000
    D) $15,800

98   What are accounts payable at the end of April?
    A) $0
    B) $7,900
    C) $10,000

D) $15,800

4.3   Cash Budget
Key Assumptions

- The company starts January with $10,000 in cash.
- SG&A expenses are $3,750 per month starting in January.
- A negative cash balance represents short-term bank borrowing.
- Interest is paid monthly on the previous month's closing cash balance; if the balance is negative, interest is 1% per month.
- No interest is earned on positive cash balances.
  - This is assumed for the sake of simplicity and can be changed.

What are net cash flows in February? Complete the "Net Cash Flow" row in the table below.

	January	February	March	April
Total Collections	$0	$0	$7,900	$15,800
OUTFLOWS:				
Payments to Suppliers	$0	$10,000	$10,000	$10,000
SG&A Expenses	$3,750	$3,750	$3,750	$3,750
Interest Expense	$0	$0		
Net Cash Flow	–$3,750			
Starting Cash	$10,000	$6,250		
Ending Cash	$6,250			

What is February's ending cash balance?

ANSWER:
February Ending Cash Balance =

How much interest is owing in March?

ANSWER:
March Interest Expense =

What is April's ending cash balance?

ANSWER:
April Ending Cash Balance =

313

What is the worst cash balance between January and April?

ANSWER:
Worst Cash Balance =

99   If you were the financial manager for the company and had prepared this
      cash budget, what would you do?
      A)   Meet with your banker and arrange a line of credit for
            approximately $15,000.
      B)   Blame the problem on your predecessor.
      C)   Get a note from your doctor.

5.   Cash Budget for Boston Whaler

Boston Whaler, Inc. manufactures powerboats. Boston Whalers are sold year
round but the bulk of the company's sales occur from April through July with
the peak in June. Experience shows that on 30% of its sales, payment is made
during the month in which the sale occurs; on 60% of its sales, payment is
made during the next month; and on 10% of its sales, payments is made
during the second month.

Rather than operate its production lines at a uniform rate throughout the year,
Boston Whaler constructs the boats one month before their sale. It purchases
raw materials, such as fibreglass, foam, metal and vinyl, in the month of
production. Raw material costs are 50% of sales. Boston Whaler pays for
construction materials one month after their purchase.

Head office and sales force salaries average $1M per month and production
wages in a given month are 12% of sales forecasted for the subsequent month.
Rent is $0.5M per month for the production facilities. Other expenses and
taxes are $0.5M per month on average. Boston Whaler plans to refurbish part
of its plant in June for an estimated outlay of $5M.

Prepare a cash budget for Boston Whaler for the months from May to July
using the sales forecast provided below. Boston Whaler starts May with a cash
balance of $10 million. What is the cash balance at the end of July?

Month	Sales ($M)
March	$3
April	$6
May	$10
June	$20
July	$10
August	$10
September	$5

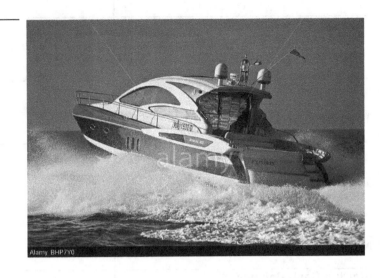

	Mar	Apr	May	June	July	August
Sales	$3	$6	$10	$20	$10	$10

CASH INFLOWS

Cash collections same month			3			
Credit collections from sales 1 month ago						
Credit collections from sales 2 months ago						
Total Cash Inflows						

CASH OUTFLOWS

OUTFLOWS FROM OPERATIONS

Purchases of Materials				
Payments for Materials				
Wages				
Total Cash Outflows for Operations				

OTHER OUTFLOWS

Rent	0.5				
Head Office Salaries	1				
Taxes and Other Expenses	0.5				
Plant Upgrades	0				
Total Other Outflows	2				

Total Cash Outflows					

NET CASH FLOW for MONTH					
Starting Cash Balance			$10		
Ending Cash Balance					

Solutions

Introduction to Sales Forecasting (3.2, 3.4, 3.6, 3.7)

Sales Revenues$_{t+1}$ = $176,801,460
Sales Revenues$_{t+1}$ = $297,641,414

Samsung:

Sales$_{t+1}$ = $71.4 billion

Lululemon:

Existing Stores Sales$_{t+1}$ = $1,144.612
New Stores Sales$_{t+1}$ = $81.371
Total Sales$_{t+1}$ = $1,225.982

Cortex:
Sales$_t$ = 4,562,250 × $2.18 = $9,945,705
Sales$_{t+1}$ = 5,018,475 × $2.2454 = $11,268,484

Cash Budget (4.1, 4.2, 4.3)

March Collections from Sales Last Month = $7,900
April Collections from Last Month = $7,900
April Collections from Two Months Ago = $7,900
April Total Collections = $15,800

	January	February	March	April
Sales Revenues	$0	$15,800	$15,800	$15,800
Raw Mats Purchases	$10,000	$10,000	$10,000	$10,000
Payments to Suppliers	$0	$10,000	$10,000	$10,000

February Net Cash Flows = –$13,750
February Ending Cash Balance = –$7,500

March Interest Expense = 0.01 × 7,500 = $75

	January	February	March	April
Total Collections	$0	$0	$7,900	$15,800

317

OUTFLOWS:				
Payments to Suppliers	$0	$10,000	$10,000	$10,000
SG&A Expenses	$3,750	$3,750	$3,750	$3,750
Interest Expense	$0	$0	$75	$134
Net Cash Flow	–$3,750	–$13,750	–$5,925	$1,916
Starting Cash	$10,000	$6,250	–$7,500	–$13,425
Ending Cash	$6,250	–$7,500	–$13,425	–$11,509

Worst Cash Balance = –$13,425

Cash Budget for Boston Whaler (5)

Cash balance at end of July = 9.7

Financial Statements Forecasting (Ch.14, LO3)

1. Introduction

In this workbook you will:

- Learn the percent-of-sales financial statements forecasting method
- Learn to forecast the interest expense
- Learn to calculate depreciation expense using the declining balance approach
- Learn the capital asset identity
- Learn to solve for the average depreciation rate
- Learn to forecast depreciation and net fixed assets
- Learn to forecast financial statements

2. Introduction to Financial Statements Forecasting

- We will use the percent-of-sales method.
- With this method, we start with a sales forecast and forecast most accounting values as a percentage of that sales forecast.
  - o Some values are forecast as a percentage of other bases. For example, taxes are a percentage of taxable income.
- The percentage of sales relationships are obtained from historical financial statements, competitor values, industry averages or management guidance.
- The forecasted statements are used for two main purposes:
  - o Financial managers use them to identify capital needs before the need arises so that the capital can be raised in a calm and orderly fashion.
  - o Financial analysts forecast financial statements as part of the discounted cash flow (DCF) method of corporate valuation.

3. Percent-of-Sales Ratios

St. Dilbert Pharmaceuticals

	Year 1		Year 2
Sales	$500		$600
Operating Expenses			
Cost of sales and SG&A	235		
Depreciation	50		
Operating Income (EBIT)	215		
Interest Expense	40		
Earnings before Income Taxes	175		
Income Taxes	36		
Net Income	$139		
Dividends (total)	$46		

In Millions of CAD	Year 1		Year 2
Total Current Assets	400		
Fixed Assets (Net)	600		
Other Assets	0		0
Total Assets	$1,000		
LIABILITIES AND SHAREHOLDERS' EQUITY			
Total Current Liabilities	0		0
Long Term Debt	450		
Common Share Capital	50		50
Retained Earnings	500		
Total Shareholders' Equity	550		
Total Liabilities & Shareholders' Equity	$1,000		

Complete the following table of ratios for Year 1.

Ratio	Year 1
*Costs/Sales	
Tax Rate (Tax/EBT)	
Dividend Payout Rate (Divs/Net Income)	
Current Assets/Sales	

*Costs = cost of goods sold + SG&A

4. Interest

4.1 Modelling Interest

Today you borrowed $900 from the bank. The bank charges an interest rate of 5%. How much interest do you owe at the end of the year?

> **ANSWER:**
> $Interest =

Last year you borrowed $800 from the bank. The bank is asking for $40 of interest today, one year after the loan. What is the interest rate on the loan?

> **ANSWER:**
> Interest Rate (%) =

How much interest did St. Dilbert pay at the end of Year 1?

> **ANSWER:**
> $Interest_1 =

At the end of Year 0, St. Dilbert had long-term debt of $374.88. What interest rate did St. Dilbert have on its loans over Year 1?

> **ANSWER:**
> Interest Rate (%) =

4.2 Forecasting the Interest Expense for St. Dilbert

How much money does St. Dilbert owe at the end of Year 1?

> **ANSWER:**
> Amount Owing =

If St. Dilbert's interest rate stays constant in Year 2 (equal to its Year 1 value that you just solved), how much interest will St. Dilbert owe at the end of Year 2?

> **ANSWER:**
> $Interest_2 =

5. Depreciation and the Capital Asset Identity

5.1 Definition: Declining Balance Depreciation

$Depr_t = dr \times Net_{t-1}$

Where

$Depr_t$ = depreciation expense in period t
dr = depreciation rate
Net_{t-1} = book value of assets at the end of period t – 1

In period 1, the beginning of period (end of last period) book value (denoted Net_0) is simply the purchase price of the asset.

5.2 Question:

100 On a balance sheet, the label used for book value of property, plant and equipment is:
- A) Gross Fixed Assets
- B) Intangible Assets
- C) Goodwill
- D) Net Fixed Assets

5.3 Question: Declining Balance Depreciation

Fritz Electric bought a new Van de Graaff generator for $11,000 at the beginning of Year 1. The machine is depreciated at 25% using the declining balance method. Ignore the half-year rule. What is the depreciation expense in the first year?

ANSWER:
$Depr_1$ =

5.4 Depreciation

Fritz Electric bought a new Van de Graaff generator for $11,000 at the beginning of Year 1. The machine is depreciated at 25% using the declining balance method. Complete the table below.

Depreciation Schedule		
	Year 1	Year 2
Book Value$_{t-1}$	$11,000	
Depr Rate (dr)	0.25	0.25
Depr		
Book Value$_t$		

5.5 Capital Asset Identity Definition

With no purchases of new plant or equipment, the capital asset identity is:

$Book_t = Book_{t-1} - Depr_t$
Or, since $Book_t = Net_t$ (by definition)
$Net_t = Net_{t-1} - Depr_t$

- Purchases of plant and equipment are called Capital Expenditures. The acronym is CAPEX.

5.6 Question

Look back at the Fritz Electric question. Does the capital asset identity work for solving for Net_1? (Reminder: In Year 1, Net_0 is the purchase price of the machine.)

ANSWER:
$Net_1 = Net_0 - Depr_1 =$

5.7 Question

Assume that Fritz Electric bought a Wimshurst machine for $5,000 at the beginning of Year 2. The machine is also depreciated at 25%. What are net fixed assets for Fritz at the end of Year 2?

Depreciation Schedule		
	Year 1	Year 2
Net (Graaff)$_{t-1}$	$11,000	
Net (Wimshurst)$_{t-1}$	n.a.	$5,000
Depr Rate (dr)	0.25	0.25
Depr		
Net (All)$_t$		

ANSWER:
Net (All)$_2$ =

5.8 Capital Asset Identity with CAPEX

With CAPEX, the capital asset identity is:

$Net_t = Net_{t-1} + CAPEX_t - Depr_t$ Eq. 1

Where
CAPEX = purchases of fixed assets

Use Eq. 1 to calculate Net_2 for Fritz in Year 2.

ANSWER:
$Net_2 =$

With CAPEX, depreciation is:
$$Depr_t = dr \times (Net_{t-1} + CAPEX_t) \qquad \text{Eq. 2}$$

5.9   Solve for the Depreciation Rate (dr)
STEP 1: Substitute Eq. 2 into Eq. 1

STEP 2: Next, we want to remove CAPEX from this equation. To simplify this further, we see from re-arranging Eq. 1 that:

$$Net_{t-1} + CAPEX_t = Net_t + Depr_t$$

Use this equality to replace $(Net_{t-1} + CAPEX_t)$ anywhere in Step 1. (There should be two replacements.)

STEP 3: Simplify for dr.

324

6. Simple Forecast of $Depr_{t+1}$ and Net_{t+1}

6.1   Question: Depreciation Rate for St. Dilbert
Look back at the financial statements for St. Dilbert. What is the depreciation rate in Year 1?

> **ANSWER:**
> dr =

6.2   Forecast Depreciation in Year 2 for St. Dilbert
St. Dilbert is planning to spend $300 on machinery and equipment in Year 2. Use Eq. 2 to forecast the depreciation expense in Year 2 using the depreciation rate solved in the last question.

> **ANSWER:**
> $Depr_2$ =

6.3   Forecast Net Fixed Assets in Year 2 for St. Dilbert
St. Dilbert is planning to spend $300 on machinery and equipment in Year 2. Use Eq. 1 and your answer to the last question to forecast net fixed assets in Year 2.

> **ANSWER:**
> Net_2 =

7. Plug Account
- Not all of the balance sheet accounts can be forecast as a percentage of sales.
- In particular, debt and equity levels in the corporation are determined by management action and are not spontaneously driven by sales.
- When a company expands its line of credit or sells new bonds, the debt accounts increase.
- If new equity is issued, the Common Shares account increases.
- In financial statements forecasting, one (or both) of the debt or equity accounts are designated "plug" accounts.
- The plug account is given whatever value is necessary to make the balance sheet balance, once all other values are forecasted.

- If the resulting value is larger than the previous year, the implication is that the company must issue new securities (debt or equity) to raise the difference.
- If the resulting value is lower, then the company is in a position to repay debt or repurchase equity.
- The primary managerial use for financial statements forecasting is to flag excess capital or a shortage of capital.
- If shortages are identified early, a company can more carefully plan its approach to the capital markets.
    - No one wants to lend to a desperate borrower!

8. F/S Forecast for St. Dilbert for Year 2

Use your answers to the earlier questions to complete the forecast for St. Dilbert. Make long-term debt the plug variable.

St. Dilbert Pharmaceuticals

	Year 1	Ratio	Year 2
Sales	$500		$600
Operating Expenses			
Cost of sales and SG&A	235	47%	
Depreciation	50		
Operating Income (EBIT)	215		
Interest Expense	40		
Earnings before Income Taxes	175		
Income Taxes	36	21%	
Net Income	$139		
Dividends (total)	$46	33%	

In Millions of CAD	Year 1		Year 2
Total Current Assets	400	80%	
Fixed Assets (Net)	600		
Other Assets	0		0
Total Assets	$1,000		
LIABILITIES AND SHAREHOLDERS' EQUITY			
Total Current Liabilities	0		0
Long Term Debt	450		
Common Share Capital	50		50
Retained Earnings	500		
Total Shareholders' Equity	550		
Total Liabilities & Shareholders' Equity	$1,000		

9. CAPEX

- Total CAPEX = Growth + Maintenance
- Maintenance CAPEX:
  - o Represents the amount of CAPEX necessary to maintain existing equipment and so hold net fixed assets constant over time.
  - o Is the amount of CAPEX necessary to make $Net_{t-1} = Net_t$
- Growth CAPEX:
  - o Represents the CAPEX needed to generate new sales.
  - o Growth CAPEX = Total – Maintenance
    - Solve growth CAPEX as a residual after maintenance CAPEX.
- In BU283, CAPEX will be given to you. In a more advanced course you will learn to forecast growth and maintenance CAPEX.

9.1 Question: Depreciation Rate

Use the selected financial information in the table to solve for Loblaw's depreciation rate in Year 6.

Selected Financial Information Loblaw Inc. ($000,000s)		
	Year 5	Year 6
Sales	$27,801	$29,210
Depreciation Expense	684	621
Net Fixed Assets	9,372	9,637

ANSWER:

dr =

10. F/S Forecast For Loblaw

	Year 5	Year 6		Year 7
Revenue	$27,801	$ 29,210	5%	$30,817
Cost of Goods Sold		22,152	0.75837	
SG&A		5,245	0.17956	
Depreciation Expense		621		
EBIT		1,192		
Interest Expense		277		
Earnings before Taxes		915		
Income Taxes		288	0.31475	
Net Earnings		$ 627		

ASSETS

Current Assets	Year 5	Year 6		Year 7
Cash	$ 920	$ 1,467		1,548
Accounts Receivable	656	649		685
Inventories	2,125	2,269		2,394
Total Current Assets	3,701	4,385	0.15012	4,626
Net Fixed Assets	9,372	9,637		
Goodwill	688	678		678
Total Assets	$ 13,761	$ 14,700		

LIABILITIES AND OWNERS' EQUITY

Current Liabilities				
Short Term Debt	$ 627	$ 715		715
Accounts payable	2,535	2,936		
Total Current Liabilities	3,162	3,651		
Long Term Debt	4,194	4,208		
Other Liabilities	519	560		560
Total Liabilities	$ 7,875	$ 8,419		
Common Stock	1,192	1,192		1,192
Retained Earnings	4,694	5,089		
Total Owners' Equity	5,886	6,281		
Liabilities & Owners' Equity	$ 13,761	$ 14,700		

How much money did Loblaw owe at the end of Year 5?

ANSWER:
Amount Owing =

How much interest did Loblaw pay at the end of Year 6?

> **ANSWER:**
> \$Interest =

What interest rate did Loblaw pay on its loans over Year 6?

> **ANSWER:**
> Interest Rate (%) =

If Loblaw's interest rate stays constant in Year 7 (equal to its Year 6 value that you just solved), how much interest will Loblaw owe at the end of Year 7?

> **ANSWER:**
> Interest_7 =

If CAPEX is \$943 in Year 7, and if Loblaw's depreciation rate in Year 7 is the same as you calculated for Year 6 above, what is the depreciation expense for Loblaw in Year 7?

> **ANSWER:**
> Depr_7 =

What is net Income for Loblaw in Year 7?

> **ANSWER:**
> Net Income =

What are net fixed assets for Loblaw in Year 7?

> **ANSWER:**
> Net_7 =

What are total assets for Loblaw in Year 7?

> **ANSWER:**
> Total Assets_7 =

Make long-term debt the plug account. What is long-term debt for Loblaw in Year 7? (Forecast other values as a percentage of sales.)

11. BONUS: F/S Forecast for Stark Industries Inc.

- Sales growth = 10%
- Unchanged: Dividends, Loans to Director, Common Shares
- LT Debt = plug
- CAPEX = 4,000
- Depreciation Rate = 14.897%

Stark Industries , Inc.		Year 2	Year 3
Revenue		161,120	177,232
Cost of Goods Sold		105,035	
General & Admin Expenses		42,957	
Depreciation		6,687	
EBIT		6,441	
Interest		787	
Net Income Before Tax		5,654	
Taxes		2,262	
Net Income After Tax		3,392	
Dividends		1,974	
Assets	Year 1	Year 2	Year 3
Cash	10,090	9,071	
Accounts Receivable	2,976	4,106	
Inventory	20,362	22,123	
Current Assets	33,428	35,300	
Equipment, Net	34,510	38,202	
Loans to Director	686	686	686
Total Assets	68,624	74,188	
Other Liabs	494	494	
Accounts Payable	10,719	12,027	
Current Liabs	11,213	12,521	
Long-term debt	7,031	9,868	
Common Shares	13,427	13,428	13,428
Retained Earnings	36,953	38,371	
Owner's Equity	50,380	51,799	
Liabilities and Owners' Equity	68,624	74,188	

Solutions

Percent-of-Sales Ratios (3)

Ratio	Year 1
*Costs/Sales	0.47
Tax Rate (Tax/EBT)	0.21
Dividend Payout Rate (Divs/Net Income)	0.33
Current Assets/Sales	0.80

Interest (4.1, 4.2)

$Interest = $45

Interest Rate = 0.05 or 5%

$Interest$_1$ = $40

Interest Rate = 0.1067 or 10.67%

Amount Owing$_1$ = Long-term Debt = $450

$Interest$_2$ = $48

Depreciation and Capital Asset Identity (5.3, 5.4, 5.6, 5.7, 5.9)

Depr$_1$ = 0.25 × $11,000 = $2,750

Depreciation Schedule		
	Year 1	Year 2
Book Value$_{t-1}$	11,000	8,250
Depr Rate (dr)	0.25	0.25
Depr	2,750	2,062.5
Book Value$_t$	8,250	6,187.5

Net$_1$ = $8,250

Depreciation Schedule		
	Year 1	Year 2
Net (Graaff)$_{t-1}$	$11,000	$8,250
Net (Wimshurst)$_{t-1}$	n.a.	$5,000
Depr Rate (dr)	0.25	0.25
Depr	2,750	3,312.50
Net (All)$_t$	8,250	9,937.50

Net$_2$ = $9,937.50

Solve for the Depreciation Rate:

$$dr = Depr_t / (Net_t + Depr_t)$$

Forecast Depreciation and Net Fixed for St. Dilbert (6.1, 6.2, 6.3, 8)

$dr = 0.076923$
$Depr_2 = \$69$
$Net_2 = \$831$

Pro Forma for St. Dilbert

	Year 1	Ratios	Year 2
Revenue	500	0.2	600.0
COGS & SGA	235	0.47	282.0
Depreciation	50	0.076923077	69.2
EBIT	215		248.8
Interest	40	0.106700811	48.0
Earnings Before Taxes	175		200.8
Taxes	36	0.21	41.3
Net Income After Tax	139		159.5
Dividends	46	0.330935252	52.8
	Year 1		**Year 2**
Current Assets	400	0.8	480.0
Fixed Assets (Net)	600	300	830.8
Total Assets	1,000		1,310.8
Current Liabilities	0	0	0.0
Long-term debt	450		654.1
Common Shares	50		50.0
Retained Earnings	500		606.7
Owner's equity	550		656.7
Liabilities and Owners' Equity	1,000		1,310.8

CAPEX (9)

$$dr = 621 / (9{,}637 + 621) = 0.060538$$

F/S Forecast for Loblaw (10)

Amount Owing$_5$ = \$627 + \$4,194
Interest$_6$ = \$277

Interest Rate $= 0.0575$
$Interest_7 = \$283$

$Depr_7 = \$640$
Net Income $= \$678$
$Net_7 = \$9,940$
Total Assets $= \$5,244$
Long-term Debt $= \$3,912$

<u>F/S Forecast for Stark Industries (11)</u>

Long-term Debt $= \$7,604$

Management of Working Capital (Ch.15 LO1)

1. Introduction

In this workbook you will:

- Learn the meaning of working capital
- Learn how to measure working capital management with net working capital, and the operating and cash cycles
- Learn about two approaches to working capital management: conservative and aggressive

2. Issues to Study

- What amounts of current assets should a firm hold?
- What types and amounts of short-term financing should a firm employ?
- How do firms ensure they have enough cash to meet on-going obligations?

3. Working Capital Management in Action

Watch the YouTube video titled "IS in Action Walmart Supply Chain."

4. Working Capital

- Gross working capital is equal to short-term assets.
- Net working capital is current assets minus current liabilities.
  - o Net working capital is the amount of long-term capital that is used to fund short-term assets.
- Net working capital is capital invested in the business that does not earn an active return because it does not produce goods (services) for sale.
- The cost of net working capital is the return on capital foregone because it is not actively invested.
- The benefit of net working capital is that it is necessary for the operation of a business.

On the balance sheet below, shade in the area that represents net working capital.

Balance Sheet

Assets	Liabilities & Owner's Equity	
Current Assets	Current Liabilities	
Fixed Assets	Long-term Liabilities	Owner's Equity

- Working capital management refers to the management of all short-term assets and liabilities.
- Working capital management is the same as short-term financial management.

5. Measuring Working Capital

5.1 Hershey's Inventory Error

Like most candy manufacturers, Hershey Foods typically has a significant percentage of sales around Halloween.

In 1998–99, Hershey spent more than $100 million on a new order management, supply chain planning and Customer Relationship Management (CRM) system to transform the company's IT infrastructure and supply chain. When disaster hit, the company was later criticized for a "big bang" approach to implementation, trying to go live with all these systems in parallel.

Expected to go live in April 1999, the schedule slipped and rather than wait until the following year, Hershey switched over in the summer. The system had major issues. In many cases, Hershey had product on the dock but couldn't get transactions to work that would enable it to put the candy in a truck and ship it to customers. Inventory was not visible to the order management system for allocation, so the orders weren't processed.

The company ultimately said at least $150 million in orders were missed. Quarterly profit dropped 19% in the 3rd quarter, and it took another hit in the

4th quarter. The fiasco made headlines across the business press. The stock dropped from $57 in August 1999 to $38 by January 2000.[1]

Selected data for Hershey are provided below.

Selected Financial Information The Hershey Company ($000s)				
	2001	2000	1999	1998
Sales	4,557,241	4,220,976	3,970,924	4,435,615
Cost of Goods Sold	2,665,566	2,471,151	2,354,724	2,625,057
Accounts receivable, net	361,726	379,680	352,750	451,324
Inventories	512,134	605,173	602,202	493,249
Total current assets	1,167,541	1,295,348	1,279,980	1,133,966
Total assets	3,247,430	3,447,764	3,346,652	3,404,098
Accounts payable	133,049	149,232	136,567	156,937
Total current liabilities	606,444	766,901	712,829	814,824

5.2   Inventory Management

The amount of time that items (raw materials and finished goods) stay in inventory is measured by the average inventory period:

$$\text{Average inventory period} = \frac{\text{Inventory}}{\dfrac{\text{COGS}}{365}}$$

- This is the average amount of time from the day a raw material arrives to the day a finished product is shipped.
- To have a low value for this ratio, a company has to have a good inventory management system, a quick and responsive supply chain, accurate sales forecasting and tight production scheduling.

What was Hershey's average inventory period for 1999? Complete the table below.

Selected Financial Information
The Hershey Company

---

[1] "The 11 Greatest Supply Chain Disasters," *Supply Chain Digest*, January 2006, p.8.

336

	2001	2000	1999	1998
Average Inventory Period	70.1	89.4		68.6

5.3 Net Working Capital

Net Working Capital = Current Assets – Current Liabilities

What was the net working capital at Hershey in 1999? Complete the table below.

Selected Financial Information The Hershey Company				
	2001	2000	1999	1998
Net Working Capital	561,097	528,447		319,142

5.4 NWC to Total Capital

The net-working-capital to total capital ratio measures the proportion of long-term capital (debt and equity) invested in short-term assets.

$$= \frac{\text{Net Working Capital}}{\text{Total Assets-Current Liabilities}}$$

This should be minimized, as short-term assets do not (usually) generate operating revenue.

What was the NWC-to-total capital ratio at Hershey in 1999? Complete the table below.

Selected Financial Information The Hershey Company				
	2001	2000	1999	1998
NWC/TC	21.2%	19.7%		12.3%

337

5.5 Gerald's Fresh Produce

In his first year of business, Gerald sold fresh produce to restaurants in the tri-city area. He bought his produce at the Food Terminal in the big city. Gerald would buy the produce early in the morning and deliver it directly to his restaurant clients the same day using his own truck (the company's only asset). Vendors at the Food Terminal didn't know Gerald so they required that he pay cash. Gerald charged a 100% markup on his costs and his typical monthly sales were $20,000. The restaurant owners demanded credit from Gerald and were very slow to pay. Gerald spent a great deal of his time collecting, and found that the restaurants would usually take two months to pay their bills. Gerald's financial statements for his first year of business are shown in the table below, under Year 1.

Gerald's New Business Plan

Reflecting on his first year of business, Gerald didn't like chasing restaurant owners for payment and didn't like tying up his equity in working capital. Gerald decided on a big change to his business. Instead of selling to restaurants, he decided to set up a produce stall at the Farmer's Market and sell for cash. Another change was that, after a year of doing business, the produce vendors at the Food Terminal were willing to let him purchase on one month's credit. In the second year, Gerald continued to have retail sales of $20,000 per month. Gerald's financials for the second year of business are shown below, under Year 2. Answer the questions that follow.

Financial Statements Gerald's Fresh Produce	Year 1	Year 2
Sales	240,000	240,000
Cost of Goods Sold	120,000	120,000
Selling, General & Admin	20,000	20,000
Depreciation	8,001	5,867
EBIT	91,999	94,133
Taxes (@30%)	27,600	28,240
Net Income	64,399	65,893
Cash	62,400	184,160
Accounts Receivable	40,000	-
Inventory	-	-
Current assets	102,400	184,160
Gross Fixed Assets	30,000	30,000
Accumulated Depr	8,001	13,868

Net Fixed Assets	21,999	16,132
Total Assets	124,399	200,292
Accounts Payable	-	10,000
Total Current Liabilities	-	10,000
Common Stock	60,000	60,000
Retained Earnings	64,399	130,292
Owner's Equity	124,399	190,292
Total Liabilities & Owner's Equity	124,399	200,292

5.6   Average Collection Period

The amount of time that it takes to collect accounts receivable is measured by the average collection period:

$$\text{Average collection period} = \frac{\text{Accounts Receivable}}{\dfrac{\text{Sales}}{365}}$$

- This is the average amount of time from the day of a sale until the customer pays the invoice.
- If customers pay in one month, then the average collection period is 30 days.
- For cash businesses, the average collection period is zero.

What is Gerald's average collection period in Year 1 and Year 2? Complete the table below.

Selected Financial Information Gerald's Fresh Produce		
	Year 1	Year 2
Average Collection Period		

5.7   Average Payable Period

The amount of time that it takes a company to pay its suppliers is measured by the average payables period:

$$\text{Average payables period} = \frac{\text{Accounts Payable}}{\dfrac{\text{COGS}}{365}}$$

- This is the average amount of time from the day of a purchase of a raw material until the company pays the supplier.
- If the company pays its invoice in one month, then the average payables period is 30 days.
- For C.O.D. purchases, the average payables period is zero.

What is Gerald's average payable period in Year 1 and Year 2? Complete the table below.

Selected Financial Information Gerald's Fresh Produce		
	Year 1	Year 2
Average Payable Period		

6.   Operating and Cash Cycle

Every business requires that money be disbursed to purchase raw materials before money is collected from the sale of finished products. That money is the investment in net working capital.

The longer products stay in inventory before they are sold and the longer it takes firms to collect their receivables, the greater the net working capital and the higher the cost. We can measure the length of time it takes cash to flow through a business using the operating and cash cycles. These measures capture the size of net working capital, but they also help identify the source of problems in working capital management.

- The operating and cash cycles capture many facets of a business, such as:
    - o inventory management
    - o supply chain integration
    - o sales forecasting

- o production scheduling
- o credit management
- o collections
- o supplier relationships

The figure below shows the operating and cash cycles. The firm, a rocket manufacturer, buys parts from its suppliers. The parts are assembled and the finished rocket is placed in inventory. The rocket is sold to a customer and money is finally received when the account is collected. The length of time from purchase of raw materials to final receipt of funds is called the operating cycle. The operating cycle does not capture the time from disbursement of funds to receipt of funds because raw materials are usually purchased on credit. Thus, the cash cycle is equal to the operating cycle less the accounts payable period (the amount of time that it takes to pay suppliers).

Operating and Cash Cycles

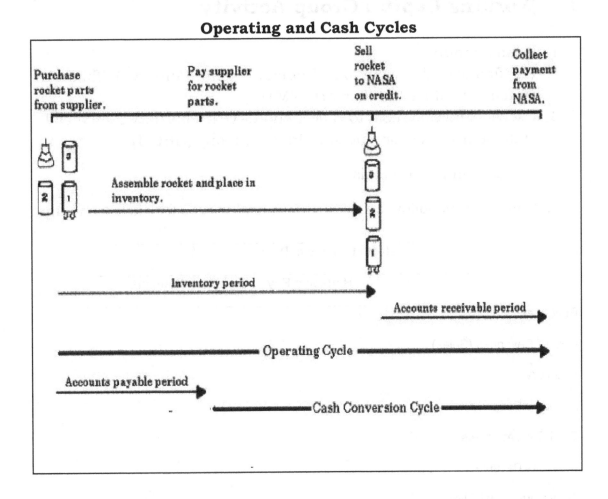

Operating Cycle = Average Inventory Period + Average Collection Period

Cash cycle = Operating Cycle – Average Payable Period

What is the cash conversion cycle for Gerald's Fresh Produce in Years 1 and 2?

ANSWER:
Cash Conversion Cycle$_1$ =
Cash Conversion Cycle$_2$ =

7. Working Capital Management

7.1 Video

- Watch the YouTube video "Working Capital Management explained" by Deutsche bank.

8. Working Capital Group Activity

1. Form a group.
2. Use finance.yahoo.com to collect end-of-year January 31 financial statement values for Walmart (WMT).
3. Use globeinvestor.com to collect end-of-year February 2 financial statement values for Hudson's Bay Company (HBC-T).

   Look under "Financials."

4. Complete the following table of financial values for each company.

	Selected Financial Data	
	Hudson's Bay	**Walmart**
Revenues		
Cost of Revenues (Sales)		
Inventory		
Accounts Receivable		
Total Current Assets		
Accounts Payable		
Total Current Liabilities		
Long-term Liabilities		

Owner's Equity

_____

5. Complete the ratio table for Hudson's Bay and Walmart.

Selected Ratios Hudson's Bay and Walmart		
	Hudson's Bay	Walmart
NWC/Total Capital*		
Average Collection Period		
Average Inventory Period		
Average Payable Period		
Operating Cycle		
Cash Cycle		

Total Capital = Long-term Liabilities + Owner's Equity

6. Why do both companies have such low collection periods?
7. Compare Walmart's days inventory to days payable. Why are they so different?
8. Compare the inventory management of the two companies. Who manages inventory better?
9. Compare the speed with which each company pays its suppliers.
10. Interpret the cash cycle values for each company. What do they imply about the management of each company?
11. Watch you tube video "Working Capital Management Explained" by Deutsche bank. How would you characterize each company's working capital management policy?
   i. Aggressive (modern)
   ii. Conservative (classic)

Solutions

<u>Working Capital</u> (4)

Balance Sheet

Assets	Liabilities & Owner's Equity	
Current Assets	**Current Liabilities**	
Fixed Assets	**Long-term Liabilities**	**Owner's Equity**

<u>Measuring Working Capital</u> (5.2, 5.3, 5.4, 5.5, 5.5, 5.6)

Average Inventory Period = 93.3

NWC = 567,151

NWC/TC = 0.215 or 21.5%

Selected Financial Information Gerald's Fresh Produce		
	Year 1	Year 2
Average Collection Period	60.83	0

Selected Financial Information Gerald's Fresh Produce		
	Year 1	Year 2
Average Payable Period	0	30.42

<u>Operating and Cash Cycle</u> (6)

Cash Conversion Cycle$_1$ = 60.83
Cash Conversion Cycle$_2$ = −30.42

Advanced Financial Statements Forecasting (Ch. 17, LO1)

1. Introduction
In this workbook you will:

- Learn how to forecast a financial statement using the percent-of-sales approach
- Learn how to forecast interest
- Learn how to forecast depreciation, maintenance CAPEX, growth CAPEX and net fixed assets
- Learn how to forecast financial statements

2. Introduction to Financial Statements Forecasting

- We will use the percent-of-sales method.
- With this method, we start with a sales forecast and forecast most accounting values as a percentage of that sales forecast.
    - Some values are forecast as a percentage of other bases. For example, taxes are a percentage of taxable income.
- The percentage of sales relationships are obtained from historical financial statements, competitor values, industry averages or management guidance.
- In this chapter we will use the forecasted statements as part of the discounted cash flow (DCF) method of corporate valuation.

2.1   Percent-of-Sales Ratios

St. Dilbert Pharmaceuticals

In Millions of CAD

	Year 1		Year 2
Sales	$500		$600
Operating Expenses			
Cost of sales and SG&A	235		
Depreciation	50		
Operating Income (EBIT)	215		
Interest Expense	40		
Earnings before Income Taxes	175		
Income Taxes	36		
Net Income	$139		
Dividends (total)	$46		

	Year 1		Year 2
Total Current Assets	400		
Fixed Assets (Net)	600		
Other Assets	0		0
Total Assets	$1,000		
LIABILITIES AND SHAREHOLDERS' EQUITY			
Total Current Liabilities	0		0
Long Term Debt	450		
Common Share Capital	50		50
Retained Earnings	500		
Total Shareholders' Equity	550		
Total Liabilities & Shareholders' Equity	$1,000		

Complete the table of ratios below for Year 1.

Ratio	Year 1
*Costs/Sales	
Tax Rate (Tax/EBT)	
Dividend Payout Rate (Divs/Net Income)	
Current Assets/Sales	
*Costs = cost of goods sold + SG&A	

346

3. Interest

3.1 Modelling Interest

Today you borrowed $900 from the bank. The bank charges an interest rate of 5%. How much interest do you owe at the end of the year?

> **ANSWER:**
> $Interest =

Last year you borrowed $800 from the bank. The bank is asking for $40 of interest today, one year after the loan. What is the interest rate on the loan?

> **ANSWER:**
> Interest Rate (%) =

How much interest did St. Dilbert pay at the end of Year 1?

> **ANSWER:**
> $Interest =

At the end of Year 0, St. Dilbert had long-term debt of $374.88. What interest rate did St. Dilbert have on its loans over Year 1?

> **ANSWER:**
> Interest Rate (%) =

3.2 Forecasting the Interest Expense for St. Dilbert

How much money does St. Dilbert owe at the end of Year 1?

> **ANSWER:**
> Amount Owing =

If St. Dilbert's interest rate stays constant in Year 2 (equal to its Year 1 value that you just solved), how much interest will the company owe at the end of Year 2?

> **ANSWER:**
> $Interest_2 =

4. Depreciation and the Capital Asset Identity

4.1 Definition: Declining Balance Depreciation

$Depr_t = dr \times Net_{t-1}$

Where

$Depr_t$ = depreciation expense in period t

dr = depreciation rate

Net_{t-1} = book value of assets at the end of period t – 1.

4.2 Question:

101 On a balance sheet, the label used for book value of property, plant and equipment is:
   A) Gross Fixed Assets
   B) Intangible Assets
   C) Goodwill
   D) Net Fixed Assets
   E) Undepreciated Capital Cost (UCC)

4.3 Question: Declining Balance Depreciation

Fritz Electric bought a new Van de Graaff generator for $11,000 at the beginning of Year 1. The machine is depreciated at 25% using the declining balance method. Ignore the half-year rule. What is the depreciation expense in the first year?

ANSWER:
$Depr_1$ =

4.4 Depreciation

Fritz Electric bought a new Van de Graaff generator for $11,000 at the beginning of Year 1. The machine is depreciated at 25% using the declining balance method. Complete the table below.

Depreciation Schedule		
	Year 1	Year 2
Book Value$_{t-1}$	$11,000	
Depr Rate (dr)	0.25	0.25
Depr		
Book Value$_t$		

4.5   Capital Asset Identity

With no purchases of new plant or equipment, the capital asset identity is:

$Book_t = Book_{t-1} - Depr_t$
Or, since $Book_t = Net_t$ (by definition)
$Net_t = Net_{t-1} - Depr_t$

- Purchases of plant and equipment are called Capital Expenditures. The acronym is CAPEX.

4.6   Question

Look back at the Fritz Electric question. Does the capital asset identity work for solving for Net_1? (Reminder: In Year 1, Net_0 is the purchase price of the machine.)

ANSWER:
$Net_1 = Net_0 - Depr_1 =$

4.7   Question

Assume that at the beginning of Year 2, Fritz Electric bought a Wimshurst machine for $5,000. The machine is also depreciated at 25%. What are net fixed assets for Fritz at the end of Year 2?

Depreciation Schedule		
	Year 1	Year 2
Net (Graaff)$_{t-1}$	$11,000	
Net (Wimshurst)$_{t-1}$	n.a.	$5,000
Depr Rate (dr)	0.25	0.25
Depr		
Net (All)$_t$		

ANSWER:
Net (All)$_2 =$

4.8   Capital Asset Identity (with CAPEX)

With additions (CAPEX) the capital asset identity is:
$Net_t = Net_{t-1} + CAPEX_t - Depr_t$ Eq. 1

With additions (CAPEX), depreciation is:
$Depr_t = dr \times (Net_{t-1} + CAPEX_t)$ Eq. 2

4.9   Solve for the Depreciation Rate (dr)

STEP 1: Substitute Eq. 2 into Eq. 1.

STEP 2: Next, we want to remove CAPEX from this equation. To simplify this further, we see from re-arranging Eq. 1. that:

$$Net_{t-1} + CAPEX_t = Net_t + Depr_t$$

Use this equality to replace $(Net_{t-1} + CAPEX_t)$ anywhere in Step 1. (There should be two replacements.)

STEP 3: Simplify for dr.

4.10   Depreciation Rate (dr) Self-Test

Check out the depreciation rate self-test on page 17.1.4 of CFO.

It's Time to Do a Self-Test

1. Practise calculating the depreciation rate.   Answer

5. Simple Forecast of $Depr_{t+1}$ and Net_{t+1}

5.1   Question: Depreciation Rate for St. Dilbert

Look back at the financial statements for St. Dilbert. What is the depreciation rate in Year 1?

ANSWER:
dr =

5.2 Forecast Depreciation in Year 2 for St. Dilbert

St. Dilbert is planning to spend $300 on machinery and equipment in Year 2 (CAPEX). Use Eq. 2 to forecast the depreciation expense in Year 2 using the depreciation rate solved in the last question.

ANSWER:

$Depr_2$ =

5.3 Forecast Net in Year 2 for St. Dilbert

St. Dilbert is planning to spend $300 on machinery and equipment in Year 2. Use Eq. 1 and your answer to the last question to forecast net fixed assets in Year 2.

ANSWER:

Net_2 =

6. F/S Forecast for St. Dilbert for Year 2

Use your answers to the earlier questions to complete the forecast for St. Dilbert. Make long-term debt the plug variable.

St. Dilbert Pharmaceuticals
In Millions of CAD

	Year 1	Ratio	Year 2
Sales	$500		$600
Operating Expenses			
Cost of sales and SG&A	235	47%	
Depreciation	50		
Operating Income (EBIT)	215		
Interest Expense	40		
Earnings before Income Taxes	175		
Income Taxes	36	21%	
Net Income	$139		
Dividends (total)	$46	33%	
	Year 1		Year 2
Total Current Assets	400	80%	
Fixed Assets (Net)	600		
Other Assets	0		0
Total Assets	$1,000		
LIABILITIES AND SHAREHOLDERS' EQUITY			
Total Current Liabilities	0		0
Long Term Debt	450		
Common Share Capital	50		50
Retained Earnings	500		
Total Shareholders' Equity	550		
Total Liabilities & Shareholders' Equity	$1,000		

351

7. CAPEX

7.1   Definition

- Total CAPEX = Growth + Maintenance
- Maintenance CAPEX is the amount of CAPEX necessary to maintain existing equipment and so hold net fixed assets constant over time.
    - Amount of CAPEX necessary to make $Net_{t-1} = Net_t$
- Growth CAPEX is the CAPEX needed to generate new sales.
    - To find growth CAPEX from historical financial statements, solve as a residual after calculating total CAPEX and maintenance:
        - Growth CAPEX = Total – Maintenance

7.2   Historical Maintenance CAPEX

From Eq. 1, the capital asset identity is:

$$Net_t = Net_{t-1} + CAPEX_t - Depr_t \qquad \text{Eq. 1}$$

Solve for the level of CAPEX that makes $Net_t = Net_{t-1}$.

$$CAPEX_t = Depr_t$$

Call this value mCAPEX, so

$$mCAPEX_t = Depr_t \qquad \text{Eq. 3}$$

- Eq. 3 is not very edifying for forecasting.
- Need to know Depr to get mCAPEX.
- Need an expression for mCAPEX that depends on known parameters and historical values.

Recall Equation 2 and let all CAPEX be maintenance CAPEX, so:

$$Depr_t = dr \times (Net_{t-1} + mCAPEX_t) \qquad \text{Eq. 4}$$

Substitute Eq. 4 into Eq. 3 and solve for mCAPEX:

7.3   Question: Depreciation Rate

Use the selected financial information in the table to solve for Loblaw's depreciation rate in Year 6.

Selected Financial Information Loblaw Inc. ($000,000s)		
	Year 5	Year 6
Sales	$27,801	$29,210
Depreciation Expense	684	621
Net Fixed Assets	9,372	9,637

ANSWER:
dr =

7.4   Question: mCAPEX

Use the equation for mCAPEX (derived above), the value for the depreciation rate derived above, and the selected financial information in the table above to solve for Loblaw's mCAPEX in Year 6.

ANSWER:
$mCAPEX_6$ =

7.5   Question: Total CAPEX

Use the capital asset identity (Eq. 1) and the selected financial information in the table above to solve for Loblaw's total CAPEX in Year 6.

ANSWER:
$CAPEX_6$ =

7.6   Historic Growth CAPEX

Recall that

Growth CAPEX = Total CAPEX – mCAPEX
Growth CAPEX = gCAPEX

Use the answers to the last two questions to solve for Loblaw's growth CAPEX in Year 6.

ANSWER:
$gCAPEX_6$ = $CAPEX_6$ – $mCAPEX_6$ =

7.7   Question: gCAPEX/ΔSales

Calculate the ratio of growth CAPEX in Year 6 to the change in sales from Year 5 to Year 6.

$$gx = gCAPEX_t / (Sales_t - Sales_{t-1})$$

ANSWER:

$gx =$

7.8   Depreciation, CAPEX and Net Fixed Assets Self-Test

Check out the fixed asset self-test on page 17.1.12 of CFO.

It's Time to Do a Self-Test

3. Practise calculating total CAPEX, the depreciation rate, maintenance CAPEX, and growth CAPEX. Answer.

8. CAPEX, Net and Depreciation for Le Chateau

Le Chateau Inc

($000s)

	Year 1	Ratio	Year 2
Sales	155,000		161,120
Cost of Goods Sold			105,035
SG&A			42,957
Depreciation			6,687
Operating Income (EBIT)			6,441
Interest Expense			787
Earnings before Income Taxes			5,654
Income Taxes			2,262
Net Income			3,392
Dividends (total)			1,974

	Year 1		Year 2
Cash	10,909		9,071
Accounts Receivables	2,976		4,106
Inventory	20,362		22,123
Total Current Assets	33,428		35,300
Fixed Assets (Net)	34,510		38,202
Other Assets	686		686
Total Assets	68,624		74,188
LIABILITIES AND SHAREHOLDERS' EQUITY			
Accounts Payable	10,719		12,027
Accruals	494		494
Total Current Liabilities	11,213		12,521
Long Term Debt	7,031		9,868
Common Share Capital	13,427		13,428
Retained Earnings	36,953		38,371
Total Shareholders' Equity	50,380		51,799
Total Liabilities & Shareholders' Equity	68,624		74,188

Calculate the values in the table below for Le Chateau in Year 2. Calculate the values in the order show, from top to bottom.

	Year 2
Total Capex$_2$	
Depr Rate, dr	
Maintenance Capex, mCAPEX	
Growth CAPEX, gCAPEX	
gCAPEX/ΔSales, gx	

9. F/S Forecast For Loblaw

	Year 5	Year 6		Year 7
Revenue	$27,801	$29,210	5%	$30,817
Cost of Goods Sold		22,152	0.75437	
SG&A		5,245	0.17956	
Depreciation		621		
EBIT		1,192		
Interest		277		
Earnings before Taxes		915		
Income Taxes		288	0.31475	
Net Earnings		$627		

ASSETS

Current Assets	Year 5	Year 6		Year 7
Cash	$920	$1,467		1,548
Accounts Receivable	656	649		685
Inventories	2,125	2,269		2,394
Total Current Assets	3,701	4,385	0.15012	4,626
Net Fixed Assets	9,372	9,637		
Goodwill	688	678		678
Total Assets	$13,761	$14,700		

LIABILITIESANDOWNERS'EQUITY

Current Liabilities				
Short-term Debt	$627	$715		715
Accounts payable	2,535	2,936		
Total Current Liabilities	3,162	3,651		
Long-term Debt	4,194	4,208		
Other Liabilities	519	560		560
Total Liabilities	$7,875	$8,419		
Common Stock	1,192	1,192		1,192
Retained Earnings	4,694	5,089		
Total Owners' Equity	5,886	6,281		
Liabilities & Owners' Equity	$13,761	$14,700		

How much money did Loblaw owe at the end of Year 5?

ANSWER:

Amount Owing =

How much interest did Loblaw pay at the end of Year 6?

ANSWER:
$Interest =

What interest rate did Loblaw pay on its loans over Year 6?

ANSWER:
Interest Rate (%) =

If Loblaw's interest rate stays constant in Year 7 (equal to its Year 6 value that you just solved), how much interest will Loblaw owe at the end of Year 7?

ANSWER:
$Interest$_7$ =

If Loblaw's depreciation rate in Year 7 is the same as you calculated for Year 6 (recall that you calculated it two sections ago), what will its maintenance CAPEX be in Year 7?

ANSWER:
mCAPEX$_7$ =

If Loblaw's ratio of growth CAPEX to incremental sales in Year 7 is the same as you calculated for Year 6 above, what will its growth CAPEX be in Year 7?

ANSWER:
gCAPEX$_7$ =

What is total CAPEX for Loblaw in Year 7?

ANSWER:
CAPEX$_7$ =

What is the depreciation expense for Loblaw in Year 7?

ANSWER:
Depr$_7$ =

What is net fixed assets for Loblaw in Year 7?

ANSWER:

$Net_7 =$

Make long-term debt the plug variable. What is long-term debt for Loblaw in Year 7?

ANSWER:

Long-term Debt$_7 =$

Solutions

Introduction to Financial Statements Forecasting (2.1)

Ratio	Year 1
*Costs/Sales	0.47
Tax Rate (Tax/EBT)	0.21
Dividend Payout Rate (Divs/Net Income)	0.33
Current Assets/Sales	0.80

Interest (3.1, 3.2)

$Interest = 0.05 \times 900 = \$45$

Interest Rate = $\$40/\$800 = 0.05$ or 5%

$Interest = \$40$

Interest Rate = $\$40/\$374.88 = 0.1067$ or 10.67%

Amount Owing$_1$ = Long-term Debt = \$450

$Interest$_2$ = $\$450 \times 0.1067 = \$48$

Depreciation and the Capital Asset Identity (4.3, 4.4, 4.6, 4.7, 4.9)

$Depr_1 = 0.25 \times \$11,000 = \$2,750$

Depreciation Schedule

	Year 1	Year 2
Book Value$_{t-}$	11,000	8,250
Depr Rate (dr)	0.25	0.25
Depr	2,750	2,062.5
Book Value$_t$	8,250	6,187.5

$Net_1 = \$11,000 - \$2,750 = \$8,250$

Depreciation Schedule

	Year 1	Year 2
Net (Graaff)$_{t-1}$	\$11,000	\$8,250
Net (Wimshurst)$_{t-1}$	n.a.	\$5,000
Depr Rate (dr)	0.25	0.25
Depr	2,750	3,312.50
Net (All)$_t$	8,250	9,927.50

$dr = Depr_t/(Net_t + Depr_t)$

Simple Forecast (5.1, 5.2, 5.3)

$dr = 50/(600 + 50) = 0.076923$

$Depr_2 = 0.076923 \times (\$600 + \$300) = \$69$
$Net_2 = \$600 + \$300 - \$69 = \$831$

F/S Forecast for St. Dilbert for Year 2 (6)

Pro Forma for St. Dilbert

	Year 1	Ratios	Year 2
Revenue	500	0.2	600.0
COGS & SGA	235	0.47	282.0
Depreciation	50	0.076923077	69.2
EBIT	215		248.8
Interest	40	0.106700811	48.0
Earnings Before Taxes	175		200.8
Taxes	36	0.21	41.3
Net Income After Tax	139		159.5
Dividends	46	0.330935252	52.8
	Year 1		**Year 2**
Current Assets	400	0.8	480.0
Fixed Assets (Net)	600	300	830.8
Total Assets	1,000		1,310.8
Current Liabilities	0	0	0.0
Long-term debt	450		654.1
Common Shares	50		50.0
Retained Earnings	500		606.7
Owner's equity	550		656.7
Liabilities and Owners' Equity	1,000		1,310.8

CAPEX (7, 7.3, 7.4, 7.5, 7.6, 7.7)

$mCAPEX_t = Net_{t-1} \times dr/(1 - dr)$

$dr = 621/(9,637 + 621) = 0.0605$

$mCAPEX_6 = 9,372 \times 0.0605/(1 - 0.0605) = 604$

$CAPEX_6 = Net_6 - Net_5 + Depr_6 = 9,637 - 9,372 + 621 = 886$

$gCAPEX_6 = CAPEX_6 - mCAPEX_6 = 886 - 604 = 282$

$gx = 282/(29,210 - 27,801) = 0.200$

CAPEX, Net and Depreciation for Le Chateau (8)

	Year 2
Total Capex$_2$	10,379
Depr Rate, dr	0.14897
Maintenance Capex, mCAPEX	6,041
Growth CAPEX, gCAPEX	4338
gCAPEX/ΔSales, gx	0.709

F/S Forecast for Loblaw (9)

Amount Owing$_5$ = \$627 + \$4,194
Interest$_6$ = \$277
Interest Rate = 277/(\$627+ \$4,194) = 0.0575
Interest$_7$ = 0.0575 × (\$715 + \$4,208) = \$283

$mCAPEX_7 = \$9,637 \times 0.0605/(1 - 0.0605) = \$621$
gCAPEX = gx × ΔSales = 0.20 × \$1,607 = \$322

CAPEX = mCAPEX + gCAPEX = \$621 + \$322 = \$943

Depr$_7$ = 0.0605 × (\$9,637 + \$943) = \$640

Net$_7$ = \$9,637 + \$943 − \$640 = \$9,940

Long-term Debt$_7$ = \$3,912

Free Cash Flow (Ch.17, LO2)

1. Introduction

In this workbook you will:

- Learn about the interest tax shield
- Learn how to calculate operating cash flow
- Learn how to calculate investments in fixed assets (CAPEX)
- Learn how to calculate the investment in net working capital
- Learn how to calculate free cash flow
- Learn the free cash flow identity

2. Free Cash Flow

2.1   Definition

Free cash flow is the amount of cash you would receive from the business if you were the sole owner or sole owner and sole lender.

+	Operating Cash Flow
−	CAPEX
−	Increase in NWC
=	Free Cash Flow

3. Operating Cash Flow

3.1   Definition

OCF = Sales – COGS – SG&A – Taxes

Let Costs = COGS + SG&A

So,

OCF = Sales – Costs – Taxes   Eq. 1

Taxes = T × (Sales – Costs – Depr)   Eq. 2

Where Dep. = depreciation expenses
T = corporate tax rate

3.2   OCF Questions

102   Substitute Eq. 2 into Eq. 1 and simplify. Which of the following is (are) a correct expression for operating cash flows? (Check them all. It might be more than one.)
   A)   = (Sales – Costs – Depr) × (1 – T)
   B)   = (Sales – Costs – Depr) × (1 – T) + Depr
   C)   = (Sales – Costs) × (1 – T) + Depr × T
   D)   = NOPAT + Depr

Definitions:
EBIT = (Sales – Costs – Depr)
NOPAT = EBIT × (1 – T)

103   What is the difference between taxes in Eq. 2 and taxes on the income statement?
   A)   There is no difference.
   B)   Income taxes are lower by an amount equal to T × $Interest Expense.
   C)   Income taxes are higher by an amount equal to T × $Interest Expense.

3.3   Definition: Interest Tax Shield
   • Taxes are reduced due to interest deductibility.
   • The amount of the reduction = T × $Interest Expense.
   • This is called the interest tax shield.

3.4   Interest Tax Shield and DCF Valuation

There are two ways to incorporate the interest tax shield into DCF valuation: Method #1: Include the interest expense in the tax calculation (in OCF) and discount at before-tax WACC.

Method #2: Ignore interest in the tax calculation (in OCF) and discount at after-tax WACC.

The two methods produce the same answer, as you will see below. We use Method #2.

Consider a company with annual (perpetual) EBIT of $217 per year.

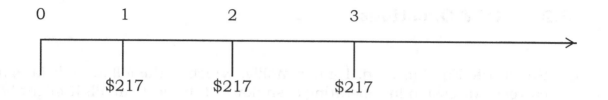

The company is worth $2,000 today. Equity is worth $1,000 and stockholders require a return of 10%. Debt (bonds) are also worth $1,000. The bonds have a face value of $1,000 and an annual coupon of $50, and bondholders require a yield of 5%. The bonds are perpetuities.

What is the before-tax cost of debt for KOT?

ANSWER:
k_d =

METHOD #1:

Complete the operating cash flow calculation for KOT Industries under Method #1, below.

KOT Industries
Method #1
Operating Cash Flows

EBIT	$217
– Interest	
Earnings Before Tax	
– Taxes (@40%)	
Net Income	
OCF = Net Income + Interest	

What is the WACC for KOT Industries using the before-tax cost of debt?

ANSWER:
WACC =

What is the present value of KOT's operating cash flows using the WACC above? (Assume that the cash flows are a perpetuity starting one year from today.)

> **ANSWER:**
> V_{KOT} =

METHOD #2:

Complete the operating cash flow calculation for KOT Industries under Method #2 below.

KOT Industries Method #2 Operating Cash Flows	
EBIT	$217
Interest	n.a.
Earnings Before Tax	
Taxes (@40%)	
Net Income	
OCF = Net Income	

What is the WACC for KOT Industries using the after-tax cost of debt?

> **ANSWER:**
> WACC =

What is the present value of KOT's operating cash flows using the WACC above? (Assume that the cash flows are a perpetuity starting one year from today.)

> **ANSWER:**
> V_{KOT} =

3.5 Question: Operating Cash Flows for Loblaw

Use the forecasted income statement below to calculate operating cash flows for Loblaw for Year 7.

	Actual	Forecast

	Year 6	Year 7
Revenue	$ 29,210	$ 30,817
Cost of Goods Sold	22,152	23,370
SG&A	5,245	5,533
Depreciation Expense	621	640
EBIT	1,192	1,272
Interest Expense	277	283
Earnings before Taxes	915	989
Income Taxes	288	311
Net Earnings	$ 627	678

ANSWER:

$OCF_{LOBLAW} =$

4. CAPEX

4.1　Definition: Declining Balance Depreciation

$Depr_t = dr \times Net_{t-1}$

Where

$Depr_t$ = depreciation expense in period t

dr = depreciation rate

Net_{t-1} = Net Fixed Assets = the book value of assets at the end of period t – 1

In period 1, the beginning of period (end of last period) book value (denoted Net_0) is simply the purchase price of the asset.

4.2　Net Fixed Assets

104　On a balance sheet, the label used for book value of assets is:
- A)　Gross Fixed Assets
- B)　Intangible Assets
- C)　Goodwill
- D)　Net Fixed Assets

4.3　Declining Balance Depreciation

Fritz Electric bought a new Van de Graaff generator for $11,000 at the beginning of Year 1. The machine is depreciated at 25% using the declining balance method. Ignore the half-year rule. What is the depreciation expense in the first year?

Fritz Electric bought a new Van de Graaff generator for $11,000 at the beginning of Year 1. The machine is depreciated at 25% using the declining balance method. Complete the table below.

Depreciation Schedule

	Year 1	Year 2
Net_{t-1}	$11,000	
Depr Rate (dr)	0.25	0.25
Depr		
Net_t		

4.4 Capital Asset Identity Definition

With no purchases of new plant or equipment, the capital asset identity is:

$Net_t = Net_{t-1} - Depr_t$

4.5 Capital Asset Identity Double Check

Look back at the Fritz Electric question. Does the capital asset identity work for solving for Net_1? (Reminder: In Year 1, Net_0 is the purchase price of the machine.)

4.6 Purchasing Another Machine (CAPEX)

Assume that at the beginning of Year 2, Fritz Electric bought a Wimshurst machine for $5,000. The machine is also depreciated at 25%. What are net fixed assets for Fritz at the end of Year 2?

Depreciation Schedule

	Year 1	Year 2

Net (Graaff)$_{t-1}$	$11,000	
Net (Wimshurst)$_{t-1}$	n.a.	$5,000
Depr Rate (dr)	0.25	0.25
Depr		
Net (All)$_t$		

ANSWER:
Net (All)$_2$ =

4.7   Capital Asset Identity with CAPEX

With CAPEX, the capital asset identity is:

$$Net_t = Net_{t-1} + CAPEX_t - Depr_t \qquad Eq.\ 1$$

Where
    CAPEX = purchases of fixed assets

Use Eq. 1 to calculate Net$_2$ for Fritz in Year 2.

ANSWER:
Net$_2$ =

We can use Eq.1 to solve for CAPEX given the other three values:

$$CAPEX_t = Net_t - Net_{t-1} + Depr_t \qquad Eq.\ 2$$

Use the partial financial statements for Loblaw below to calculate CAPEX in Year 7.

ANSWER:

CAPEX$_7$ =

Selected Financial Information
Loblaw Inc.

	Year 6	Year 7
Revenue	$ 29,210	$ 30,817
Cost of Goods Sold	22,152	23,370
SG&A	5,245	5,533
Depreciation Expense	621	640
EBIT	1,192	1,272
Interest Expense	277	283
Earnings before Taxes	915	989
Income Taxes	288	311
Net Earnings	$ 627	678

ASSETS		
Current Assets	Year 6	Year 7
Cash	$ 1,467	$ 1,548
Accounts Receivable	649	685
Inventories	2,269	2,394
Total Current Assets	4,385	$ 4,626
Net Fixed Assets	9,637	9,939
Goodwill	678	678
Total Assets	$ 14,700	$ 15,243

5. Net Working Capital

5.1 Definition

- Net working capital increases in current assets require cash (e.g., build-up of inventory or accounts receivable).
- Some of increased inventory is financed through supplier credit – accounts payable.
- Difference = NWC
- The increase in NWC is a use of free cash flow.

The accounting definition of net working capital is:

NWC = C.A. – C.L.
Where
C.A. = current assets
C.L. = current liabilities

To calculate free cash flow, we use this definition:

NWC = [C.A. – Cash] – [C.L. – Short-term Debt]

5.2   NWC Questions

105   Fritz Electric doubled its inventory of wire. It paid for the wire by withdrawing from its chequing account. What is the change in the accounting definition of NWC from before these two transactions to afterwards?
   A)   NWC increased
   B)   NWC decreased
   C)   NWC remained unchanged

106   Fritz Electric doubled its inventory of wire. It paid for the wire by withdrawing from its chequing account. What is the change in the FCF definition of NWC from before these two transactions to afterwards?
   A)   NWC increased
   B)   NWC decreased
   C)   NWC remained unchanged

107   Fritz Electric doubled its inventory of wire. It paid for the wire by withdrawing from its line of credit. What is the change in the accounting definition of NWC from before these two transactions to afterwards?
   A)   NWC increased
   B)   NWC decreased
   C)   NWC remained unchanged

108   Fritz Electric doubled its inventory of wire. It paid for the wire by withdrawing from its line of credit. What is the change in the FCF definition of NWC from before these two transactions to afterwards?
   A)   NWC increased
   B)   NWC decreased
   C)   NWC remained unchanged

5.3   Question: Net Working Capital

Use the selected financial information below to calculate the change in net working capital for Loblaw for Year 7.

ASSETS		Forecast	
Current Assets		Year 6	Year 7
Cash		$ 1,467	$ 1,548
Accounts Receivable		649	685
Inventories		2,269	2,394
		4,385	4,626
LIABILITIES AND STOCKHOLDERS' EQUITY			
Current Liabilities			
Short Term Debt		$ 715	$ 715
Accounts payable		2,936	3,097
Total Current Liabilities		3,651	3,812

ANSWER:

$\Delta NWC_7 =$

6. Free Cash Flow for Loblaw in Year 7

+	Operating Cash Flow	
−	CAPEX	
−	Increase in NWC	
=	Free Cash Flow	

7. Free Cash Flow for Le Chateau

Le Chateau Inc
($000s)

	Year 1	Ratio	Forecasted Year 2
Sales	155,000		161,120
Cost of Goods Sold			105,035
SG&A			42,957
Depreciation			6,687
Operating Income (EBIT)			6,441
Interest Expense			787
Earnings before Income Taxes			5,654
Income Taxes			2,262
Net Income			3,392
Dividends (total)			1,974

	Year 1		Year 2
Cash	10,909		9,071
Accounts Receivables	2,976		4,106
Inventory	20,362		22,123
Total Current Assets	33,428		35,300
Fixed Assets (Net)	34,510		38,202

371

Other Assets	686		686
Total Assets	68,624		74,188
LIABILITIES AND SHAREHOLDERS' EQUITY			
Accounts Payable	10,719		12,027
Accruals	494		494
Total Current Liabilities	11,213		12,521
Long Term Debt	7,031		9,868
Common Share Capital	13,427		13,428
Retained Earnings	36,953		38,371
Total Shareholders' Equity	50,380		51,799
Total Liabilities & Shareholders' Equity	68,624		74,188

What is operating cash flow for Le Chateau in Year 2?

ANSWER:
$OCF_{Le Chateau} =$

What is CAPEX for Le Chateau in Year 2?

ANSWER:
$CAPEX_2 =$

What is the change in net working capital for Le Chateau in Year 2?

ANSWER:
$\Delta NWC_{Le Chateau} =$

What is free cash flow for Le Chateau in Year 2?

ANSWER:
$FCF_{Le Chateau} =$

8. Free Cash Flow Identity

8.1   Definition

Free Cash Flow = ΔCash + Cash Flow to (from) Claimholders – (T * $Int)

- Free cash flow is derived from the cash flow statement.
- Claimholders are stockholders and the firm's lenders.
- Lenders get interest and principal payments.

372

- Stockholders get dividends and have their shares repurchased (by the firm).
- There is interest tax shield on RHS because FCF omits interest tax shield, but cash flow statements start with Net Income which includes interest tax shield.
- Payments to claimholders are +ve. Money received from claimholders is –ve.

8.2 FCF Identity for Loblaw

	Year 6	Year 7
Revenue	$ 29,210	$ 30,817
Cost of Goods Sold	22,152	23,370
SG&A	5,245	5,533
Depreciation Expense	621	640
EBIT	1,192	1,272
Interest Expense	277	283
Earnings before Taxes	915	989
Income Taxes	288	311
Net Earnings	$ 627	678

ASSETS

Current Assets	Year 6	Year 7
Cash	$ 1,467	$ 1,548
Accounts Receivable	649	685
Inventories	2,269	2,394
Total Current Assets	4,385	$ 4,626
Net Fixed Assets	9,637	9,939
Goodwill	678	678
Total Assets	$ 14,700	$ 15,243

Current Liabilities		
Short Term Debt	$ 715	$ 715
Accounts payable	2,936	3,097
Total Current Liabilities	3,651	3,812
Long Term Debt	4,208	3,912
Other Liabilities	560	560
Total Liabilities	$ 8,419	$ 8,284
Common Stock	1,192	1,192
Retained Earnings	5,089	5,767
Total Owners' Equity	6,281	6,959
Liabilities & Owners' Equity	$ 14,700	$15,243

What is the change in cash (Year 7 minus Year 6)?

ANSWER:

ΔCash =

How much interest did Loblaw pay at the end of Year 7?

ANSWER:

$Interest =

How much money did Loblaw repay (borrow) from its lenders in Year 7?

ANSWER:

Principal Repayment (New borrowing) =

What is the aggregate amount of dividends paid to stockholders in Year 7?

ANSWER:

$Dividends$_7$ =

What is the change in the common stock account (Year 7 minus Year 6)? An increase indicates money raised from new issues and a decline indicates a stock repurchase.

ANSWER:

ΔCommon Stock =

What is the tax shield in Year 7?

ANSWER:

Tax Shield =

What is free cash flow using the identity?

Free Cash Flow = ΔCash + Cash Flow to (from) Claimholders – (T * $Int)

ANSWER:

FCF$_7$ =

9. Bonus Free Cash Flow Exercise

Use the financial statements to calculate Cadbury's free cash flow in Year 2.

Cadbury PLC Financial Statements
at December 31,

(in millions of GBP)	Year 1	Year 2
Revenue	£5,436	£6,011
Cost of Goods Sold	2,709	3,018
SG&A	1,933	2,005
Depreciation Expense	161	192
Restructuring Costs	193	253
EBIT	440	543
Interest Expense	50	172
Earnings before taxes	390	371
Income taxes	30	103
Net Income	360	268

(in millions of GBP)	Year 1	Year 2
ASSETS		
Cash and cash equivalents	£498	£266
Accounts receivable	1,067	978
Inventories	767	748
Other current assets	303	133
Total current assets	2,635	2,125
Property, plant and equipment	1,761	1,869
Intangible assets	3,973	3,802
Other assets	526	333
TOTAL ASSETS	£8,895	£8,129
LIABILITIES		
Short-term debt	£1,189	£267
Accounts payable	1,551	1,577
Other current liabilities	648	590
Total current liabilities	3,388	2,434
Long-term debt	1,194	1,394
Other liabilities	779	779
TOTAL LIABILITIES	5,361	4,607
SHAREHOLDERS' EQUITY		
Paid in capital	1,036	908
Retained earnings	2,498	2,614
Total Owner's Equity	3,534	3,522
Total Liabilities and Owner's Equity	£8,895	£8,129

What is operating cash flow in Year 2?

ANSWER:
OCF =

What is CAPEX in Year 2?

ANSWER:
$CAPEX_2 =$

What is the change in net working capital in Year 2?

ANSWER:
$\Delta NWC =$

What is free cash flow in Year 2?

ANSWER:
FCF =

Solutions

Operating Cash Flow (3.4, 3.5)

	Method #1	Method #2
EBIT	$217	$217
Int. Expense	$50	$0
EBT	$167	$217
Tax @40%	$67	$87
Net Income	$100	$130
OCF	$150	$130
WACC	0.5 * 5% + 0.5 * 10% = 7.5%	0.5 * (1 – T) * 5% + 0.5 *10% = 6.5%
PV	$150/0.075 = $2,000	$130/0.065 = $2,000

Loblaw:

NOPAT = EBIT * (1 – T)
NOPAT = 1,272 * (1 – 0.3147) = $871.8

OCF = NOPAT + $D
OCF = 871.8 + 640 = $1,512

CAPEX (4.3, 4.5, 4.6, 4.7)

$Depr_1 = 0.25 \times \$11,000 = \$2,750$

Depreciation Schedule

	Year 1	Year 2
Net_{t-1}	11,000	8,250
Depr Rate (dr)	0.25	0.25
Depr	2,750	2,062.5
Net_t	8,250	6,187.5

$Net_1 = \$11,000 - \$2,750 = \$8,250$

Depreciation Schedule

	Year 1	Year 2
Net (Graaff)$_{t-1}$	$11,000	$8,250
Net (Wimshurst)$_{t-1}$	n.a.	$5,000
Depr Rate (dr)	0.25	0.25
Depr	2,750	3,312.50
Net (All)$_t$	8,250	9,927.50

$Net_t = Net_{t-1} + CAPEX_t - Depr_t = 8,250 + 5,000 - 3,312.50 = \$9,927.50$

Loblaw:

$CAPEX_7 = Net_t - Net_{t-1} + Depr_t = 9,939 - 9,637 + 640 = \$942$

Net Working Capital (5.2, 5.3)

Fritz:

1) No Change; 2) Increased; 3) No Change; 4) Increased

Loblaw:

$\Delta NWC_7 = -19 - (-18) = -\$1$

Free Cash Flow for Loblaw (6)

+	Operating Cash Flow	1,512
−	CAPEX	−942.63
−	Increase in NWC	−(−1)
=	Free Cash Flow	570.64

Free Cash Flow for Le Chateau (7)

$OCF_{Le\ Chateau} = \$10,551.14$
$CAPEX_2 = Net_t - Net_{t-1} + Depr_t = 38,202 - 34,510 + 6,687 = \$10,379$
$\Delta NWC_2 = 13,708 - 12,125 = \$1,583$
$FCF = 10,551.14 - 10,379 - 1,583 = -\$1,411$

Free Cash Flow Identity (8.2)

Loblaw:

ΔCash = \$81

\$Interest = \$283

Repay (borrow) = \$296

Dividends = \$0

Repurchase (new issue) = \$0

Tax Shield = \$89

FCF = 81 + 283 + 296 + 0 + 0 − 89 = \$571

<u>Bonus Exercise (9)</u>

OCF = (Sales − Costs − Depr) × (1 − T) + Depr = \$584.248

$\text{CAPEX}_2 = \text{Net}_t - \text{Net}_{t-1} + \text{Depr}_t = 1{,}869 - 1{,}761 + 192 = \$300$

$\Delta\text{NWC}_2 = -308 - (-62) = -\$246$

FCF = 584.248 − 300 − (−246) = \$530

DCF Valuation (Ch.17, LO3)

1. Introduction

In this workbook you will:

- Learn the discounted cash flow valuation (DCF) method
- Learn about redundant assets
- Value Apple Inc.

2. Discounted Cash Flow Valuation

2.1 Definition

- In capital budgeting:
  - Project Value = PV of **incremental** free cash flows (FCF_t)
  - Discounted @ WACC
- Corporate valuation treats a firm as a large project:
  - Value = PV of Free cash flow @ WACC
  - $Value_0 = [FCF_1/(1 + k)^1] + [FCF_2/(1 + k)^2] + \ldots$
  - FCF is cash flow from the **assets** of the firm.
  - The "value" is the value of the "assets" not the equity ownership.

2.2 Value of the firm (assets)

Total Firm Value

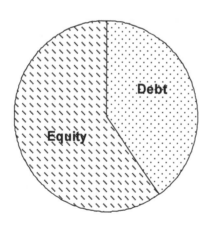

109 To control the board of directors you need to buy:
  A) All of the voting equity.
  B) 51% of the voting equity.

C) All of the equity and all of the debt.

D) All of the debt.

110 To receive all of the free cash flow you need to buy:

A) All of the voting equity.

B) 51% of the voting equity.

C) All of the equity and all of the debt.

D) All of the debt.

2.3 DCF Valuation

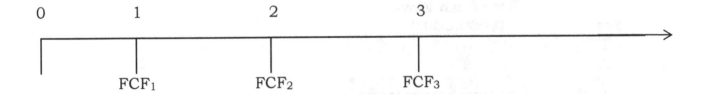

$$V = Redundant\ Assets + \sum_{n=1}^{\infty} \frac{FCF_n}{(1+k)^n}$$

2.4 Forecasting Free Cash Flow

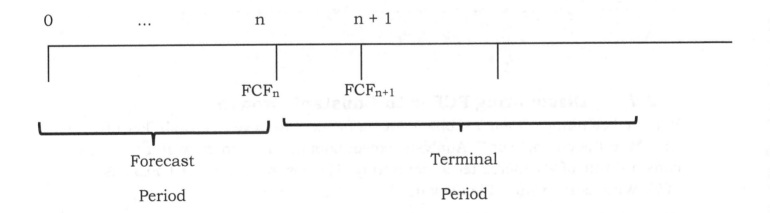

381

We typically assume that free cash flow grows at a constant annual rate during the terminal period and that the terminal period is a perpetuity. In that case, the present value of terminal period free cash flow (as of Year n) is equal to:

$$V_n = \frac{FCF_{n+1}}{k - g}$$

V_n is called the terminal value.

2.5 Value with Non-constant Growth

Your junior analyst has prepared a cash flow forecast for Fritz Electric in the table below. After Year 3, the free cash flow will grow at a constant rate of 2.5% in perpetuity. The company's cost of capital is 9%. What is the value of Fritz Electric?

Year	Free Cash Flow ($000,000s)
1	$10
2	$20
3	$30

ANSWER:

$V_0 =$

2.6 Valuation Self-Test

Check out the non-constant growth valuation self-test on page 17.3.5 of CFO.

It's Time to Do a Self-Test

7. Practise calculating the value of a company. Answer

2.7 Discounting FCF with Constant Growth

It is the beginning of Year 7. Loblaw Inc. is forecast to have free cash flow of $571M at the end of Year 7. Analysts expect Loblaw's FCF to grow at a constant rate of 2% thereafter in perpetuity. The cost of capital for Loblaw is 10%. What is the value of Loblaw Inc.?

ANSWER:

$V_0 =$

2.8　Redundant Assets

- DCF considers future operations but ignores non-operational assets (i.e., land and cash).

How much cash and short-term investments does Microsoft have as of December 31, 2013?

ANSWER:
Cash =

Microsoft Corporation (MSFT) - NasdaqGS ★ Follow

37.10 ↑0.62(1.70%) 9:34AM EST - Nasdaq Real Time F

Balance Sheet

View: Annual Data | **Quarterly Data**

Period Ending	Dec 31, 2013
Assets	
Current Assets	
Cash And Cash Equivalents	10,059,000
Short Term Investments	73,885,000
Net Receivables	17,314,000
Inventory	1,594,000
Other Current Assets	4,018,000
Total Current Assets	**106,870,000**
Long Term Investments	14,607,000
Property Plant and Equipment	11,567,000
Goodwill	14,680,000
Intangible Assets	2,945,000
Accumulated Amortization	-
Other Assets	2,874,000
Deferred Long Term Asset Charges	-
Total Assets	**153,543,000**

2.9　Stock Price

V = E + D

Where

E = market value of equity

D = market value of debt (use book value if market unavailable)

Therefore

E = V – D

P = E/(Shares Outstanding)

2.10 Loblaw's Stock Price

It is the beginning of Year 7. The present value of future free cash flows for Loblaw Inc. is $7,137.5M. Loblaw has $1,467M of cash, $4,923M of debt and 274.1M shares outstanding at the end of Year 6. What is the fair price for one share of Loblaw Inc.?

> **ANSWER:**
> $P_0 =$

3. Valuation of Apple Inc.

Forecast the financial statements for Apple for 2014. Then value its shares. Use the assumptions that follow.

	2012	2013	Ratios	2014
Revenue	$156.5	$170.9		$177.7
Cost of Goods Sold	87.8	106.6		
SG&A	10.1	8.5		
Depreciation Expense	3.3	6.8		
EBIT	55.2	49.0		
Interest Expense	0.0	0.0		
Other Income	0.5	1.2		0.0
Earnings before Taxes	55.8	50.2		
Provision for Income Taxes	14.0	13.1		
Net Earnings	$41.7	$37.0		

ASSETS

Current Assets	2012	2013	Ratios	2014
Cash	$29.1	$40.5		
Accounts Receivable	10.9	13.1		
Inventories	0.8	1.8		
Other	16.8	17.9		
Total Current Assets	57.7	73.3		
Long-term Marketable Assets	92.1	106.2		110.5
Property, Plant & Equipment, Net	15.5	16.6		
Goodwill	5.4	5.8		5.8
Other	5.5	5.1		5.1
Total Assets	$ 176.1	$ 207.0		

LIABILITIES AND STOCKHOLDERS' EQUITY

Current Liabilities

Accounts payable	$21.2	$22.4	
Other	17.4	21.3	
Total Current Liabilities	38.5	43.7	
Long Term Debt	0.0	17.0	17.0
Other Liabilities	19.3	22.8	22.8
Total Liabilities	57.9	83.5	
Shareholders' Equity			
Common Stock	16.4	19.8	19.8
Retained Earnings	101.8	103.8	
Total Shareholders' Equity	118.2	123.5	
Total Liabilities & Shareholders' Equity	$ 176.1	$ 207.0	

Apple's sales in 2014 will be 4% higher, or $177.7 billion. After that, Apple's free cash flow will grow at 2% in perpetuity. Apple has 892 million shares outstanding. Apple's cost of debt is 3% and it will make interest payments in 2014. Use cash as the plug account. Apple's WACC is 10%. Over the last 10 years, Apple's average depreciation rate has been 13% and the ratio of growth CAPEX to the change in sales has been 10%.

What is Total CAPEX for 2014?

ANSWER:
CAPEX =

What is the depreciation expense for 2014?

ANSWER:
Depr =

What is net income for 2014?

ANSWER:
Net Income =

What are retained earnings (from the Balance Sheet) for 2014?

ANSWER:
Retained Earnings =

What are total liabilities and owners' equity for 2014?

> **ANSWER:**
> Total Liabilities and Owners' Equity =

What is cash for 2014?

> **ANSWER:**
> Cash =

What is operating cash flow in 2014?

> **ANSWER:**
> OCF =

What is free cash flow in 2014?

> **ANSWER:**
> FCF =

What is the present value of free cash flow in 2014? ($g = 2\%$, $k = 10\%$)

> **ANSWER:**
> PV of FCF =

What is the value of Apple at the beginning of fiscal year 2014? (Don't forget redundant assets.)

> **ANSWER:**
> V =

Given these assumptions, what is the fair price for one share of Apple Inc.?

> **ANSWER:**
> P_0 =

Solutions

Discounted Cash Flow Valuation (2.5, 2.7, 2.8, 2.10)

Fritz:

$V_0 = \$10/(1.09) + \$20/(1.09)^2 + \$30/(1.09)^3 + [\$30(1.025)/(0.09 - 0.025)] \times 1/(1.09)^3$
$V_0 = \$414.48$

Loblaw:

$V_0 = \$571/(0.10 - 0.02) = \$7,137.50$

Microsoft:

Cash = $83.9 billion

Loblaw Stock Price:

$P = E/SO = (V - D)/SO = (7,137.5 + 1,467 - 4,923)/274.1 = \$13.43$

Valuation of Apple Inc. (3)

$CAPEX = mCAPEX + gCAPEX = 16.6 \times 0.13/(1 - 0.13) + 0.1 \times 6.84 = \$3.164$
Depr $= 0.13 \times (16.6 + 3.164) = 2.6$
Net Income = $40.5
Retained Earnings = $144.3
Total Liabilities & Owners' Equity = $249.3
Cash = $76.7
OCF = $43.49
FCF = $40.76
PV_FCF = $509.56
V = $656.32
E = $639.36
Price = $716.77

Advanced Capital Structure (Ch. 18)

1. Introduction

- Learn Proposition I and II with taxes and a constant D/V ratio
- Learn how leverage affects systematic risk
- Learn how leverage affects firm value by affecting incentives. First look at the impact of leverage on management's incentives, then look at how leverage affects shareholder and bondholder incentives.

2. M&M with Tax and D/V = constant

- M&M assume that debt is a constant dollar amount for the life of the firm.
- It is more realistic to assume that D/V is constant.
- That is what we do in DCF/WACC valuation.
- This assumption affects the functional forms of Propositions I and II.

2.1 M&M Proposition I

Assuming no redundant assets,

$$V_L = \sum_{n=1}^{\infty} \frac{FCF_n}{(1 + k_w)^n}$$

Where

$$k_w = \frac{D}{V_L} k_D (1 - T) + \frac{E}{V_L} k_E$$

- Note: This is the DCF (aka WACC) method of valuation.
- There are no restrictions on FCF_n. It can grow with any pattern.
  - Recall that with M&M, FCF is a level perpetuity.

2.2 DCF/WACC Valuation

Consider the following data for GloboChem:

- D = 0 (All equity firm)
- FCF_1 = $3M (paid annually starting in one year)
- Perpetual annual growth rate of FCF, g, = 2.5%
- k_U = 6.25%
- T = 35%

- Shares outstanding = 4M

What is the WACC for GloboChem?

> **ANSWER:**
> $k_W =$

What is the value of GloboChem?

> **ANSWER:**
> $V_U =$

What is the stock price for GloboChem?

> **ANSWER:**
> $P =$

2.3 PV of Tax Shields

It is also true that the levered firm's value is additively separable into two parts:

$V_L = V_U +$ PV of Tax Shields

- PV of tax shields is hard to estimate.
- The firm's cash flows are not constant (as M&M assume) and so interest tax shields may grow. It is not necessarily a level perpetuity.

CALCULATING PV of TAX SHIELDS METHOD 1:

Step 1: Calculate V_L.
Sept 2: Calculate V_U.
Step 3: PV of Tax Shields = $V_L - V_U$

CALCULATING PV of TAX SHIELDS METHOD 2:

STEP 1: Simultaneously solve for V_L and D in each year.
STEP 2: Then, once you have debt, calculate interest and the interest tax shield.
STEP 3: Find the PV of the interest tax shields.

This is difficult to do and beyond the scope of the course. And, since we know how to get V_L with the DCF (WACC) method, it is not really important.

For either of Method #1 or Method #2, you need k_E and k_U. In other words, you need a Proposition II.

2.4 M&M Proposition II (w/ tax and D/V constant)

Proof uses a law of one price argument. If two assets are identical, then they should be priced equally and should generate the same (expected) return.

From Proposition I:
$$V_L = V_U + PV_{TS} \qquad \text{Eq. 1}$$

We also know that:
$$V_L = E_L + D \qquad \text{Eq. 2}$$

Think of Eq. 1 as a portfolio of two assets: the unlevered firm and the tax shields.

Think of Eq. 2 as a portfolio of two assets: the levered company's equity and its debt.

Eq. 1 should equal Eq. 2 (since both give the value of the levered firm), so their returns should be equal. This proof has three more steps:

1) Find the return on the first portfolio.

2) Find the return on the second portfolio.

3) Equate the returns and simplify to solve for Proposition II.

STEP 1: Return on Portfolio 1 (Eq.1)

- The dollar return on a portfolio equals the amount invested times the rate of return. If you invest $100 and earn 5%, then your return is $5.
- For portfolio 1, there are two investments: V_U and PV_{TS}.
- The return on the unlevered firm, V_U, is k_U, the return required by unlevered shareholders.
- Q: What is the return on PV_{TS} ?
  - o Q: How risky are the tax shield cash flows?
  - o A: Since debt varies with V_L (we assume D/V is constant) and since V_L varies with FCF, it is logical that tax shields are as risky as the free cash flows. Therefore, return on $PV_{TS} = k_U$.
- The return on the first portfolio is $k_U V_U + k_U\, PV_{TS}$.

- For portfolio 2, there are two investments: E_L and D.
- The return on the levered equity, E_L, is k_E, the return required by levered shareholders.
- The return required by lenders is k_D.
- The return on the second portfolio is $k_D D + k_E E$.

STEP 3: Equate Returns and Solve for k_E

$$k_U V_U + k_U PV_{TS} = k_D D + k_E E_L$$
$$k_U[V_U + PV_{TS}] = k_D D + k_E E_L \qquad \text{Eq. 3.}$$

Recall that:
$$V_U + PV_{TS} = E_L + D \qquad \text{(Eq. 1 = Eq. 2)}$$

Use this equality to substitute for the amount in the square brackets in Eq.3. Then simplify for k_E.

ANSWER:
$k_E =$

---

111 This is the same expression for the required return to equity, k_E, as:
  A) M&M with no taxes.
  B) M&M with taxes.
  C) This isn't the same as anything.

2.5 Proposition II Explore It
Check out the Proposition II Explore It on page 18.1.4.

2.6 Proposition II Self-Test
Check out the Proposition II self-test It on page 18.1.5.

It's Time to Do a Self-Test

2. Practise M&M Proposition II. [Answer]

2.7 Proposition II Example

- GloboChem (the company from the earlier example) decides to borrow to attain a D/V ratio of 40% (debt-to-equity of 0.6667). It pledges to maintain that proportional capital structure in perpetuity. Thus, as the value of the company rises, it will issue new debt each year. $k_D = 5\%$.
- The new debt is used to repurchase an equal value of shares at the prevailing market price (open market repurchase).

What is the return on equity for the levered firm, k_E? (Prop II)

> **ANSWER:**
> $k_E =$

What is the WACC for GloboChem?

> **ANSWER:**
> $k_W =$

What is the market value of the firm after the debt issue and repurchase? (Hint: Use a DCF valuation.)

> **ANSWER:**
> $V_L =$

What is the market value of the debt? (Recall that D/V = 40%)

> **ANSWER:**
> $D =$

The company uses the proceeds from the debt issue to repurchase shares. How many shares are repurchased and how many are left outstanding if the company repurchased shares at $20/share?

> **ANSWER:**
> Number Shares$_{AFTER} =$

What is the percentage increase in the stock price after the debt issue and repurchase?

> **ANSWER:**
> $\%\Delta P =$

112   Given what you just learned, would you have sold any shares during the repurchase for $20 per share?
   A)   Yes
   B)   No

Now assume that GloboChem offers to repurchase shares at $24.5843.

How many shares are repurchased and how many are left outstanding?

> **ANSWER:**
> Number Shares$_{AFTER}$ =

What is the stock price after the repurchase?

> **ANSWER:**
> $P_{AFT} =$

113   Given what you just learned, would you have sold any shares during the repurchase for $24.58 per share?
   A)   Yes
   B)   No
   C)   I am indifferent (within $0.01) between tendering shares to the firm in the repurchase or holding.

BONUS: What is the equation to solve for P_{REPO} such that $P_{REPO} = P_{AFT}$?

2.8 Conclusions

114   Under the assumptions of taxes and a fixed D/V ratio, we find that firm value rises with increased debt.
   A)   True
   B)   False

115 Under the assumptions of taxes and a fixed D/V ratio, we find that WACC falls with increased debt. (Recall WACC as defined on page 1.)
A) True
B) False

116 With the assumption of positive corporate taxes and a fixed D/V ratio, what is the optimal capital structure? That is, what D/V ratio maximizes the value of the levered firm?
A) D/V = 0
B) D/V = 0.5
C) D/V = 1
D) D/V = ∞

3. Systematic Risk (Beta) and Leverage

Recall Eq.3:

$$k_U[V_U + PV_{TS}] = k_D D + k_E E_L \qquad \text{Eq. 3}$$

and recall Eq. 1:

$$V_L = [V_U + PV_{TS}] \qquad \text{Eq. 1}$$

Subsitute Eq.1 into Eq.3:

$$k_U V_L = k_D D + k_E E_L$$

Or

$$k_U = \frac{D}{V_L} k_D + \frac{E}{V_L} k_E$$

- The left-hand side is the return on the unlevered firm.
- The right-hand side is the return on a portfolio of the levered firm's debt and equity.
- Since these returns are equal, the betas of the assets are equal.
- What is the beta of the unlevered firm?
  - Call it β_U, AKA the "unlevered" beta or "asset" beta.
- What is the beta of the RHS portfolio?
  - From portfolio theory we know that the beta of a portfolio is a weighted average of the asset betas:

$$\text{Beta of RHS Portfolio} = \frac{D}{V_L} \beta_D + \frac{E}{V_L} \beta_E$$

- Equate the two betas:

$$\beta_U = \frac{D}{V_L} \beta_D + \frac{E}{V_L} \beta_E \qquad \text{Eq. 4}$$

- The unlevered beta is the beta that a company would have if it had no debt. Thus, the systematic risk is driven by the company's assets and not by leverage. That is why it is also called an asset beta.
- Asset betas are thought to be fundamental to each industry.
- Leverage makes the equity beta different from the asset beta.
- The equity beta, β_E, is the beta estimated from the company's stock returns.
- To get asset beta, you need to calculate the equity beta for an unlevered company that is a "pure play" in an industry
  OR
- "Unlever" equity betas for levered companies in the same industry (with same assets).

3.1 Unlevering an Equity Beta ($\beta_D = 0$)

Assume that the debt beta is zero: $\beta_D = 0$. Then, Eq. 4 simplifies to:

$$\beta_U = \frac{E}{E + D} \beta_E \qquad \text{Eq. 5}$$

The Broken Glass Toy Co. (BGT) has debt worth \$20M and equity worth \$60M. BGT's debt beta is zero and its equity beta is 1.5. What is its unlevered beta?

> **ANSWER:**
> $\beta_U =$

3.2 Self-Test for Unlevering a Beta
Check out the self-test for unlevering a beta on page 18.2.4 in CFO.

It's Time to Do a Self-Test

4. Practise unlevering betas. [Answer]

3.3 Levering an Asset Beta ($\beta_D = 0$)

Rearrange Eq. 5 to solve for βE:

$$\beta_E = \left(1 + \frac{D}{E}\right) \beta_U$$

The BW Toilet Paper Company is all equity financed. Its beta is $\beta_U = 0.6$. The company is considering a debt issue. It will use the proceeds to repurchase shares. If it issues debt, the beta of the bonds will be zero. After the debt issue, the company's D/E ratio will be 0.25. What will BW's equity beta be after the debt issue and repurchase?

ANSWER:
$\beta_E =$

3.4 Self-Test for Levering a Beta
Check out the self-test for levering a beta on page 18.2.4 in CFO.

5. Practise levering betas. Answer

3.5 Example: Divisional Beta
Marriott Corp. needs an equity (levered) Beta for its restaurant division to calculate a WACC for internal capital budgeting. The restaurant division has debt and equity of D = $0.5B and E = $1B. An analyst has collected the following data for three pure play restaurant companies.

Data for Pure Play Firms ($B)

	β_E	Debt	E	V
Burger King	0.75	0.004	0.096	0.100
McDonald's	1.00	2.300	7.700	10.000
Wendy's	1.08	0.210	0.790	1.000

117 The analyst suggests that you use a beta of 0.9433, which he calculated as (0.75 + 1 + 1.08)/3. Is this correct?
   A)   Yes
   B)   No

What is the unlevered beta for each company assuming that debt betas are zero?

β_E	β_U

396

Burger King	0.75	0.72
McDonald's	1.00	
Wendy's	1.08	

What is the average of the unlevered betas?

> **ANSWER:**
> Avg β_U =

What is the best estimate of Marriott's restaurant equity beta?

> **ANSWER:**
> β_E =

3.6 Unlevering and Relevering Betas ($\beta_D \neq 0$)

GloboChem is a multinational chemical company. The unlevered beta for the chemical industry is $\beta_U = 0.5$. GloboChem has a capital structure with 60% equity and 40% debt. The debt beta is $\beta_D = 0.27273$. What is GloboChem's equity beta using Eq. 4?

> **ANSWER:**
> β_E =

The expected return on the market is 9% and the risk free rate is 3.5%. What is the expected return on GloboChem's (levered) equity given its equity beta?

> **ANSWER:**
> $E(k_E)$ =

118   How does your answer to the last question compare to your estimate of GloboChem's return to (levered) equity under Proposition II (in Section 1.5)?
    A)   It is different.
    B)   It is the same.

The expected return on the market is 9% and the risk free rate is 3.5%. What is the expected return on GloboChem's unlevered equity given its unlevered equity beta?

> **ANSWER:**
> E(k$_U$) =

119 How does your answer to the last question compare to GloboChem's return to unlevered equity given in Section 1.2 on page 1?
   A)   It is different.
   B)   It is the same.

3.7 Conclusion

120 The equity holder's risk increases with the company's debt-equity ratio.
   A)   True
   B)   False

4. Criticisms of Capital Structure Models

All of the models presented thus far are subject to the following critiques:

- Personal taxes are ignored. (Miller addressed this later, but we do not!)
- Lenders charge a higher interest rate for borrowers with more leverage; it is not constant.
- M&M assume costless bankruptcy and financial distress.
   o Costs of bankruptcy:
      ▪ Administrative, legal and accounting costs
      ▪ Loss of value due to distress sales
   o Costs of financial distress:
      ▪ Customers buy elsewhere for fear that warranties will not be honoured.
      ▪ Suppliers demanding cash payments for inputs fearing they may not be paid otherwise.
- M&M ignore the fact that the amount of debt can affect the incentives of managers and stockholders. These are called agency problems.
- The present value of these expected costs reduce slightly the benefits of the debt tax shield.

5. Principal Agent Problems

- An agency relationship is a contract under which one person (the principal) engages another person (the agent) to perform some service on their behalf, which involves delegating some decision-making authority to the agent.
- The agency problem is when an agent maximizes his own utility by acting in a way that is not in the best interests of the principal.
- There are two agency relationships:
  - o Owner and manager
  - o Bondholders and stockholders

5.1 Owner-Manager Conflicts and Leverage

- What can managers do that benefits themselves but hurts the shareholders?
  - o Effort exertion (slack off)
  - o Inefficient investment (perquisite consumption, e.g., Leaf's season tickets, corporate jets, etc.)
  - o Overinvestment (empire building)
- Michael Jensen's "free cash flow" hypothesis:
  - o Interest on debt reduces the free cash flow at the managers' discretion leaving them less cash to waste.
  - o Increased debt can actually raise the value of equity by reducing managerial waste.

5.2 Bondholder v. Stockholder Conflicts and Leverage

- High leverage and financial distress exacerbate conflict between bondholders and shareholders (Jensen & Meckling (1976)).
- The problems we shall examine:
  - o Asset Substitution (Risk Shifting or Gambling)
  - o Debt overhang (Underinvestment)

6. Asset Substitution

- When leverage is high and bankruptcy is close, shareholders have an incentive to take big risks.
- Their downside is capped due to limited liability.

6.1 Example

- Fed-Ex owes $1M due at the end of the week.

- Fed-Ex has cash of $900,000.
- Assume a discount rate of 0%.

When the end of the week comes, what will the lenders get?

> **ANSWER:**
> Cash Flow to Lenders = D =

When the end of the week comes, what will the stockholders get? (Recall that stockholders are residual claimants. They get what is left after lenders get paid.)

> **ANSWER:**
> Cash Flow to Stockholders = E =

Those answers are also the market values of the two securities (D and E) at the beginning of the week, since we are assuming a discount rate of 0%.

What is the value of the firm, V, at the beginning of the week?

> **ANSWER:**
> V = D + E =

- Fred Smith, CEO, calls an emergency meeting at the beginning of the week and suggests a new project to shareholders.
  - Project code name: Las Vegas
  - Take the cash ($900,000) to Las Vegas and bet it on the following game of chance:

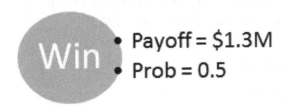

Win · Payoff = $1.3M · Prob = 0.5

Lose · Payoff = $0.3M · Prob = 0.5

What is the expected payoff from the game above? (The expected payoff is just the probability weighted average payoff.)

ANSWER:
E(Payoff) =

What is the NPV of the game? NPV = E(Payoff) – $Bet. $Bet = $900,000

ANSWER:
NPV =

121   Is Project Las Vegas a positive NPV project or a negative NPV project?
   A)   Positive NPV
   B)   Negative NPV

Assume that Mike Smith goes ahead with Project Las Vegas. What is the company's cash position at the end of the week under the two states of nature (win or lose)? Complete the following table.

	Fed-Ex's Cash	
	Win	**Lose**
Cash	**$1,300,000**	

What will lenders get at the end of the week under the two states of nature? Complete the following table. (Recall that face value of loan is $1M.)

Cash Flows to Claimholders		
	Win	**Lose**
Company's Cash	$1,300,000	
Cash to Lenders		

What is the expected value of the cash to lenders? (That is the market value of the debt, since k = 0%). Recall that the expected value is just the probability weighted average of the cash flows in each state of nature.

ANSWER:
E(Cash Flow to Lenders) = D =

What will stockholders get at the end of the week under the two states of nature? Complete the following table. (The stockholders are residual claimants, so they get what is left after the lenders are paid.)

Cash Flows to Claimholders		
	Win	**Lose**
Company's Cash	$1,300,000	$300,000
Cash to Lenders		
Cash to Stockholders		

What is the expected value of the cash to stockholders? (That is the market value of the equity, since k = 0%). Recall that the expected value is just the probability weighted average of the cash flows in each state of nature.

ANSWER:
E(Cash Flow to Stockholders) = E =

Given your estimates of D and E above, what is the value of the company, V?

ANSWER:
V = E + D =

What is the change in the value of debt from before the adoption of Project Las Vegas to after?

> **ANSWER:**
> $D_{AFT} - D_{BEF} =$

What is the change in the value of equity from before the adoption of Project Las Vegas to after?

> **ANSWER:**
> $E_{AFT} - E_{BEF} =$

What is the change in the value of the firm, V, from before the adoption of Project Las Vegas to after?

> **ANSWER:**
> $V_{AFT} - V_{BEF} =$

6.2 Conclusions

122   How is the change in the value of the firm related to the NPV of the project?
    A)   They are the same
    B) $\Delta V > NPV$
    C) $\Delta V < NPV$

123   Would the stockholders approve of the Las Vegas project?
    A)   Yes
    B)   No

124   Is it possible that stockholders in companies that are near bankruptcy might approve negative NPV projects?
    A)   Yes
    B)   No

125   If stockholders of companies that are near bankruptcy adopt high risk, negative NPV projects, then who gains and who loses?
    A)   Stockholders gain at lender's expense
    B)   Lenders gain at stockholders' expense

C) Everybody gains
D) Everybody loses

126 Why isn't the loss to lenders equal to the gain to stockholders?
A) Because lenders absorb the loss associated with accepting a negative NPV project.
B) Answer A is correct.
C) Answer A really is correct.

127 How might bondholders (lenders) protect themselves given this possibility?
A) Put covenants in the loan agreements (bond indentures) that restrict the company's ability to undertake new capital projects without lender approval.
B) Answer A is correct.

6.3 Asset Substitution Explore It

Check out the asset substitution Explore It on page 18.3.2 of CFO.

7. Debt Overhang

- Telefunken GmgH has debt outstanding with a face value of $1M due in one year.
- Telefunken has a project that is expected to generate $900,000 of free cash flow in one year.
- Assume a discount rate of 0%.

When the end of the year comes, what will the lenders get?

> **ANSWER:**
> Cash Flow to Lenders = D =

When the end of the year comes, what will the stockholders get? (Recall that stockholders are residual claimants. They get what is left after lenders get paid.)

> **ANSWER:**
> Cash Flow to Stockholders = E =

Those answers are also the market values of the two securities (D and E) at the beginning of the year, since we are assuming a discount rate of 0%.

What is the value of the firm, V, at the beginning of the year?

> **ANSWER:**
> $V = D + E =$

- Telefunken's owners have identified a safe positive NPV project (the U-47).
  - Project investment at year 0 = $100,000
  - Project payoff at Year 1 = $150,000
  - NPV = $50,000

Assume that Telefunken goes ahead with the U-47 project. What is the company's cash position at the end of the year?

> **ANSWER:**
> Cash at end of year =

When the end of the year comes, what will the lenders get?

> **ANSWER:**
> Cash Flow to Lenders = D =

When the end of the year comes, what will the stockholders get? (Recall that stockholders are residual claimants. They get what is left after lenders get paid.)

> **ANSWER:**
> Cash Flow to Stockholders = E =
>
> What is the change in the value of debt from before the adoption of Project U-47 to after?

> **ANSWER:**
> $D_{AFT} - D_{BEF} =$

128 Given your answer to the last question, will the bondholders be willing to invest an additional $100,000 in order to fund Project U-47?
   A) Yes, the benefit to them is greater than $100,000.
   B) No, the benefit to them is less than or equal to $100,000.

What is the change in the value of equity from before the adoption of Project U-47 to after?

> **ANSWER:**
> $E_{AFT} - E_{BEF} =$

129 Given your answer to the last question, will the stockholders be willing to invest an additional $150,000 in order to fund Project U-47?
   A)   Yes, the benefit to them is greater than $100,000.
   B)   No, the benefit to them is less than or equal to $100,000.

7.1 Conclusions

130 Is it possible that stockholders (and bondholders) in companies that are near bankruptcy might forego positive NPV projects?
   A)   Yes
   B)   No

131 Which claimholder suffers more from this problem?
   A)   Stockholders
   B)   Bondholders

132 How might bondholders (lenders) protect themselves given this possibility?
   A)   Put covenants in the loan agreements (bond indentures) that restrict the company's debt load. First, restrictions on more borrowing. Second, restrictions on debt ratios like D/E.
   B)   Answer A is correct.

7.2 Debt Overhang Explore It

Check out the debt overhang Explore It on page 18.3.3 of CFO.

406

Solutions

M&M with Tax and D/V = constant (2.2)

$k_W = k_U$ (all equity firm)
$V = FCF_1/(k_U - g) = \$3/(0.0625 - 0.025) = \$80$
$P = V_U/N = 80/4 = \$20$

Proposition II:

$$k_E = k_U + [k_U - k_D]\frac{D}{E}$$

GloboChem:
$k_E = 0.07083$
$k_W = 0.0555$
$V_L = \$98.3607$
$D = \$39.3443$
Shares repurchased = 1.96721M
Shares outstanding after = 2.03279
Price after = \$29.0323
Percentage Change in Price = (\$29.0323/\$20) − 1 = 65.152%

Shares repurchased = 1.600383M
Shares outstanding after = 2.399617M
Price after = \$24.59

$B_U = 1.125$
$B_E = 0.75$

Systematic Risk (Beta) and Leverage (3.5, 3.6)

	β_E	β_A
Burger King	0.75	0.72
McDonald's	1.00	0.77
Wendy's	1.08	0.85

Avg $\beta_U = 0.78$

$B_E = (1 + 0.5/1) \times 0.78 = 0.75 = 1.17$

GloboChem:

$B_A = E/V \times B_E + D/V \times B_D$

$B_E = V/E \times B_A - D/E \times B_D$

$B_E = 1.66667 \times 0.5 - 0.66667 \times 0.27273$

$B_E = 0.6515153$

CAPM: $E(k) = k_f + B \times [E(k_m) - k_f] = 0.035 + 0.6515153 \times [0.09 - 0.035] = 7.08\%$

Asset Substitution (6.1)

$D = \$900,000$

$E = \$0$

$V = 900,000 + 0 = \$900,000$

$E(Payoff) = 0.5 * 1.3M + 0.5 \times 0.3M = \$800,000$

$NPV = -\$0.9 + \$0.8 = -\$0.1$

Fed-Ex's Cash		
	Win	**Lose**
Cash	**\$1,300,000**	**\$300,000**

Cash Flows to Claimholders		
	Win	**Lose**
Company's Cash	**\$1,300,000**	**\$300,000**
Cash to Lenders	**\$1,000,000**	**\$300,000**

$E(Cash\ Flow\ to\ Lenders) = D = 0.5 \times \$1M + 0.5 \times \$0.3M = \$650,000$

Cash Flows to Claimholders		
	Win	**Lose**
Company's Cash	**\$1,300,000**	**\$300,000**
Cash to Lenders	**\$1,000,000**	**\$300,000**

Cash to Stockholders	**$300,000**	**$0**

E(Cash Flow to stockholders) = E = 0.5 × $0.3M + 0.5 × $0 = $150,000

$V = E + D = 0.65 + 0.15 = 0.8M$
$D_{AFT} - D_{BEF} = 650,000 - 900,000 = -\$250,000$
$E_{AFT} - E_{BEF} = 150,000 - 0 = \$150,000$
$V_{AFT} - V_{BEF} = 800,000 - 900,000 = -\$100,000$

Debt Overhang (7)

Cash Flow to Lenders = D = $900,000
Cash Flow to Stockholders = E = $0
V = D + E = $900,000 + $0 = $900,000

Cash at end of year = $1,050,000

Cash Flow to Lenders = D = $1,000,000
Cash Flow to Stockholders = E = $50,000
$D_{AFT} - D_{BEF} = 1,000,000 - 900,000 = \$100,000$
$E_{AFT} - E_{BEF} = 50,000 - 0 = \$50,000$

Futures (Ch.19, LO1–LO3)

1. Introduction

In this workbook you will:

- Learn the basic features of forward contracts
- Learn the basic features of futures contracts
- Learn how to read grain futures price quotes
- Learn about the most popular futures contracts
- Learn about the roll of the clearinghouse
- Learn about margin accounts and marking to market
- Learn how to calculate profits on futures trades
- Learn about offset trades
- Learn about convergence
- Learn about hedging price risk with futures

2. Hedging Price Risk

Definition:

Price risk can affect inputs or outputs. Input price risk is the possibility that the price of a production input (i.e., a commodity) will rise and so reduce profits. Output price risk is the possibility that the product price of a business will fall and so reduce sales revenues and profits.

Example: A wheat farmer faces output price risk if the price of wheat falls.

Example: A bakery faces input price risk if the price of wheat rises.

Definition:

Hedging means to reduce a pre-existing price risk exposure.

Definition:

Speculating means to accept price risk with the expectation of making a profit.

Forward and futures contracts can be used to hedge price risk.

2.1 Hedging Video

Watch the hedging Explain It video on page 19.0.2 of CFO.

3. Forward Contract

3.1 Terminology

Example: If you dial 747–1111 (Pizza Pizza) and order a medium pepperoni pizza for $10.99, then you take a "long" position in the forward pizza market.

- A forward contract is an agreement to buy or sell an asset (pizza) at a future maturity date (30 minutes) at a certain price ($10.99).
- At maturity, the buyer takes delivery of the underlying asset and the seller must make delivery.
- The maturity date of the forward is also called its settlement date (30 minutes).
- The fixed buy or sell price for the underlying asset is the forward's price.
- Forward contracts are part of the class of derivative securities because the forward derives its price from the underlying asset (the pizza).

3.2 Rights and Obligations

BUYER (LONG POSITION)	SELLER (SHORT POSITION)
Pays price at settlement date	Receives price on settlement date
Has OBLIGATION to BUY	Has OBLIGATION to SELL
an underlying asset at a fixed price on a specified settlement date.	

3.3 Problems with Forwards Solved with Futures

- Forward contracts are not exchange traded. They are traded over-the-counter or privately negotiated.
- They are customized and thus not standardized. Even if you could trade them, you probably wouldn't like the specifics of someone else's contract.
- Forward contracts can only be completed by making/taking delivery.

- In contrast, Futures contracts are standardized. Futures contracts are exchange-traded. Futures contracts provide a means of completion that does not involve physical delivery. (More on that below.)

4. Futures Contracts

4.1 Standardized. CBT Soybeans Contract
- Quantity = 5,000 bushels
- Maturity Date = January, March, May, July, August, September and November (last business day in the month prior to 15th day of the contract month)
- Type = #2 Yellow at contract price, #1 Yellow at 6 cent/bushel premium, #3 Yellow at a 6 cent/bushel discount
- Price: Prices are reported in dollars, cents and quarter cents per bushel.
  - A typical price quote is something like: 1533'2.
  - The digit after the apostrophe is eighths of a cent, but the minimum change is a quarter cent, so you only see '0, '2, '4 and '6.
  - 1533'2 = $15.33 + 2/8 = $15.3325 (per bushel)
- Delivery = when buyer receives registered warehouse receipt from seller. Warehouses must be in Chicago Switching District or Toledo Switching District.
- Last delivery date (for seller) = 7 business days after final trading date

What is the dollar equivalent of the following price quote: 1536'6.

ANSWER:
$Price per bushel =

4.2 Soybeans Futures Price Quote

Month	Last	Change	Prior Settle	Open	High	Low	Volume
NOV-14	1499'0	+1'2	1497'6	1498'0	1508'6	1493'2	41,606
JAN-15	1432'6	+4'4	1428'2	1430'2	1439'6	1425'4	5,223
MAR-15	1294'2	−0'4	1294'6	1296'0	1304'4	1291'6	1,843

MAY-15	1243'0	0	1243'0	1242'4	1252'2	1241'0	24,383
JUL-15	1248'2	–0'2	1248'4	1247'2	1256'6 b	1246'4	1,528

- The Month column designates the month and year that the contract matures.
- The Last column displays the price of the most recent trade.
- The Change column displays the change in price between the most recent "last" and the previous day's settlement price.
- The Prior Settle column displays the final settlement price calculated at the end of the previous trading day.
- The Open column displays the first trade price of the session for the contract.
- The High (Low) column displays the highest (lowest) trade price for the contract during the trading day.
- The Volume column displays the total number of contracts traded during the trading day.

What was yesterday's closing price for the contract maturing in March 2015?

ANSWER:
$Price per bushel =

How many of the November contracts have traded today?

ANSWER:
Volume =

If you went long today (at the Last price) in one November contract for Soybeans and took delivery in the middle of November, how much will you pay for all of the soybeans? (We call this the cash value of the contract.)

ANSWER:
Total cost = cash value =

4.3 Popular Contracts

- Go to www.cmegroup.com
  - Look for Market Data.
  - Under "Reports" select "Volume."
  - Under "Futures Only" select "Interest Rate."

Sum the volume for 10-year T-Note Future, 5-year T-Note Future and 2-year T-Note Future. Look in the Overall Combined Total column.

ANSWER:
Total Volume in 2-, 5- and 10-year T-Notes =

- Click on the hyperlinked row label for "10-Year T-Note Future."
- Click on "Contract Specs."

What is the face value of the bond that underlies the 10-year T-Note Future contract?

ANSWER:
Face value of underlying =

What is the economic value of trading in the 10-year T-Note Future contracts yesterday? (Hint: multiply the total volume traded by the face value of each contract.)

ANSWER:
Economic value of trading in the 10-year T-Note Future =

133   The GDP of the U.S. was about $16 trillion last year. Which is larger: the value of all goods and services produced in the U.S. last year or yesterday's trading in T-Note futures?
A)   GDP
B)   T-Notes

What is the volume of trading for the "Eurodollar Future"? Look in the Overall Combined volume column.

ANSWER:
Total Volume in the Eurodollar Future =

- Click on the hyperlinked row label for "Eurodollar Future."
- Click on "Contract Specs."

What is the principal amount of a Eurodollar deposit that underlies the futures contract?

ANSWER:
$Principal =

What is the economic value of trading in the Eurodollar Future contracts yesterday?

ANSWER:
Economic value of trading in the Eurodollar Future =

134 Which is larger: the value of U.S. GDP last year or yesterday's trading in Eurodollar futures?
   A)   GDP
   B)   Eurodollars

5.   Performance Bond (Margin Deposit)

5.1 Clearing House

Definition:

The Clearing House is the division of the exchange that manages settlement (final delivery and payment) and daily trading profits.

- After a trade, the Clearing House (CH) takes the role of counter-party to each trade.
    o At maturity, CH matches the remaining buyers and sellers for delivery.
    o Delivery is made to the CH.
    o Since all contracts have two sides, the CH has no net exposure.
- To guarantee performance, CH requires a margin deposit or performance bond of about 5%.
    o This value varies by contract; the broker may require more.
    o The trader deposits that amount into the account with the broker.
    o The broker maintains an account with the Clearing House.
- The Clearing House "marks accounts to market" daily.
    o The loser account is debited. The winner account is credited.
    o Funds are transferred between accounts.

5.2 Terminology

Definition:

The initial margin is the amount of the margin deposit when a futures position is first initiated.

Definition:

The maintenance margin is the minimum balance of the margin account.

Definition:

A margin call occurs if the balance in the account falls below the maintenance margin level. The logic of the margin call is as follows:

IF the Temporary account balance < maintenance margin,
THEN the trader must deposit funds to raise the balance to the initial margin level.

- Temporary balance$_t$ = Closing Balance$_{t-1}$ + Daily Profit$_t$
- Closing balance = Temporary balance + deposit

5.3 Marking to Market Example

- Contract = S&P 500 Mini
- Cash value = $50 × S&P 500 Futures quote
- Position = Long
- Number of Contracts = 1
- Initial margin = $4,000
- Maintenance margin = $3,200

If the S&P 500 Future contract trades at a level of 1,700, what is the cash value of one contract?

ANSWER:
$Cash Value =

On Day 1 you take a long position in one contract of the S&P 500 futures and make the required $4,000 initial margin deposit in your trading account. On Day 2 the futures closes down at 1,690. What is your daily profit? (Hint: The

416

change in the cash value. Since you are long, increases are a profit and decreases are a loss.)

> **ANSWER:**
> Daily Profit =

What is the temporary balance at the end of Day 2?

> **ANSWER:**
> Temporary Balance$_2$ =

135 Is there a margin call on Day 2?
   A)   Yes
   B)   No

What is the closing balance at the end of Day 2?

> **ANSWER:**
> Closing Balance$_2$ =

On Day 3 the futures closes down at 1,680. What is your daily profit?

> **ANSWER:**
> Daily Profit$_3$ =

What is the temporary balance at the end of Day 3?

> **ANSWER:**
> Temporary Balance$_3$ =

136 Is there a margin call on Day 3?
   A)   Yes
   B)   No

What is the size of the deposit?

> **ANSWER:**
> Deposit =

What is the closing balance at the end of Day 3?

> **ANSWER:**
> Closing Balance$_3$ =

On Day 4 the futures closes up at 1,700. What is your daily profit?

ANSWER:
Daily Profit$_4$ =

What is the temporary balance at the end of Day 4?

ANSWER:
Temporary Balance$_4$ =

137   Is there a margin call on Day 4?
     A)   Yes
     B)   No

What is the closing balance at the end of Day 4?

ANSWER:
Closing Balance$_4$ =

5.4 Marking-to-Market Explore It

Check out the marking-to-market Explore It on page 19.2.9 of CFO.

5.5 Cumulative Profit

$$\text{Cumulative Profit} = \sum_{t=1}^{T} \text{Daily Profits}_t$$

For a long position:

Cumulative profit = $(CV_2 - CV_1) + (CV_3 - CV_2) + \ldots + (CV_T - CV_{T-1})$
Cumulative profit = $CV_T - CV_1$

Where
CV_t = the cash value of the position on day t

For a short position:

418

Cumulative profit = $(CV_1 - CV_2) + (CV_2 - CV_3) + ... + (CV_{T-1} - CV_T)$
Cumulative profit = $CV_1 - CV_T$

What is the sum of the daily profits for the S&P 500 position from the example in the last section?

ANSWER:
Sum of profits =

What is the difference between the cash value at the end of the fourth day and the value at the end of the first day?

ANSWER:
Difference in CV =

What would the cumulative profit have been if you had shorted the S&P 500 Futures?

ANSWER:
Cumulative Profit =

6. Completing a Futures Trade

- There are two ways to complete a futures trade:
  - o Take/make delivery
  - o Offset (reversing) trade
    - An offset trade is a trade in the opposite direction in the same quantity and contract.
- More than 99% of contracts do not result in delivery. These contracts are closed using an offset or reversing trade.

6.1 Offset Trade Example

TRADE #1

Trader A buys one wheat contract for September delivery. Quantity of wheat = 5,000 bushels. Trader B is the seller.

TRADE #1 with Clearing House (CH)

At maturity, CH receives money from A and pays it to B. CH receives wheat from B and gives it to A.

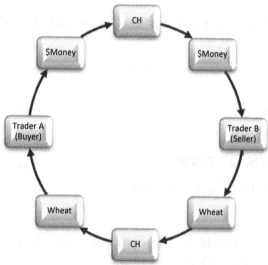

TRADE #2: The Offset Trade

Trader C buys one wheat contract for September delivery. Quantity of wheat = 5,000 bushels. Trader A is the seller.

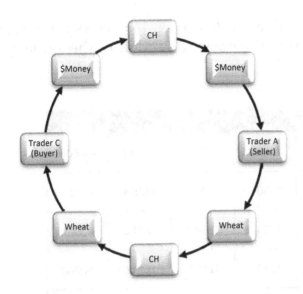

END OF TRADING

Each Trader's Obligations with Clearing House			
	Trader's Action		
	Deliver	Receive	Net Obligation
Trader A			
	5,000bu to complete short position in Trade #2	5,000bu to complete long position in Trade #1	None
Trader B			
	5,000bu to complete short position in Trade #1		Deliver 5,000bu
Trader C			
		5,000bu to complete long position in Trade #2	Receive 5,000bu

- Clearing House's Actions:
  - No action with Trader A
  - Pair Trader B with Trader C
- By executing an offset trade, Trader A has avoided any delivery obligation.

421

- o It's not clear if she profited or lost because prices are not given.
- An offset trade is a trade in the opposite direction in the same quantity and contract.

Month	Last	Change	Prior Settle	Open	High	Low	Volume
NOV-14	**1499'0**	**+1'2**	1497'6	1498'0	1508'6	1493'2	41,606
JAN-15	**1432'6**	**+4'4**	1428'2	1430'2	1439'6	1425'4	5,223
MAR-15	**1294'2**	**–0'4**	1294'6	1296'0	1304'4	1291'6	1,843
MAY-15	**1243'0**	0	1243'0	1242'4	1252'2	1241'0	24,383
JUL-15	**1248'2**	**–0'2**	1248'4	1247'2	1256'6 b	1246'4	1,528

You are short 10 soybean futures contracts (see table above). What is the offset trade?

ANSWER:
Offset trade =

7. Convergence

If you buy a soybean futures contract on the maturity date, when do you get the soybeans?

ANSWER:
Delivery date =

If you order 5,000bu of soybeans from Great Lakes Grain in Ayr, Ontario, when will you receive the soybeans? (Hint: It takes approximately five semi-trailers to carry 5,000bu.)

ANSWER:
Delivery date =

138   What is the difference in delivery time between a futures contract (purchased on its settlement day) and a spot contract?

139 According to the "Law of One Price," if two contracts are identical then their prices should be_____.
   A) The same
   B) Identical
   C) Equal
   D) All of the above

140 According to the "Law of One Price," the futures price (on its settlement day) should be _____ the spot price.
   A) The same as
   B) Identical to
   C) Equal to
   D) All of the above

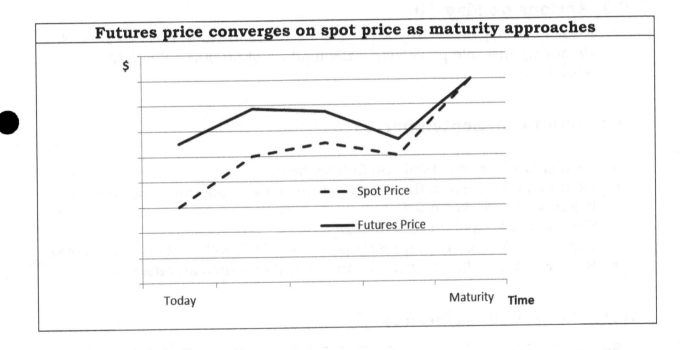

Futures price converges on spot price as maturity approaches

8. Futures Video

Watch the video titled "A Window on Futures" by the Chicago Board of Trade, 1993. VHS. 17 minutes.

9. Farmer Gulke's Short Hedge

- Farmer Gulke farms about 2,000 acres near Rockford, IL. He expects to harvest 50,000 bushels of soybeans in mid-September.
- Today is May 10.

Soybean Prices on May 10		
Contract	Delivery	Price
Spot	Immediate	208'4
Futures	July	211'4
Futures	Sept	213'6

- Farmer Gulke is exposed to price risk. He fears that soybean prices will decline before September.
- He will make a fair profit if he can sell his beans for $2.1375/bu
- To lock in that price and so hedge the price risk, he sells 10 September soybean futures contracts. Recall that each contract is for 5,000bu.

9.1 Actions on May 10

- He sells 10 September soybean futures contracts at a price of $2.1375
- He anticipates sale proceeds, in September, of 50,000 × $2.1375 = $106,875.

9.2 Actions on September 15

- Farmer Gulke harvests his 50,000 soybeans.
- He transports them to the nearest grain elevator operator and sells the beans at the market price.
- Say the market price is $2.00/bu.
- Farmer Gulke receives total sale proceeds of 50,000 × $2.00 = $100,000.
- Next, Farmer Gulke phones his broker and executes an offset trade.

What is Farmer Gulke's offset trade?

> **ANSWER:**
> Offset trade =

9.3 Cumulative Profits and Total Proceeds

Because of convergence, the futures price on the September contract's settlement day will equal the spot price ($2.00). What are Farmer Gulke's cumulative profits on the soybeans futures trades?

> **ANSWER:**

Cumulative profit =

What is the sum of Farmer Gulke's proceeds from the sale of the soybeans and the profit (loss) on the futures transactions?

ANSWER:
Total Proceeds =

If Farmer Gulke had delivered his soybeans to Chicago in fulfillment of his short contract instead of executing the offset trade, what would his total proceeds have been?

ANSWER:
Total Proceeds =

141　Why didn't Farmer Gulke physically deliver his soybeans to Chicago? (Hint: Rockford is 86 miles from Chicago and it would require 50 semi-trailers to move 50,000bu of soybeans.)
　　A)　　Transportation costs
　　B)　　Last time he took soybeans to Chicago they got drunk at a blues club and vomited in his car on the way home.

Assume that the spot price of soybeans was $2.50 in September. What is the sum of Farmer Gulke's proceeds from the sale of the soybeans and the profit (loss) on the futures transactions?

ANSWER:
Total Proceeds =

10. Unilever's Long Hedge

- Unilever manufactures margarine at a plant in Olathe, Kansas. The purchasing manager expects to need 50,000 bushels of soybeans in mid-September.
- Today is May 10.

Soybean Prices on May 10		
Contract	Delivery	Price
Spot	Immediate	208'4

Futures	July	211'4
Futures	Sept	213'6

- Unilever is exposed to price risk. If soybean prices rise, then profits will fall.
- Unilever will make a fair profit if they can buy beans for $213.75/bu.
- To lock in that price and so hedge the price risk, Unilever buys 10 September soybean futures contracts.

10.1 Actions on May 10

- Unilever buys 10 September soybean futures contracts at a price of $2.1375.
- They anticipate a purchase cost, in September, of 50,000 × 2.1375 = $106,875.

10.2 Actions on September 15

- The purchasing manager buys 50,000 soybeans from ADM Collingwood Grain Inc. in Overland Park, Kansas and has the beans trucked to Olathe (12 miles).
- Assume that the market price is $2.40/bu.
- Unilever pays a total of 50,000 × $2.40 = $120,000.
- Next, the purchasing manager phones his broker and executes an offset trade.

What is the purchasing manager's offset trade?

> **ANSWER:**
> Offset trade =

10.3 Cumulative Profits and Total Proceeds

Because of convergence, the futures price on the September contract's settlement day will equal the spot price ($2.40). What are Unilever's cumulative profits on the soybeans futures trades?

> **ANSWER:**
> Cumulative profit =

What is the sum of Unilever's cash outlay to buy the soybeans and the profit (loss) on the futures transactions?

ANSWER:
Total cost =

Assume that the spot price of soybeans was $2.00 in September. What is the sum of Unilever's cash outlay from the purchase of the soybeans and the profit (loss) on the futures transactions?

ANSWER:
Total cost =

Solutions

<u>Futures Contracts</u> (4.1, 4.2)

Price = $15.3675

Price = 1294'6 or $12.9475
Volume = 41,606
Total cost = $74,950

<u>Performance Bond (Margin Deposit)</u> (5.3, 5.5)

Cash Value = $85,000
Daily profit$_2$ = –$500
Temp Balance$_2$ = $3,500
Closing Balance$_2$ = $3,500

Daily profit$_3$ = –$500
Temp Balance$_3$ = $3,000
Deposit = $1,000
Closing Balance$_3$ = $4,000

Daily profit$_4$ = $1,000
Temp Balance$_4$ = $5,000
Closing Balance$_4$ = $5,000

Sum of profits = 0
$CV_4 - CV_1 = 0$

Sum of profits = 0
$CV_1 - CV_4 = 0$

<u>Completing a Futures Trade</u> (6.1)

Not sufficient information. The offset trade will involve a long position, but the question does not indicate the delivery month for the short position, so the offset trade cannot be determined. The offset must be in the exact same contract, which includes the same delivery month.

<u>Convergence</u> (7)

Delivery date = by 7 business days after the 15th of the month
Delivery date = a few days

<u>Farmer Gulke's Short Hedge</u> (9.2, 9.3)

428

Offset trade = Buy 10 September soybean futures contracts.
Cumulative profits = $6,875
Total proceeds = $106,875
Total proceeds = $106,875
Total proceeds = $106,875

Unilever's Long Hedge (10.2, 10.3)

Offset trade = Sell 10 September soybean futures contracts.
Cumulative profits = $13,125
Total cost = $106,875
Total cost = $106,875
Total cost = $106,875

Options (Ch.19, LO4–LO6)

1. Introduction

In this workbook you will:

- Learn the basics of option contracts
- Learn about types of options, options markets and options pricing
- Understand the payoffs and profits to long and short positions in calls
- Understand the payoffs and profits to long and short positions in puts
- Understand intrinsic value
- Understand moneyness
- Understand the time premium of an option
- Understand some basics of option pricing
- Understand how to complete an option trade
- Understand the inherent leverage in options

2. Option Contract Basics

2.1 Terminology

- An option is a contract giving its owner a right. There are two different kinds:
  - A call option gives the owner the right to buy an asset at a fixed price before a given date.
  - A put option gives the owner the right to sell an asset at a fixed price before a given date.

Definition:
Exercising the option is the act of buying or selling the underlying asset.

Definition:
The fixed buy or sell price for the underlying asset is the option's "strike" or "exercise" price. The strike price is paid when the option is exercised.

Definition:
The option's "premium" or "price" is the amount that the owner must pay to have the option. The premium is paid when the contract is initiated.

- The maturity date of the option is its expiration date.
- An American option can be exercised anytime until expiration.
- A European option can only be exercised on the exercise date.

2.2 Rights and Obligations of Options Positions

	HOLDER, BUYER (LONG POSITION)	WRITER, SELLER (SHORT POSITION)
	Pays premium	Receives premium
CALL	Has RIGHT to BUY	Has OBLIGATION to SELL
	an underlying asset at a fixed price before a specified time period.	
	Pays premium	Receives premium
PUT	Has RIGHT to SELL	Has OBLIGATION to BUY
	an underlying asset at a fixed price before a specified time period.	

142 A put gives the owner the right to sell and a call gives the owner the right to buy.
A) True
B) False

143 Regardless of type, the long position pays the premium and the short position receives the premium.
A) True
B) False

144 Only owners have an option. Option writers have an obligation (at the election of the owner).
A) True
B) False

145 If a call option holder exercises, then they pay twice: first the premium and second the strike price.
A) True
B) False

146 If a put option holder exercises, who buys the underlying asset?
A) Call owner
B) Call writer
C) Put owner
D) Put writer

147 Do you have to own the underlying asset before you can write a call?
A) Yes
B) No

431

2.3 Types of Options and Markets

- Check out:
  - A) http://www.cboe.com/
  - B) http://www.nasdaqtrader.com → search "PHLX"
  - C) https://www.m-x.ca/accueil_en.php → Trading → Options List

148 Approximately how many equity options are listed on the NASDAQ PHLX market?
  - A) 1,000
  - B) 2,000
  - C) 3,000
  - D) 4,000

149 Approximately how many equity options are listed on the Montreal Exchange?
  - A) 100
  - B) 200
  - C) 300
  - D) 400

2.4 Option Price Quotes

- Go to www.cboe.com.
- Choose "Quotes & Data."
- Then select "Delayed Quotes."
- In the "Get Quote" box (upper right-hand corner), type "AAPL."
- This brings up stock information. Click on [Options Chain]

Find the call option with the nearest exercise date and with a strike price that is nearest to (but just above) the current stock price for Apple. (Be careful not to select a "Mini" option. Those have "AAPL7" at the beginning of the chain.) What was the last traded option premium and the volume of contracts traded?

ANSWER:
Last premium =
Volume =

3.   Introduction to Calls

- Go to http://www.cboe.com/.
- At the top, select "Trading Resources."
- Choose "CBOETV" from the pull-down menu.
- At the bottom, choose the "Education: Basic" tab.
- Watch the video titled: "Buying a Call."

4.   Payoffs and Profits to Calls

4.1 Notation

- We are working with the same time line in all of the payoff/profit diagrams, shown below.
- An option position is taken at time $t = 0$ and held until expiration at time $t = T$.

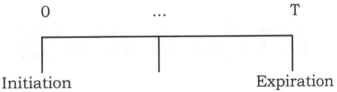

- The asset underlying the options is a stock.
- Assume that there is only one share in a stock option. (In fact, there are 100.)
- S_0 = Stock price at initiation
- S_T = Stock price at expiration
- X = Exercise price
- 0 = Initiation date
- T = Expiration date
- C_0 = Call premium at initiation
- P_0 = Put premium at initiation

4.2 Long 1 Share
Definition:

The payoff is the proceeds from selling = S_T.

Definition:

Profit = Payoff − purchase price = $S_T - S_0$

You buy one share of XYZ for $60 at time t = 0. You sell it later at time t = T for $70. What is the payoff at Time T and the profit from the transactions?

| **ANSWER:** |
| Payoff = |
| Profit = |

Plot the profit you just calculated on the graph below. The x-axis shows the price at expiration. Plot the profits for all of the other x-axis values and connect them with a line.

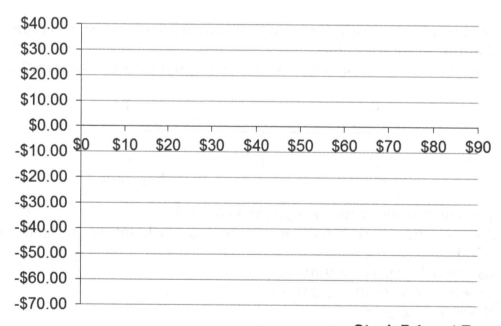

Profit Diagram for Long 1 Share

What is the y-axis intercept of your line? How do you interpret the value?

| **ANSWER:** |
| Intercept = |
| Interpretation = |

4.3 Long 1 Call

Definition:

The payoff is the proceeds from exercising. (This is the monetary value of what you have when you exercise.)

Definition:

Profit = Payoff – purchase price (the option premium)

The payoff to a call owner is:

$$\text{Payoff} = \text{MAX}(0, S_T - X)$$

- The MAX function selects the greater of the two items in the brackets.
- If $S_T > X$, then the owner exercises the option and buys the share for $X when it is worth more, S_T. The monetary value of this is the difference, $S_T - X$.
- If $S_T <$ or $= X$, then the owner does not exercise the option and receives nothing. The monetary value of this is $0.

The profit to the call owner is:

$$\text{Profit} = \text{payoff} - \text{option premium (purchase price)}$$

You buy one call on stock of XYZ for $3 at time $t = 0$. The strike price of the option is $60. At expiration, the stock is trading for $70. What is the payoff at Time T and the profit?

ANSWER:
Payoff =
Profit =

Long Call Profit Self-Test
Check out the long call profit self-test on page 19.5.3 in CFO.

It's Time to Do a Self-Test

16. Practise calculating the profit to a long position in a call option. `Answer`

Plot the payoff and profit you just calculated on the graph below. The x-axis shows the price at expiration. Repeat the calculations for stock prices of $60 and $80. Make two lines, one for payoffs and one for profits, by connecting your points. Extend both lines to the y-axis.

Profit Diagram for Long 1 Call

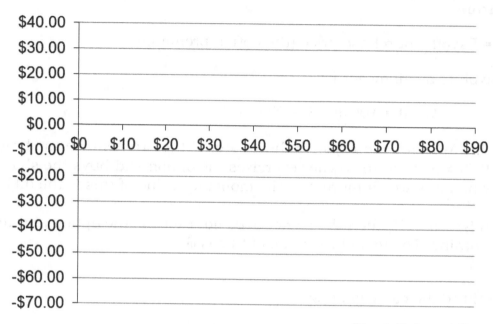

Stock Price at T

What is the y-axis intercept of the profit line? How do you interpret the value?

ANSWER:
y-axis intercept =
Interpretation =

What is the x-axis intercept of the profit line? How do you interpret the value?

ANSWER:
x-axis intercept =
Interpretation =

4.4 Short 1 Call

Definition:

The payoff is the proceeds from exercising.

Definition:

Profit = Payoff – the option premium

The payoff to a call writer is:

$$\text{Payoff} = -1 \times \text{MAX}(0, S_T - X)$$

- It is easiest to think of the call writer's payoff by thinking about what the call owner will do, since the call owner has the choice.
- If $S_T > X$, then the owner exercises the option and buys the share for \$X when it is worth more, S_T. The Call writer is the one who sells the share for less than it is worth, so the monetary value of this is: $-1 \times (S_T - X)$.
- If $S_T <$ or $= X$, then the owner does not exercise the option and the call writer has to do nothing. The monetary value of this is \$0.

The profit to the call writer is:

$$\text{Profit} = \text{payoff} + \text{option premium}$$

We add the premium because the writer receives the premium.

You sell one call on stock of XYZ for \$3 at time t = 0. The strike price of the option is \$60. At expiration, the stock is trading for \$80. What is the payoff at Time T and the profit?

> **ANSWER:**
> Payoff =
> Profit =

Short Call Profit Self-Test
Check out the short call profit self-test on page 19.5.6 in CFO.
It's Time to Do a Self-Test

18. Practise calculating the profit to a short position in a call option. [Answer]

Plot the payoff and profit you just calculated on the graph below. The x-axis shows the price at expiration. Repeat the calculations for stock prices of $60 and $70. Make two lines, one for payoffs and one for profits, by connecting your points. Extend both lines to the y-axis.

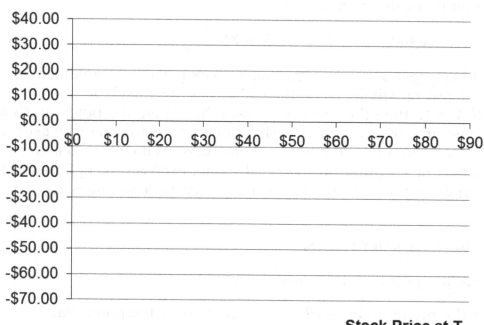

Profit Diagram for Short 1 Call

Stock Price at T

What is the y-axis intercept of the profit line? How do you interpret the value?

ANSWER:
y-axis intercept =
Interpretation =

What is the x-axis intercept of the profit line? How do you interpret the value?

ANSWER:
x-axis intercept =
Interpretation =

5. Introduction to Puts

- Go to: http://www.cboe.com/.
- At the top, select "Trading Resources."
- Choose "CBOETV" from the pull-down menu.
- At the bottom, choose the "Education: Basic" tab.
- Watch the video titled: "Buying a Put."

5.1 Long 1 Put

Definition:

The payoff is the proceeds from exercising.

Definition:

Profit = Payoff – option premium

The payoff to a put owner is:

$$\text{Payoff} = MAX(0, X - S_T)$$

- If $S_T < X$, then the owner exercises the option and sells the share for $X when it is worth less, S_T. The monetary value of this is the difference, $X - S_T$.
- If $S_T >$ or $= X$, then the owner does not exercise the option and receives nothing. The monetary value of this is $0.

The profit to the put owner is:

$$\text{Profit} = \text{payoff} - \text{option premium}$$

You buy one put on stock of XYZ for $2.25 at time t = 0. The strike price of the option is $35. At expiration the stock is trading for $30. What is the payoff at Time T and the profit?

ANSWER:
Payoff =
Profit =

Long Put Profit Self-Test
Check out the long put profit self-test on page 19.5.8 in CFO.

21. Practise calculating the profit to a long position in a put option. [Answer]

Plot the payoff and profit you just calculated on the graph below. The x-axis shows the price at expiration. Repeat the calculations for stock prices of $40 and $50. Make two lines, one for payoffs and one for profits, by connecting your points. Extend both lines to the y-axis.

Profit Diagram for Long 1 Put

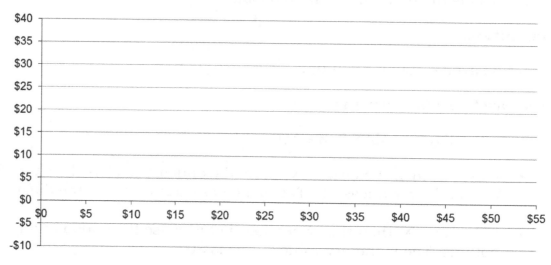

Stock Price at T

What is the y-axis intercept of the profit line? How do you interpret the value?

ANSWER:
y-axis intercept =
Interpretation =

What is the x-axis intercept of the profit line? How do you interpret the value?

ANSWER:
x-axis intercept =
Interpretation =

5.2 Short 1 Put

Definition:

The payoff is the proceeds from exercising.

Definition:

Profit = Payoff – the option premium

The payoff to a put writer is:

$$\text{Payoff} = -1 \times \text{MAX}(0, X - S_T)$$

- It is easiest to think of the put writer's payoff by thinking about what the put owner will do, since the call owner has the choice.
- If $S_T < X$, then the owner exercises the option and sells the share for $X when it is worth less, S_T. The put writer is the one who buys the share for more than it is worth, so the monetary value of this is: $-1 \times (X - S_T)$.
- If $S_T >$ or $= X$, then the owner does not exercise the option and the put writer has to do nothing. The monetary value of this is $0.

The profit to the put writer is:

Profit = payoff + option premium

We add the premium because the writer receives the premium.

You sell one put on stock of XYZ for $2.25 at time t = 0. The strike price of the option is $35. At expiration the stock is trading for $25. What is the payoff at Time T and the profit?

ANSWER:
Payoff =
Profit =

Short Put Profit Self-Test
Check out the short put profit self-test on page 19.5.12 in CFO.
It's Time to Do a Self-Test

24. Practise calculating the profit to a short position in a put option. `Answer`

Plot the payoff and profit you just calculated on the graph below. The x-axis shows the price at expiration. Repeat the calculations for stock prices of $40 and $50. Make two lines, one for payoffs and one for profits, by connecting your points. Extend both lines to the y-axis.

Profit Diagram for Short 1 Put

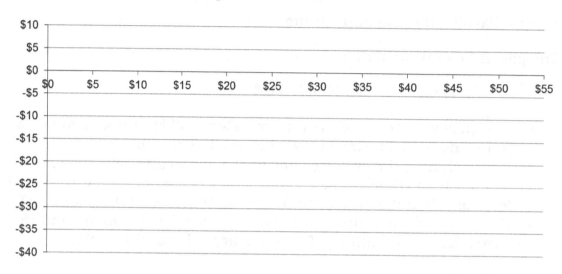

Stock Price at T

What is the y-axis intercept of the profit line? How do you interpret the value?

ANSWER:
y-axis intercept =
Interpretation =

What is the x-axis intercept of the profit line? How do you interpret the value?

ANSWER:
x-axis intercept =
Interpretation =

6. Intrinsic Value

- Intrinsic value$_t$ = payoff to option holder if option exercised at time t.
  - Call: MAX (0, St – X)
  - Put: MAX (0, X – St)

442

- The value can't be negative since the holder can't be forced to exercise.

You buy one call on stock of IBM for $3.50 at time t = 0. The strike price of the option is $120. Today the stock is trading for $123.50. What is the intrinsic value of the option?

ANSWER:
Intrinsic Value =

You sell one put on stock of IBM for $6.375 at time t = 0. The strike price of the option is $130. Today the stock is trading for $123.50. What is the intrinsic value of the option?

ANSWER:
Intrinsic Value =

Intrinsic Value Self-Test
Check out the intrinsic value self-test on page 19.6.4 in CFO.
It's Time to Do a Self-Test

28. Practise computing intrinsic and time values for call options. Answer

29. Practise computing intrinsic and time values for put options. Answer

7. Moneyness

An option is in-the-money if its intrinsic value is positive.

	$S_t > X$	$S_t < X$
CALL	In-the-money	Out-of-the-money
	Intrinsic value > 0	Intrinsic value = 0
PUT	Out-of-the-money	In-the-money
	Intrinsic value = 0	Intrinsic value > 0

150 A call on stock of IBM has a strike price of $130. Today the stock is trading for $123.50. The option is _____.
A) In-the-money
B) Out-of-the-money

151 A call on stock of IBM has a strike price of $120. Today the stock is trading for $123.50. The option is _____.
A) In-the-money
B) Out-of-the-money

152 A put on stock of IBM has a strike price of $120. Today the stock is trading for $123.50. The option is _____.
A) In-the-money
B) Out-of-the-money

153 A put on stock of IBM has a strike price of $130. Today the stock is trading for $123.50. The option is _____.
A) In-the-money
B) Out-of-the-money

8. Time Value (Premium)

We think of an option premium as the sum of two pieces: the intrinsic value and the time value:

$$\$C/P = IV + TV$$

Where

TV = Time value
IV = Intrinsic value
$C/P = Call or put premium

We observe the premium from the market and can calculate the IV, so we solve for the TV as:

$$TVP = \$C/P - IV$$

444

- The table below shows option premium price quotes for calls and puts on IBM.
- Today is January 15, so the January options are about to expire.
- n.a. = not available
- n.t. = no trade

Market Price	Strike Price	Calls			Puts		
		Jan	April	July	Jan	April	July
123.5	95	29.3750	n.a.	n.a.	n.t.	n.a.	n.a.
123.5	100	23.7500	26.0000	n.a.	0.0625	0.1250	n.a.
123.5	110	13.5000	15.5000	17.2500	n.t.	0.5625	1.4375
123.5	120	3.5000	7.5000	10.3750	0.0625	2.5625	3.8750
123.5	130	0.0625	2.8750	5.6250	6.3750	8.1250	8.5000
123.5	140	n.t.	0.8125	2.5000	n.t.	n.t.	16.5000

What is the time value for the January call with a strike price of $120? Note that the stock is trading for $123.50.

ANSWER:
Time value =

What are the time value for the April and July calls with a strike price of $120?

ANSWER:
Time value$_{April}$ =
Time value$_{July}$ =

What is the time value for the January put with a strike price of $130?

ANSWER:
Time value =

Consider the following trades: 1) buy IBM today for $123.50; 2) buy the
January put with the $130 strike; 3) exercise the put. What is your profit?

ANSWER:
Profit =

154 Can time values be negative?
  A)   Sure
  B)   No, because a negative time value implies an arbitrage trading
       opportunity. The resulting trading will change the option and asset
       prices to eliminate the negative time value.

155 What happens to time values over time?
  A)   When there is more time to expiration, time values are larger,
       ceteris paribus.
  B)   When there is less time to expiration, time values are larger, ceteris
       paribus.
  C)   Time values are not affected by time.

Why does time make options more expensive?

ANSWER:

| **Time Value Self-Test** |
| Check out the time value self-test on page 19.6.4 in CFO. |

It's Time to Do a Self-Test

28. Practise computing intrinsic and time values for call options. Answer

29. Practise computing intrinsic and time values for put options. Answer

9.   Pricing of Puts and Calls

9.1 The Minimum Bound for Option Premiums

Given what we learned from the previous time premium example for the
January put, we know that option premium must equal or exceed its intrinsic
value:

$$Ct \geq MAX (0, St - X)$$

$$Pt \geq MAX (0, X - St)$$

Otherwise, an arbitrage opportunity exists.

Assume that the January call on IBM with the $120 strike price was trading for a $2 premium. IBM is trading for $123.50. What trades would you make to take advantage of this and what profit would you earn?

ANSWER:
Profit =

If you repeat the above trades, what will happen to the option premium?

ANSWER:

9.2 Four Factors that Determine Option Premiums

- Stock price
- Exercise price
  - o Calls decrease in value as exercise price rises.
  - o Put options decrease in value as exercise price falls.
- Time to expiration date
  - o Greater time to expiration increases the chance that an option will expire in-the-money or deep in-the-money.
- Volatility
  - o Options with underlying assets that have more volatile prices have a larger chance of being in-the-money. Option prices increase with volatility.

156 What happens to call premiums as the stock price rises, all else held constant?
   A)   Increases
   B)   Decreases
   C)   Stays the same

157 What happens to put premiums as the stock price rises, all else held constant?
A) Increases
B) Decreases
C) Stays the same

158 All else held constant, options with more time to expiration are worth
_____.
A) More
B) Less
C) The same

159 All else held constant, options with more volatile underlying assets have _____ premiums.
A) Higher
B) Lower

10. Completing an Option Trade

- There are two choices when completing an option trade:
  o Exercise
  o Reversing (offset) trade

10.1   Early Exercise

Consider the IBM Call with April expiry and $120 strike price. Refer to the table above for more information. You entered a long position in October. IBM's stock price was $110 and you paid a premium of $12. Today (January 15) you think that IBM has reached its peak price at $123.50. See the graph below. (The dashed line is your forecast.) You want to get out of your long option position today because as the price drops, the intrinsic value will fall.

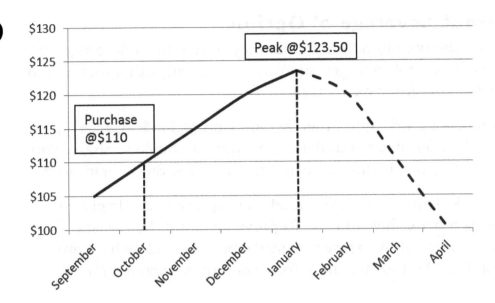

If you exercise today, how much is your payoff and what is your profit?

> **ANSWER:**
> Payoff =
> Profit =

If you execute an offset trade today, what are the proceeds from the offset and what is your profit?

> **ANSWER:**
> Proceeds =
> Profit =

160 When you exercise early you _____ the _____ of the option.
   A) Gain, intrinsic value
   B) Gain, time premium
   C) Give up, intrinsic value
   D) Give up, time premium

- Since the time premium is positive up to the exercise date, it is (almost) never optimal to exercise an American option except on the exercise date.
   o The "almost" exception is a technicality that we will leave for a more advanced course.

11. The Inherent Leverage of Options

Because you only pay the premium for options, they have built-in leverage. A given amount of money controls a larger quantity of an asset with options than with a simple long position in the asset itself.

It is May 21 and shares of Stark Industries Inc. are trading for $63.03. You believe that Stark Industries stock is undervalued and you buy one share. You think that the price will rise to its fair value (a little over $64.50) by mid-July.

Your friend, Tony Stark, tells you that you made a huge mistake. He claims that buying options is a better investment. To prove his point, he invests $63.03 in Stark call options (July expiry and strike price of $62), which are trading for $1.93 on May 21. (Assume that Tony can buy a fraction of a contract.)

On July 20, the stock trades for $64.67. It has exceeded your target so you sell. Coincidentally, July 20 is the expiry date for Tony's option, which closes at a premium of $2.67.

What is your holding period return for your stock investment?

ANSWER:
HPR = $(P_1 - P_0)/P_0$ =

What is Tony's holding period return for his option investment?

ANSWER:
HPR =

Solutions

Payoffs and Profits to Calls (4.2, 4.3, 4.4))

Long 1 Share:

Payoff$_T$ = $70
Profit = $10
Y-axis intercept = –$60
This is your maximum loss if the company goes bankrupt.

Long 1 Call:

Payoff = $10
Profit = $7
y-axis intercept = –$3
This is the lost premium if the option is not exercised.
x-axis intercept = $63
This is the break-even stock price. The stock price must be at least $63 for the call owner to make a positive profit.

Short 1 Call:

Payoff = –$20
Profit = –$17
y-axis intercept = $3
This is the premium if the option is not exercised.
x-axis intercept = $63
This is the break-even stock price. The stock price must be $63 or less for the writer to make a positive profit on the short call.

Introduction to Puts (5.1, 5.2)

Long 1 Put:

Payoff = $5
Profit = $2.75
y-axis intercept = $32.75
This is the payoff from selling a worthless stock for the strike price minus the premium.
x-axis intercept = $32.75

This is the break-even stock price. The stock price must $32.75 (or lower) for the put owner to make a positive profit.

Short 1 Put:

Payoff = –$10
Profit = –$7
y-axis intercept = (–X + Premium) = –$32.75
This is the cost of buying a worthless stock for the strike price plus the premium.
x-axis intercept = $32.75.

This is the break-even stock price. The stock price must be $32.75 or higher for the writer to make a positive profit on the short put.

Intrinsic Value (6)

Intrinsic value = 3.50
Intrinsic value = 6.50

Time Value (Premium) (8)

Time value = 0
Time value = 4.00
Time value = 6.875
Time value = –0.125

Profit = 0.125

Greater time means there is a bigger chance that an option will move into the money or deeper into the money. You are willing to pay more for that higher probability.

Pricing of Puts and Calls (9.1)

Trades: 1) buy the January call with the $120 strike for $2; 2) exercise the call; and 3) sell the share.

Profit = –2 – 120 + 123.50 = $1.50

Your buying will create excess demand, which will cause the premium to rise.

Payoff = $3.50
Profit = –$8.50

Proceeds from offset = $7.50
Profit = –$4.50

The Inherent Leverage of Options (11)

STOCK Holding Period Return
HPR = 0.026 or 2.60%

OPTION RETURN IF EXERCISE

Each contract is for 100 shares, so the cost of 1 contract is $100 \times \$1.93 = \$193$ in May. Tony buys $\$63.03/\$193 = 0.32658$ of a contract.

The fractional purchase doesn't affect the return calculation, so it is simplest to do the calculation as if the fraction is 1/100 or one share.

Investment = Call Premium = $1.93
Payoff = $MAX(0, S - X) = \$64.67 - \$62 = \$2.67$

Return = (Payoff – Premium)/Premium
Return = ($2.67 – $1.93)/$1.93
Return = $0.74/$1.93 = 0.3834 or 38.34%

OPTION RETURN IF REVERSE

HPR = (Sell premium – Buy Premium)/Buy Premium
HPR = ($2.67 – $1.93)/$1.93
HPR = 0.3834 or 38.34%